AGES
8–9

SCHOLASTIC

Fourth Grade
Jumbo Workbook

This book belongs to

Justin Basarmeta

Cover design by Sequel Creative
Cover art by Patrick Girouard
Interior illustrations by Elizabeth Adams, Maxie Chambliss, Chris Cole/Duomo/Corbis (page 131), Steve Cox, Duomo/Corbis (page 136), Michael Denman, Kate Flanagan, Greg Harris, Hulton Archive (page 132, 140), Anne Kennedy, Jared Lee, Margeaux Lucas, Kathy Marlin, Bob Masheris, Mike Moran, Sherry Neidigh, Richard Porteus, Karen Sevaly

ISBN 978-0-545-91026-2

5 6 7 8 9 10   08   22 21 20 19 18 17

Dear Parents,

The power to succeed is in every child! The question is: How can you help your child achieve this success and become an independent, lifelong learner?

You have already taken the first step! This *Fourth Grade Jumbo Workbook* is the perfect way to support the learning your child needs to be successful in school.

Research shows that independent practice helps children gain mastery of essential skills. This book includes carefully selected, teacher-tested activities that give fourth grade students exactly the practice they need. Topics covered include:

- Spelling
- Vocabulary
- Reading Comprehension
- Grammar and Writing
- Multiplication and Division
- Fractions and Decimals

You'll also find assessments to help you keep track of your child's progress—and provide important practice with standardized test formats.

Let's get started! Your involvement will make this a valuable educational experience and will support and enhance your child's learning.

Enjoy!

Hindie

Hindie Weissman
Educational Consultant,
27+ years teaching experience

Learn and Succeed

Welcome!

Grade 4 is a critical stepping stone on the road to learning success! This workbook has been carefully designed to help ensure your child has the tools he or she needs to soar in school. On the 300-plus pages that follow, you'll find plenty of practice in each of these must-know curriculum areas:

SPELLING	VOCABULARY	READING SKILLS	GRAMMAR
• Recognizing Short & Long Vowel Spellings • Recognizing Unusual Vowel Sounds • Forming Plurals	• Understanding Synonyms, Antonyms, Homonyms, & Homophones • Recognizing Latin/Greek Roots • Recognizing Prefixes & Suffixes • Understanding Analogies	• Recognizing Main Idea/Details • Recognizing Cause/Effect • Using Context Clues • Making Predictions • Summarizing	• Recognizing Types of Sentences • Understanding Parts of Speech • Subject/Verb Agreement • Using Punctuation
WRITING	**ADDITION/SUBTRACTION**	**MULTIPLICATION/DIVISION**	**FRACTIONS/DECIMALS**
• Sentence Building • Understanding Parts of a Story • Writing a Paragraph	• Adding & Subtracting Multi-Digit Numbers • Solving Word Problems Using Addition & Subtraction	• Multiplying With Regrouping • Dividing With Remainders • Solving Word Problems Using Multiplication & Division	• Identifying & Comparing Decimals • Adding Fractions • Adding & Subtracting Decimals

Helping your child build essential skills is easy!

These teacher-approved activities have been specially developed to make learning both accessible and enjoyable. On each page, you'll find:

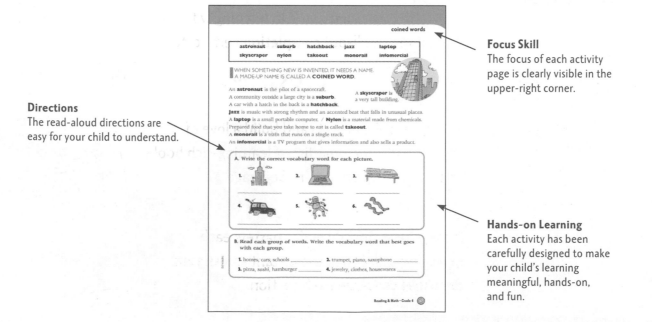

Focus Skill
The focus of each activity page is clearly visible in the upper-right corner.

Directions
The read-aloud directions are easy for your child to understand.

Hands-on Learning
Each activity has been carefully designed to make your child's learning meaningful, hands-on, and fun.

Scholastic

with Scholastic!

These great extras are guaranteed to make learning extra engaging!

This workbook is loaded with lots of motivating, special components including:

SPECIAL ACTIVITIES TO GET READY FOR FIFTH GRADE ▶

Give your child a head start in fifth grade with this BONUS assortment of get-ready activities.

◀ CONNECTION TO ONLINE LEARNING

Boost computer literacy with this special link to a treasury of skill-building online activities at www.scholastic.com/success.

MOTIVATING STICKERS ▶

Mark the milestones of your child's learning path with these bright, kid-pleasing stickers.

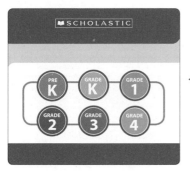

◀ INSTANT FLASH CARDS

Promote reading fluency with these fun flash cards.

REWARD CERTIFICATE ▶

Celebrate your child's leap in learning with this colorful, pull-out completion certificate.

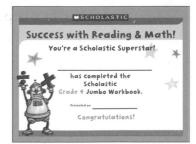

◀ LIST OF THE BEST BOOKS FOR YOUNG LEARNERS

Reinforce key concepts and build a love of reading with this great list of learning-rich books selected by top educators. See page 12.

QUICK ASSESSMENT TESTS ▶

Make sure your child *really* masters each must-know skill with the instant assessment tests that conclude each section.

Scholastic

Table of Contents

Scholastic

Scholastic

MATHEMATICS

Scholastic

Scholastic

Tips for Success

Here are some tips to help your child get the most out of this workbook:

- Provide a quiet, comfortable place for your child to work.

- Make sure your child understands the directions.

- Encourage your child to use colorful pencils and markers to make learning fun.

- Check completed work as soon as possible and review corrected work with your child.

- Pay attention to areas where your child is having difficulty. Spend extra time to help him or her master those skills.

- Provide a special area at home where your child's work can be displayed.

- Be positive and encouraging. Praise your child for his or her efforts and good work.

Scholastic

Read with Your Child

Reading to your child and having him or her read to you is an extremely effective way of supporting your child's learning. When you read with him or her, make sure your child is actively participating. Here are five ways to support your child's reading:

1. Let your child choose the book.

2. Look at the cover of the book and ask your child what he or she thinks the story will be about.

3. As you read the book, locate a good stopping point and ask your child to predict what will happen next. Then read to confirm the prediction or correct it.

4. Discuss the characters in the story: Are they kind? good? bad? clever? Are they like characters in another book?

5. When you finish the story, have your child summarize it.

Scholastic

Read with Your Child

Looking for a great book to read with your child? Here are some top teacher picks:

- *Because of Winn-Dixie* by Kate DiCamillo (Candlewick Press, 2000).

- *Bubba the Cowboy Prince: A Fractured Texas Tale* by Helen Ketteman (Scholastic, 1997).

- *Catwings* by Ursula K. LeGuin (Scholastic, 1988).

- *Ella Enchanted* by Gail Carson Levine (HarperCollins, 1997).

- *Harriet the Spy* by Louise Fitzhugh (HarperTrophy, 1990).

- *Harry Potter and the Sorcerer's Stone* by J. K. Rowling (Scholastic, 1998).

- *The Secret Garden* by Frances Hodgson Burnett. Illustrated by Tasha Tudor (HarperCollins, 1987).

- *Shiloh* by Phyllis Reynolds Naylor (Dell, 1991).

- *A Single Shard* by Linda Sue Park (Clarion, 2001).

- *Tales of a Fourth Grade Nothing* by Judy Blume (Dutton, 1972).

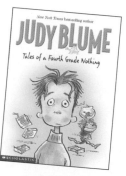

Spelling

Sometimes spelling isn't straightforward. In this section, your child will get practice spelling a variety of vowel sounds as well as irregular plurals and some commonly misspelled words.

What to Do

Have your child complete the activity pages. Review your child's answers. Remember, answers to the activities are in the back of the book if you need them.

The last page in this section is the Grade 4 spelling list. You might make flash cards to review the words with your child throughout the year.

Keep On Going!

Have your child create a list of the words he or she finds especially tricky to spell. Then create word searches using those words for him or her to solve. Invite your child to create word searches for you to solve, too!

e-i-g-h-t-h

h-a-l-v-e-s

b-r-e-a-t-h-e

The **long-*a* sound** /ā/ *can be spelled with the letters* a, a_e, ai, ay, ey, *or* eigh.

A. Read and write each word. Then organize the list words by the correct long-*a* sound group.

List Words	**a**	**ai**
1. basic	_____	_____	_____
2. eighth	_____	_____	_____
3. erase	_____	_____	_____
4. crayon	_____		
5. obey	_____	**a_e**	**ay**
6. daily	_____	_____	_____
7. radio	_____	_____	_____
8. escape	_____		
9. brain	_____	**ey**	**eigh**
10. stray	_____	_____	_____
11. they	_____	_____	_____
12. neighbor	_____		_____
13. glacier	_____		
14. explain	_____		
15. freight	_____		

B. **Challenge Words**
Read and write each word. Place a star next to words with the long-*a* sound.

16. precipitation _____

17. temperature _____

18. thermometer _____

19. humidity _____

20. hail _____

...MORE RAIN IN TODAY'S FORECAST...

Scholastic

A. Use the shape of the letters to fit a list word into each puzzle.

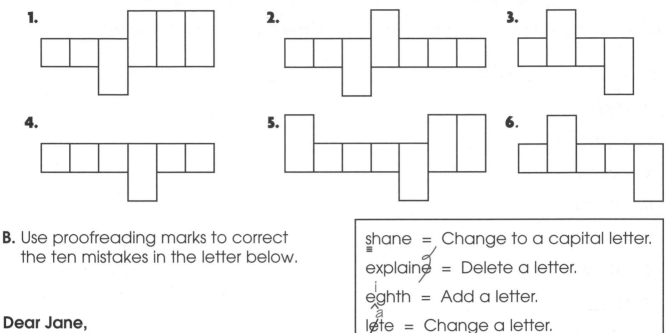

1.
2.
3.
4.
5.
6.

B. Use proofreading marks to correct the ten mistakes in the letter below.

shane = Change to a capital letter.
explaine = Delete a letter.
eghth = Add a letter.
lete = Change a letter.

Dear Jane,

I saw a glashier on the basik dailey boat tour. I cannot erais the magnificent

image from my brane. I asked the captain and crew if i could raydio my neighber.

However, thay were too busy trying to excap the bad weather. Talk to you soon.

Sincerely,

Daisy

C. Write the challenge word for each definition. Then use the number code to learn a fact about an incredible storm.

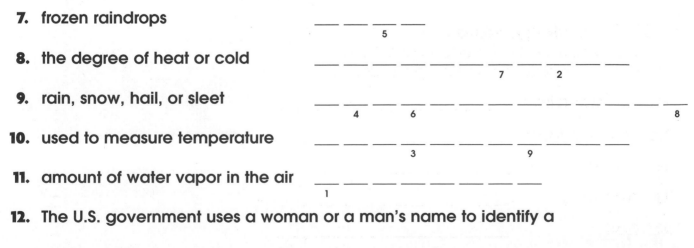

7. frozen raindrops

___ ___ ___ ___

    5

8. the degree of heat or cold

___ ___ ___ ___ ___ ___ ___ ___ ___ ___ ___

                 7   2

9. rain, snow, hail, or sleet

___ ___ ___ ___ ___ ___ ___ ___ ___ ___

  4   6   8

10. used to measure temperature

___ ___ ___ ___ ___ ___ ___ ___ ___ ___

           3   9

11. amount of water vapor in the air

___ ___ ___ ___ ___ ___ ___ ___

1

12. The U.S. government uses a woman or a man's name to identify a

___ ___ ___ ___ ___ ___ ___ ___ ___ .

1   2   3   4   5   6   7   8   9

The **long-**e **sound** /ē/ *can be spelled with the letters* e, ea, ee, ei, ie, *or* ey.

Guide Words *are listed at the top of each dictionary page. They tell the first and last words found on that page.*

A. Read and write each word. Then organize the list words using the guide words.

List Words   about/family

1. species _____ _____ _____

2. beach _____ _____ _____

3. jockey _____ _____

4. ecology _____

5. eager _____   famous/nibble

6. neither _____ _____ _____

7. field _____ _____ _____

8. monkey _____ _____

9. secret _____

10. agreed _____   niche/young

11. queen _____ _____ _____

12. either _____ _____ _____

13. yield _____ _____

14. feast _____

15. seaweed _____

B. **Challenge Words**
Read and write each word.

16. rhinoceros _____

17. crocodile _____

18. leopard _____

19. orangutan _____

20. biologist _____

Scholastic

Write the list word in the puzzle that completes each sentence below. Then unscramble the letters from the shaded boxes and write them on the blanks to spell another word for *seaweed* with the long-*e* sound.

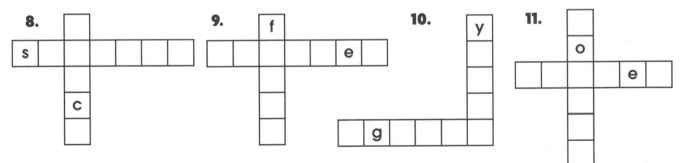

1. We saw a _____ at the zoo.

2. _____ is the study of how living things relate to their environment.

3. Ramon is _____ to complete his science project.

4. Our family celebrates with a _____ at Thanksgiving.

5. Princess Claire was crowned _____.

6. _____ provides fish with food and oxygen.

7. John wants _____ pizza or a hamburger.

Write two list words that share a common letter in each puzzle.

Write the challenge word that matches each picture.

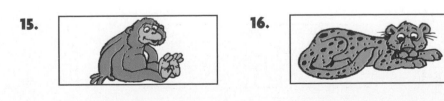

12.

13.

14.

15.

16.

Scholastic

The **long-**i **sound** /ī/ *can be spelled with the letters* i, i_e, ai, igh, *or* y.

A **syllable** *is a unit of spoken language that is spoken without interruption.*
The word excited *has three syllables.*

A. Read and write each word. Then organize the list words by their number of syllables.

List Words	one syllable	two syllables
1. flight	_____	_____
2. type	_____	_____
3. delight	_____	_____
4. icicle	_____	_____
5. mile	_____	_____
6. surprise	_____	
7. idea	_____	**three syllables**
8. rhyme	_____	_____
9. decided	_____	_____
10. apply	_____	_____
11. finally	_____	_____
12. prize	_____	_____
13. myself	_____	
14. diagram	_____	
15. mighty	_____	

B. **Challenge Words**
   Read and write each word.
Place a star next to words with the long-*i* sound.

16. dictionary _____

17. library _____

18. glossary _____

19. fiction _____

20. biography _____

IT'S ABOUT TIME!

Scholastic

A. Circle each list word in the puzzle. The words go forward, backward, down, and diagonally. Then write each word in the correct group below.

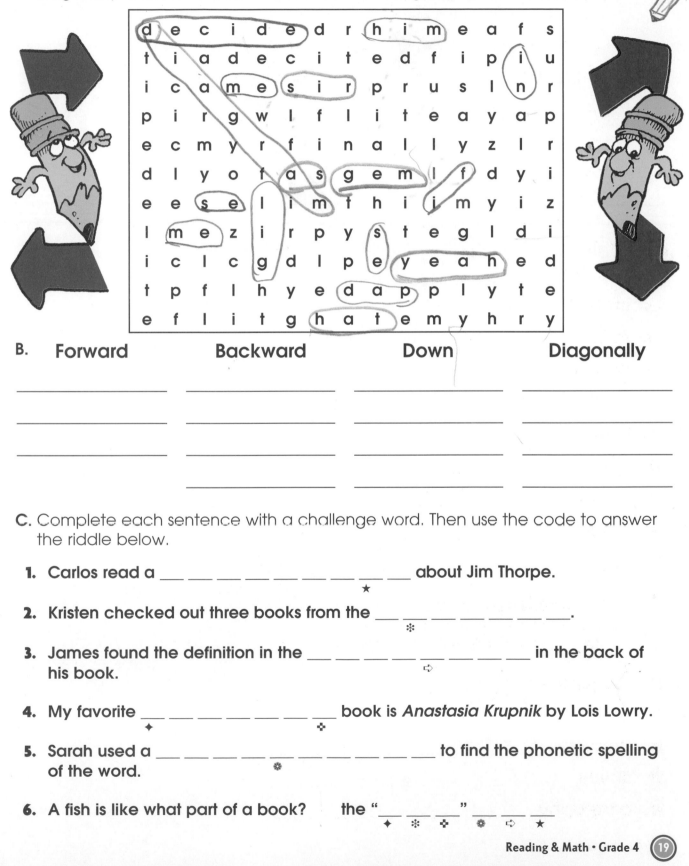

```
d  e  c  i  d  e  d  r  h  i  m  e  a  f  s
t  i  a  d  e  c  i  t  e  d  f  i  p  i  u
i  c  a  m  e  s  i  r  p  r  u  s  l  n  r
p  i  r  g  w  l  f  l  i  t  e  a  y  a  p
e  c  m  y  r  f  i  n  a  l  l  y  z  l  r
d  l  y  o  f  a  s  g  e  m  l  f  d  y  i
e  e  s  e  l  i  m  t  h  i  j  m  y  i  z
l  m  e  z  i  r  p  y  s  t  e  g  l  d  i
i  c  l  c  g  d  l  p  e  y  e  a  h  e  d
t  p  f  l  h  y  e  d  a  p  p  l  y  t  e
e  f  l  i  t  g  h  a  t  e  m  y  h  r  y
```

B.

Forward	Backward	Down	Diagonally
_____	_____	_____	_____
_____	_____	_____	_____
_____	_____	_____	_____
	_____	_____	_____

C. Complete each sentence with a challenge word. Then use the code to answer the riddle below.

1. Carlos read a ___ ___ ___ ___ ___ ___ ___ ___ about Jim Thorpe.
   ★

2. Kristen checked out three books from the ___ ___ ___ ___ ___ ___ ___.
   ✳

3. James found the definition in the ___ ___ ___ ___ ___ ___ ___ in the back of his book.
   ⇨

4. My favorite ___ ___ ___ ___ ___ ___ ___ book is *Anastasia Krupnik* by Lois Lowry.
   ◆   ❖

5. Sarah used a ___ ___ ___ ___ ___ ___ ___ ___ ___ to find the phonetic spelling of the word.
   ❋

6. A fish is like what part of a book?   the "___ ___ ___" ___ ___ ___
   ◆ ✳ ❖   ❋ ⇨ ★

➡️ The **long-**o **sound** /ō/ *can be spelled with the letters* o, o_e, oa, *and* ow.

A. Read and write each word. Look for the word with two long-*o* sounds. Then organize the list words by the correct long-*o* sound group.

List Words   o   o_e

1. shown
2. coast
3. spoke
4. throat
5. wrote
6. poem   *oa*   *ow*
7. narrow
8. echo
9. goal
10. tomorrow
11. awoke
12. introduce   **two long-*o* sounds**
13. grove
14. cocoa
15. shadow

B. 🏆 **Challenge Words**
Read and write each word. Place a star next to words with the long-*o* sound.

16. ocean
17. continent
18. geography
19. valley
20. discovery

Complete each analogy with a list word.

1. *Ice cream* is to *milk shake* as _____ is to *hot chocolate*.

2. A *novel* is to *Judy Blume* as a _____ is to *Shel Silverstein*.

3. *River* is to *bank* as *ocean* is to _____.

4. *Yesterday* is to _____ as *past* is to *future*.

5. *Batch* is to *bunch* as _____ is to *group*.

6. To *make known* is to _____ as to *look closely* is to *investigate*.

7. *Write* is to _____ as *bring* is to *brought*.

Unscramble each group of code symbols to write a list word.

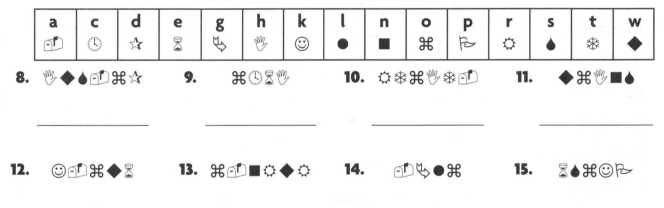

8. _____   **9.** _____   **10.** _____   **11.** _____

12. _____   **13.** _____   **14.** _____   **15.** _____

Write the challenge word for each definition. Then use the number code to complete the fact below about the earth's surface.

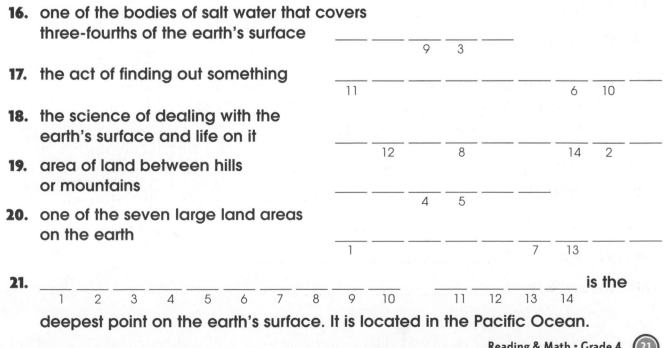

16. one of the bodies of salt water that covers three-fourths of the earth's surface

____ ____ ____ ____
     9   3

17. the act of finding out something

____ ____ ____ ____ ____ ____ ____ ____ ____ ____
11   6 10

18. the science of dealing with the earth's surface and life on it

____ ____ ____ ____ ____ ____ ____ ____ ____
  12   8   14 2

19. area of land between hills or mountains

____ ____ ____ ____
  4 5

20. one of the seven large land areas on the earth

____ ____ ____ ____ ____ ____ ____
 1   7 13

21. ____ ____ ____ ____ ____ ____ ____ ____ ____ ____   ____ ____ ____ ____ is the
  1 2 3 4 5 6 7 8 9 10   11 12 13 14

deepest point on the earth's surface. It is located in the Pacific Ocean.

long-*u* and /oo/
sounds

The **long-**u **sound** /ū/ *as in* beauty *can be spelled with the letters* u_e, ew, iew, *or* ue.

The **u sound** /oo/ *as in* move *and* proof *can be spelled with the letters* o_e, ue, ew, oo, ui, *or* ui_e.

A. Read and write each word. Then organize each list word under the correct *u* group.

List Words	/ū/	/oo/
1. clue	_____	_____
2. huge	_____	_____
3. view	_____	_____
4. school	_____	_____
5. prove	_____	_____
6. juice	_____	_____
7. rescue	_____	_____
8. few	_____	_____
9. fruit	_____	
10. refuse	_____	
11. crew	_____	
12. issue	_____	
13. value	_____	
14. bruise	_____	
15. accuse	_____	

B. **Challenge Words**

Read and write each word.

16. musical _____

17. harmony _____

18. performance _____

19. orchestra _____

20. rhythm _____

22 Reading & Math · Grade 4

A. Write the list word that belongs with each group of words.

1. milk, water, _____

2. gigantic, vast, _____

3. team, band, _____

4. suggestion, hint, _____

5. save, recover, _____

6. vegetable, meat, _____

7. blister, scratch, _____

8. scene, picture, _____

B. Use proofreading marks to correct the ten mistakes in the story.

Proven Clean

Luke just read the latest issew of the skool newspaper. An author of one of the articles was trying to acuse Luke's class of making the mess in the lunchroom last tuesday. Luke knew this was not true He decided he must pruve it to more than a fuw students. Luke interviewed the custodian. The custodian agreed that Luke's class did not refuze to clean up. In fact, the custodian added that they knew the valew of a clean lunchroom. Luke now had his proof

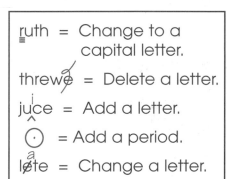

ruth = Change to a capital letter.

threwe = Delete a letter.

juce (i) = Add a letter.

⊙ = Add a period.

lete (a) = Change a letter.

C. Write the challenge word for each definition. The shaded boxes will spell the name of the musician who began composing at the age of five.

orderly repeating of sounds

a pleasing combination of musical notes

having to do with music

a public presentation

a group of musicians playing together

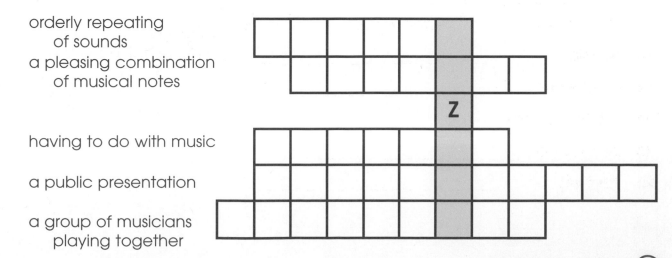

Z

Scholastic

The **/ou/ sound** *can be spelled with the letters* ow *or* ou.
The **/oi/ sound** *can be spelled with the letters* oi *or* oy.

A **noun** *is a word that names a person, place, or thing. A* **verb** *is a word that shows an action.*

A. Read and write each word. Look for the word that can be both a noun and a verb. Then organize the list words as nouns or verbs.

List Words	nouns	verbs
1. moisture	_____	_____
2. destroy	_____	_____
3. allow	_____	_____
4. council	_____	_____
5. avoid	_____	_____
6. employ	_____	_____
7. boundary	_____	_____
8. downtown	_____	
9. boiled	_____	
10. voyage	_____	
11. mountain	_____	
12. disappoint	_____	
13. allowance	_____	
14. found	_____	
15. oyster	_____	

both noun and verb

_____

B. **Challenge Words**
Read and write each word.

16. exercise _____

17. heartbeat _____

18. muscle _____

19. oxygen _____

20. breathe _____

Scholastic

A. Complete each analogy with a list word.

1. *Studied* is to *observed* as _____ is to *discovered*.

2. *Lake* is to *ocean* as *hill* is to _____.

3. *Seed* is to *apple* as *pearl* is to _____.

4. *Laugh* is to *comedian* as _____ is to *enemy*.

5. *Cookie* is to *snack* as *money* is to _____.

6. *Heal* is to *doctor* as _____ is to *boss*.

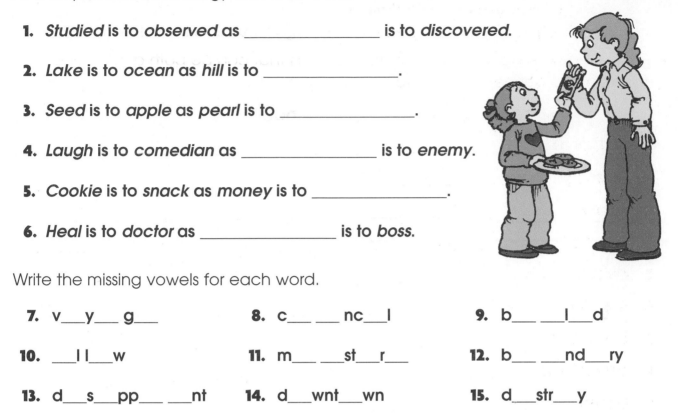

Write the missing vowels for each word.

7. v__y__ g__

8. c__ __ nc__l

9. b__ __l__d

10. __l l__w

11. m__ __st__r__

12. b__ __nd__ry

13. d__s__pp__ __nt

14. d__wnt__wn

15. d__str__y

B. Circle each challenge word on the track. Then write the remaining letters on the blanks below to learn an interesting fact about exercising.

About s e v h e a r t b e a t e n q u a r b r e a t h e t s o
d e r e s i c r e x e i u q e r e r a n e g e l c s u m y x o f
t o r u n a o n e h u n d o x y g e n r e d y a r d d a s h

START   FINISH

_____ _____ _____ _____ _____ _____ _____

_____ _____ _____ _____ ____ _____ _____ _____ _____ _____ __

_____ _____ __ _____ _____-_____ _____ _____ _____-_____ _____ _____ _____ _____ .

The /k/ **sound** *can be spelled with the letters* c, k, *or* ck.

A. Read and write each word. Then organize the list words using the guide words.

List Words

atomic/freckle

1. nickel _____ _____ _____
2. tractor _____ _____ _____
3. picnic _____ _____
4. cracker _____
5. clerk _____

handicap/picture

6. heroic _____ _____ _____
7. hockey _____ _____ _____
8. rocket _____ _____
9. shriek _____

pink/trademark

10. attic _____
11. frantic _____ _____ _____
12. attack _____ _____ _____
13. hawk _____ _____
14. plastic _____
15. stack _____

B. **Challenge Words**
Read and write each word.

16. Olympic _____
17. snowboarding _____
18. skiing _____
19. competition _____
20. athletes _____

Scholastic

A. Look at the shape of the list words. Write the word that fits in each set of letter boxes.

1.

2.

3.

4.

5.

6.

7.

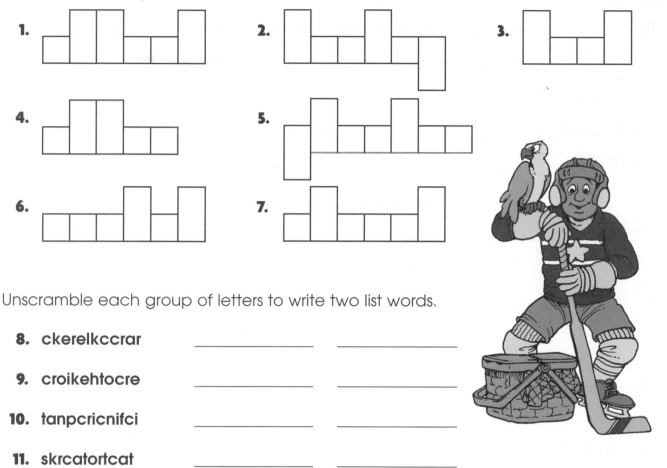

Unscramble each group of letters to write two list words.

8. ckerelkccrar   _____   _____

9. croikehtocre   _____   _____

10. tanpcricnifci   _____   _____

11. skrcatortcat   _____   _____

B. Complete the passage using the challenge words. Then use the number code to learn about an exciting winter sport.

The first Winter ___ ___ ___ ___ ___ ___ ___ Games were held in 1924.
                                                    4

The ___ ___ ___ ___ ___ ___ ___ ___ ___ ___ featured skating and
                   3   6

___ ___ ___ ___ ___ . In 1998, ___ ___ ___ ___ ___ ___ ___ ___ ___ ___ ___
  2   8   1   7

became an Olympic sport. ___ ___ ___ ___ ___ ___ ___ from about 80
                                 5

countries competed in the 2002 Winter Olympic Games. Athletes

sled headfirst at speeds over 80 miles per hour in the

___ ___ ___ ___ ___ ___ ___ ___ event!
 1 2 3 4 5 6 7 8

Scholastic

The **/j/ sound** *can be spelled with the letters* ge *or* dge.

A. Read and write each word. Then organize the list words by their number of syllables.

List Words		one syllable	two syllables
1. ledge	_____	_____	_____
2. package	_____	_____	_____
3. message	_____	_____	_____
4. pledge	_____	_____	_____
5. garbage	_____	_____	_____
6. bridge	_____	_____	_____
7. average	_____	_____	
8. judge	_____		
9. damage	_____	**three syllables**	
10. luggage	_____	_____	
11. edge	_____	_____	
12. discourage	_____		
13. budge	_____		
14. manage	_____		
15. urge	_____		

B. **Challenge Words**

Read and write each word.

16. vegetable _____

17. mineral _____

18. protein _____

19. vitamin _____

20. nutrition _____

A **synonym** is a word with the same or almost the same meaning as another word.

A. Write the list words in each puzzle that are synonyms for the clue words.

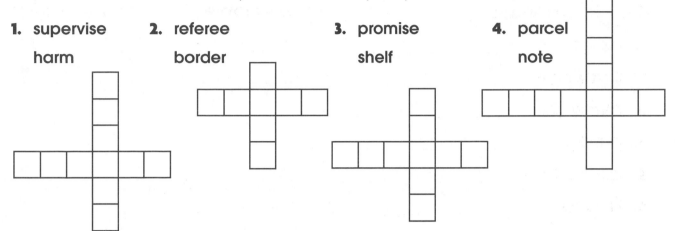

1. supervise

harm

2. referee

border

3. promise

shelf

4. parcel

note

Underline the misspelled words in each sentence. Then write them correctly on the lines.

5. I urdge you to pin a badg on your luggege.

_____   _____   _____

6. The averige length of a bridg in our city is 100 meters.

_____   _____

7. Mom tried to discourije George from putting his hat in the garbadge.

_____   _____

B. Write the challenge word for each phonetic spelling in the puzzle. Then write the shaded letters in order on the blanks below to complete the fact.

1. noo 'tri shən

2. 'vej tə bəl

3. 'min ər əl

4. 'vī tə mən

5. 'prō tēn

6. When you eat, you are feeding about a hundred__ __ __ __ __ __ __ __
cells in your body!

The /s/ **sound** can be spelled with the letters s or c.

A. Read and write each word. Then organize the list words in alphabetical order.

List Words

1. since _____ _____
2. recess _____ _____
3. sentence _____ _____
4. spice _____ _____
5. distance _____ _____
6. succeed _____ _____
7. slice _____ _____
8. princess _____ _____
9. silence _____ _____
10. surface _____ _____
11. instance _____ _____
12. science _____ _____
13. saucer _____ _____
14. source _____ _____
15. spruce _____ _____

B. **Challenge Words**
Read and write each word.

16. insects _____
17. grasshopper _____
18. ladybug _____
19. antenna _____
20. cricket _____

Write the list word that is related to each group of words.

1. queen, king, _____

2. math, reading, _____

3. cup, plate, _____

4. break, rest, _____

5. sugar, flour, _____

6. word, paragraph, _____

7. pine, fir, _____

8. cut, tear, _____

Use the code to write each word.

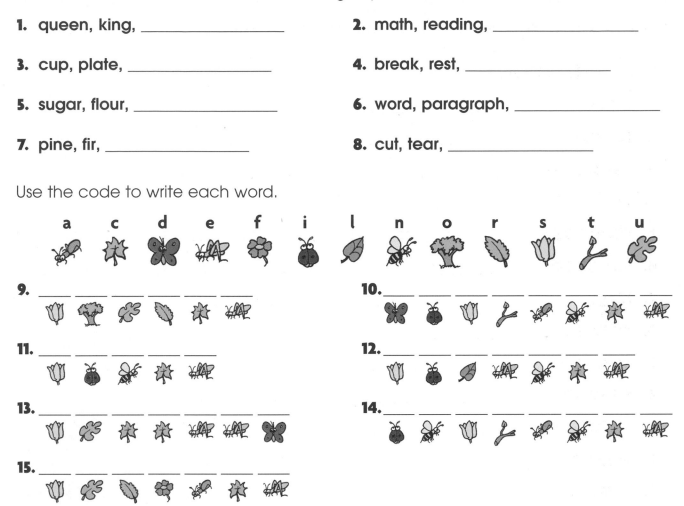

9. _____

10. _____

11. _____

12. _____

13. _____

14. _____

15. _____

Complete each sentence using a challenge word. Then use the number code to answer the riddle below.

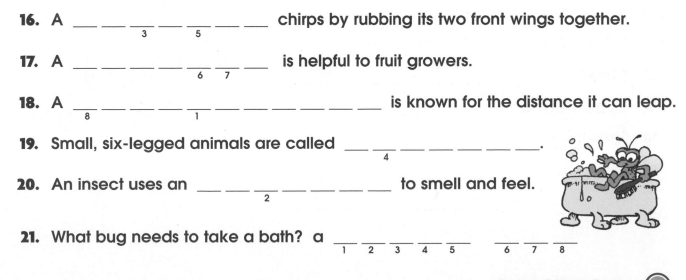

16. A __ __ __ __ __ __ chirps by rubbing its two front wings together.
      3   5

17. A __ __ __ __ __ __ is helpful to fruit growers.
               6 7

18. A __ __ __ __ __ __ __ __ __ is known for the distance it can leap.
      8   1

19. Small, six-legged animals are called __ __ __ __ __ __ .
                                            4

20. An insect uses an __ __ __ __ __ __ to smell and feel.
                          2

21. What bug needs to take a bath? a __ __ __ __ __   __ __ __
                                      1 2 3 4 5   6 7 8

Scholastic

The **schwa sound** /ə/ *can be spelled with the letters* a, e, *or* o. *This sound can be found in many unstressed syllables.*

A. Read and write each word. Then organize the list words by the letter making the schwa sound.

List Words   *a*   *e*

1. garden _____ _____ _____
2. person _____ _____ _____
3. custom _____ _____ _____
4. woman _____ _____ _____
5. problem _____ _____ _____
6. students _____
7. bottom _____ *o*
8. balance _____ _____
9. animal _____ _____
10. season _____ _____
11. frighten _____ _____
12. different _____ _____
13. instant _____
14. opinion _____
15. hospital _____

B. **Challenge Words**
Read and write each word.

16. division _____
17. multiplication _____
18. geometry _____
19. graph _____
20. fraction _____

Scholastic

A. Write the missing vowels for each list word.

1. b___l___nc___

2. pr___bl___m

3. h___sp___t___l

4. w___m___n

5. ___n___m___l

6. ___nst___nt

7. b___tt___m

8. c___st___m

9. ___p___n___ ___n

B. Use proofreading marks to correct the ten mistakes in the word problem. Then solve the problem.

All the studints from Mr. melby's class met in front of the school early saturday morning. It was spring, the seson to plant their class gardon. Each persan was to plant a diferent kind of seed. Mr. Melby was in charge of creating a scarecrow to frightin the crows away They calculated that if every student planted 50 seeds, the class would plant 1,250 seeds altogether. How many students are in Mr. Melby's class. _____

C. Fit the challenge words into the puzzle. Then unscramble the shaded letters on the blanks to spell a number with one hundred zeros. Use a dictionary to check your answer.

6. ___ ___ ___ ___ ___ ___

Some words do not follow common sound-spelling patterns. The spellings of these words must be memorized.

A. Read and write each word. Then organize the list words by the number of vowels in them.

 List Words　　　　**one vowel**　　　　**two vowels**

1. once _____ _____ _____

2. forty _____ _____ _____

3. meant _____ _____

4. young _____ **three vowels** _____

5. island _____ _____ _____

6. another _____ _____ _____

7. truly _____ _____ _____

8. against _____ _____

9. beauty _____ _____

10. toward _____ _____

11. calendar _____

12. answer _____

13. often _____

14. machine _____

15. cousin _____

B. **Challenge Words**
　　　Read and write each word.

16. portrait _____

17. sculpture _____

18. artistic _____

19. landscape _____

20. masterpiece _____

Scholastic

A. Write the list word that belongs with each group of words.

1. peninsula, mountain, _____

2. aunt, uncle, _____

3. twenty, sixty, _____

4. equipment, appliance, _____

5. pretty, handsome, _____

6. month, date, _____

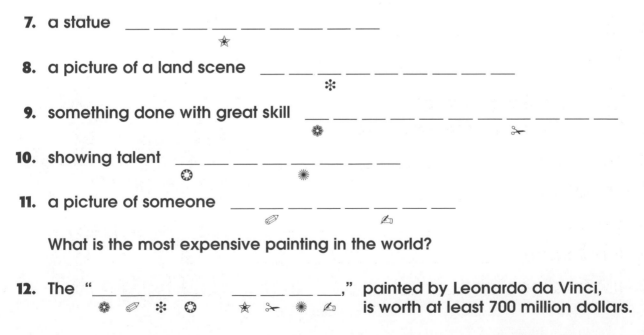

B. Use proofreading marks to correct the 11 mistakes in the paragraph.

Wunce upon a time there was a yung boy who would not study. He ment to study, but he always forgot. Thus, he would ofen need to guess an anser because he truely did not know it. While walking tward his house after school, he decided to lean aginst a tree. He watched a squirrel nibble on a nut. Anuther squirrel scampered up the tree. the squirrels were so fascinating the boy decided to learn about them That night he discovered how interesting it is to study.

C. Write the challenge word for each definition. Then use the picture code to answer the question below.

7. a statue __ __ __ __ __ __ __ __ __
                      ☆

8. a picture of a land scene __ __ __ __ __ __ __ __ __
                                      ❋

9. something done with great skill __ __ __ __ __ __ __ __ __ __ __
                                            ❀   ✄

10. showing talent __ __ __ __ __ __ __ __
                    ❁   ✹

11. a picture of someone __ __ __ __ __ __ __ __
                                  ✐   ✎

What is the most expensive painting in the world?

12. The "__ __ __ __   __ __ __ __," painted by Leonardo da Vinci,
        ❀ ✐ ❋ ❁   ☆ ✄ ✹ ✎   is worth at least 700 million dollars.

There are different ways to form the plurals of words. To form the plural of most words ending in f or fe, change the f or fe to v and add -es. Example: leaf, leaves

Some words have unusual plural forms. Example: man, men

A. Read and write each word. Then organize the list words alphabetically using the guide words below.

List Words   **caboose/knee**

1. loaves   _____   _____   _____

2. geese   _____   _____   _____

3. wolves   _____   _____

4. calves   _____

5. oxen   _____   **knew/scene**

6. children   _____   _____

7. halves   _____   _____   _____

8. teeth   _____   _____

9. thieves   _____

10. scarves   _____   **shallow/wonderful**

11. cacti   _____   _____   _____

12. mice   _____   _____   _____

13. knives   _____   _____

14. women   _____

15. shelves   _____

B. **Challenge Words**
   Read and write each word.

16. reptiles   _____

17. tortoises   _____

18. alligators   _____

19. predators   _____

20. vertebrates   _____

Scholastic

A. Write the list word in the puzzle for each singular form below. Then write the letters in the shaded boxes in order on the blanks below to complete the fact.

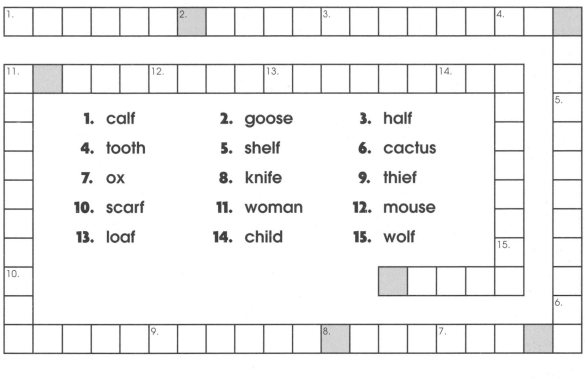

1. calf	**2.** goose	**3.** half
4. tooth	**5.** shelf	**6.** cactus
7. ox	**8.** knife	**9.** thief
10. scarf	**11.** woman	**12.** mouse
13. loaf	**14.** child	**15.** wolf

16. __ __ __ __ __ __ can run across ceilings

because their feet are like suction cups.

B. Use proofreading marks to correct the seven mistakes in the paragraph below. Then write the misspelled words correctly on the lines provided.

Reptils are cold-blooded vertebraetes. this means that their body temperatures stay about the same temperature as their surroundings. Alligaters, lizards, snakes, and tortuises are examples of these scaly-skinned animals Many reptiles are preddators, which means they hunt other animals for food.

_____

_____

_____

_____

Scholastic

Throughout the year, see if you can learn all the words on this Grade 4 spelling list.

accuse	chocolate	faithful	icicle	ocean	rewind	they
activities	clerk	families	idea	often	rhinoceros	they're
against	cloudburst	fearless	Illinois	Olympic	rhyme	thieves
agreed	cloudless	feast	insects	once	rhythm	thoughtful
alligator	clue	few	instance	opinion	rocket	threw
allow	coast	fiction	instant	orangutan	sandwiches	throat
allowance	cocoa	field	introduce	orchestra	saucer	through
anchor	competition	finally	island	outline	scarves	tomorrow
animal	consonant	flight	issue	oxen	school	tortoises
another	continent	forth	jockey	oxygen	science	touchdown
answer	council	forty	journeys	oyster	sculpture	toward
antenna	countries	foul	judge	package	season	tractor
apply	cousin	found	juice	painful	seaweed	truly
artistic	cracker	fourth	knives	peace	secret	turkeys
asteroids	crayon	fowl	ladybug	Pennsylvania	senator	type
astronaut	crew	fraction	landscape	performance	sentence	unbeaten
athletes	cricket	frantic	ledge	person	shadow	uncertain
atmosphere	crocodile	freight	leopard	photocopy	shelves	unequal
attack	custom	frighten	libraries	picnic	shown	unfair
attic	daily	fruit	library	piece	shriek	unfinished
average	damage	galaxy	loaves	plastic	silence	unfriendly
avoid	decided	galleries	luggage	pledge	since	universe
awoke	delicious	garbage	machine	poem	skiing	unknown
background	delight	garden	manage	portrait	skillful	unwrap
balance	dessert	geese	Massachusetts	powerful	slice	urge
basic	destroy	geography	masterpiece	precipitation	snowboarding	useless
beach	diagram	geometry	meant	predators	source	valley
beauty	dictionary	glacier	message	prefix	species	value
biography	different	glossary	mice	president	spice	vegetable
biologist	disappoint	goal	mighty	princess	spoke	vertebrates
boiled	discourage	government	mile	principal	spotless	view
bottom	discovery	governor	miner	principle	spruce	vitamin
boundary	distance	graph	mineral	prize	stack	vowel
brain	division	grasshopper	Minnesota	problem	stray	voyage
brainstorm	downtown	grove	minor	protein	students	windward
breathe	eager	guesses	moisture	prove	submarine	wolves
breathless	earphone	hail	monkey	queen	succeed	woman
bridge	earthquake	halves	monkeys	radio	successful	women
bruise	echo	harmful	mountain	radishes	suffix	wonderful
budge	ecology	harmony	multiplication	raisins	surface	wrote
buzzes	edge	hawk	muscle	reappear	surprise	yacht
cacti	eighth	headquarters	musical	rearrange	syllable	yardstick
calendar	either	heartbeat	myself	recess	tasteless	yield
calves	employ	heroic	narrow	recycle	taxes	yogurt
capitol	erase	highways	neighbor	refuse	teeth	young
capsize	escape	hockey	neither	remove	temperature	
careless	everybody	holidays	New Jersey	replace	their	
cheerleader	everywhere	hospital	nickel	reptiles	themselves	
chessboard	exercise	huge	nutrition	rescue	there	
children	explain	humidity	obey	review	thermometer	

Scholastic

Spelling Practice Test

Fill in the bubble next to the correct answer.

1. Which word does NOT have the long-*a* sound?

    ○ **A**   crayon

    ● **B**   neighbor

    ○ **C**   ahead

    ◑ **D**   obey

2. Which word does NOT have a long-*e* sound?

    ○ **F**   feast

    ○ **G**   leopard

    ○ **H**   beach

    ○ **J**   yield

3. Which word has the long-*i* sound?

    ○ **A**   fiction

    ○ **B**   myself

    ○ **C**   humidity

    ○ **D**   daily

4. Which word has the /s/ spelled with the letter c?

    ○ **F**   surface

    ○ **G**   cricket

    ○ **H**   beach

    ○ **J**   fraction

Scholastic

Spelling Practice Test

Fill in the bubble next to the correct answer.

5. Between which guide words would you find *frantic*?

    ○ **A**   plead/quit

    ○ **B**   feast/giant

    ○ **C**   friend/glue

    ○ **D**   able/bend

6. Which word is the correct plural form of ox?

    ○ **F**   oxs

    ○ **G**   oxes

    ○ **H**   oxen

    ○ **J**   ox

7. Which word is misspelled?

    ○ **A**   truly

    ○ **B**   equiptment

    ○ **C**   statue

    ○ **D**   against

8. Which word is misspelled?

    ○ **A**   geese

    ○ **B**   cacti

    ○ **C**   loafes

    ○ **D**   knives

Scholastic

Vocabulary

Are you a slugabed? Do you like mayo? Do you have a laptop? Words can do many things. They can name people, places, and things. They can describe our experiences. They can show opposites. Some come to us from other languages. Words can be clipped, coined, or funny. They can imitate sounds (onomatopoeias) and they can be arranged in interesting and unusual ways (idioms and oxymorons) all to help us communicate.

The activities in this section introduce your child to all kinds of words. Some are very common, some are not. Some are put together in interesting ways, and some are just fun. Your child will have fun with the words in this section. And remember, children who know lots of words become strong readers.

What to Do
Have your child complete the activity pages. Check his or her work. Cut out the Vocabulary Flash Cards on pages 87–92. Review them with your child throughout the year. Have your child make additional cards as he or she learns new words during the year.

Keep On Going!
Have your child put the Vocabulary Flash Cards into categories such as Words From Other Languages, Funny Words, Onomatopoetic Words, Coined Words, Clipped Words, Oxymorons, and so on. Encourage him or her to add new flash cards to each category throughout the school year. Your child can have fun challenging family and friends with questions about the words such as *What does the word mean? Give me another example of that kind of word. What language does this word come from? Do you know another word that came from that language?* and so on.

A word can have parts. The main part of a word, or **root**, *contains the basic meaning. Here are some common roots.*

> **spec, vid, vis, scop** = see
>
> **aud** = hear
>
> **phon, son** = sound
>
> **tact** = touch
>
> **clam, claim** = shout
>
> **dic** = speak

A. The root is missing from one word in each sentence. Use context clues and the meaning of the roots above to complete each word with its root.

1. My grandfather listens to his old 45s on a _____ograph.

2. NASA lost con_____ with the astronauts during reentry.

3. The _____or of the crowd was almost deafening.

4. We heard a piano _____ata by Beethoven at the concert.

5. Everyone in the _____ience seemed to enjoy the play.

6. Hometown _____tators cheered as their team ran onto the field.

7. The crack in the plate is barely _____ible.

8. Why don't you come over and watch a _____eo with us?

9. The suspect pro_____ed that he was not guilty of the charges.

10. The students used a micro_____e to study the plant cells.

11. I will _____tate the list of words so listen carefully.

B. On another sheet of paper, list the words you made. Define each one in your own words. Then use a dictionary to check your definitions. Make corrections if needed.

C. **Here are some more common roots. Find out what each root means. This will help you figure out the meaning of unfamiliar words.**

1. act	4. aero	7. aqua	10. bio	13. cycl	16. fac	19. form	22. geo	25. gram
2. liber	5. loc	8. mar	11. mob	14. nat	17. pod	20. photo	23 ques	26. san
3. saur	6. scribe	9. sign	12. terr	15. therm	18. trib	21. voc	24. void	27. volv

Scholastic

A **prefix** *is a word part that is added to the beginning of a word and changes its meaning. Here are some common prefixes and their meanings.*

a-	on	mis-	wrong	re-	again, back
anti-	against	**multi-**	many, much	**super-**	above, beyond
im-	not	**non-**	not	**trans-**	across
in-	not	**over-**	too much	**un-**	not
inter-	among, between	**pre-**	before	**under-**	below, less than

Here are some words with these prefixes. Use the information from the chart above to write what you think each word means. Then use a dictionary to check your definitions. Make corrections if needed.

1. aboard _____

2. supervisor _____

3. multicolored _____

4. misunderstood _____

5. international _____

6. preheat _____

7. nonstop _____

8. transcontinental _____

9. uncomfortable _____

10. overpriced _____

11. review _____

12. unbelievable _____

13. inexpensive _____

14. underweight _____

15. impatient _____

16. antifreeze _____

TRANSCONTINENTAL EXPRESS • GATE 2

ALL ABOARD!

Scholastic

*The prefix **dis-** can mean "not" or "opposite of." Draw a line between the prefix and base word in the chart below. Think about how the meaning of the base word changes when **dis-** is added.*

discontinued	disagree	dislike
discover	dishonest	disconnect
disobey	disappear	disapprove

Now use the words to complete the sentences.

1. Activities at the recreation center have been _____ until further notice.

2. You can _____ the electric clock by pulling out the plug.

3. Instead of studying, the _____ student cheated by copying the test answers from another student.

4. My brother always seems to _____ from sight whenever there is work to be done around the house.

5. If you would at least taste the soup, you might _____ that it is really quite good.

6. My parents sometimes _____ with me about which CDs to buy because they _____ of the content.

7. I really _____ doing homework as soon as I get home from school and would rather do something fun.

8. What is the punishment if you _____ the rules?

Scholastic

A **suffix** is a group of letters that is added to the end of a word and can add meaning to it. Some common suffixes and their meanings are listed in the box below.

-ous	full of	**-ward**	direction
-less	without	**-ity**	condition of
-ment	action or process	**-en**	to make
-ent	one who	**-ology**	science or study of
-an	relating to	**-ily**	in what manner

One state grows enough apples each year to circle the earth at least 25 times. Do you know which state this is? To find out, use the suffixes to write a word for each definition. The letters in the boxes will answer the question.

1. in the direction of the east   __ __ __ __ ☐ __ __ __

2. in a hearty manner   __ __ ☐ __ __ __ __ __

3. one who resides in a place   __ __ ☐ __ __ __ __ __

4. full of treachery   __ __ __ __ __ __ ☐ __ __ __

5. relating to America   __ __ __ __ ☐ __ __

6. action of governing   __ __ __ __ __ ☐ __ __ __

7. the study of animals   __ __ __ __ __ __ ☐ __

8. the condition of being necessary   __ __ __ __ __ __ __ ☐ __

9. without noise   __ ☐ __ __ __ __ __ __

10. to make weak   __ __ __ __ __ ☐

11. Name of state   _____

Scholastic

| kinship | remarkable | envious | brotherhood | frailty |
| leadership | profitable | joyous | neighborhood | royalty |

-ship and **-ty** mean "condition of being"
-able means "that can be"

-ous means "full of"
-hood means "a state of being"

Kinship means "related by blood."

Someone who is a good leader shows **leadership**.

Remarkable means "special."

If something is **profitable**, you make money on it.

If you are **envious**, you want what someone else has.

When you are happy, you are **joyous**.

Brotherhood means "fellowship."

A **neighborhood** is an area in a community.

Frailty is weakness.

Royalty means "being royal."

A. Read the vocabulary word. Find and underline two other words in the row that mean almost the same thing.

1. remarkable	extraordinary	uncommon	regular
2. envious	desiring	generous	jealous
3. kinship	relation	family	kindling
4. frailty	favor	feebleness	fragility
5. profitable	money-making	loss	prosperous
6. joyous	journalist	glad	cheerful
7. royalty	kingliness	monarchy	citizen
8. brotherhood	friendship	enemy	fellowship

B. Underline the suffix in each word.

1. leadership   2. neighborhood

Scholastic

kinship	remarkable	envious	brotherhood	frailty
leadership	profitable	joyous	neighborhood	royalty

A. Use what you know. Write the best word to complete each sentence.

1. After so many years, the childhood friends had a _____ reunion.

2. Some people are unhappy with the _____ of our state government.

3. It was an amazing and _____ story.

4. The _____ among the cousins was very strong.

5. The owner hoped her new business would soon be _____ .

6. We know almost all of the people who live in our _____ .

7. The prince walked proudly as did other members of the _____ .

8. Greg was discontented and _____ when his classmates were chosen for the team.

9. The kitten's _____ made it difficult for it to stand very long.

10. The students sang of _____ toward the people they supported.

B. Read each question. Choose the best answer.

1. Which one has street signs? ❏ brotherhood ❏ neighborhood

2. Which one is royalty? ❏ princess ❏ principal

3. What does a country need? ❏ lectureship ❏ leadership

4. Which one might be envious? ❏ giver ❏ taker

Scholastic

aquarium	aquamarine	aqueduct	transport	comport
aquatic	aquanaut	portable	porter	report

MANY WORDS HAVE LATIN ROOTS.

An **aquanaut** is an underwater explorer.

Root:

Aqua means "water."

A tank for fish is called an **aquarium**.

Something that is **aquatic** is related to water.

Aquamarine is a blue-green color like water.

An **aqueduct** is a pipe or channel that carries water.

Port means "carry."

When something is easily moved from place to place, it is **portable**.

If you **transport** something, you take it from one place to another.

A **porter** is someone who carries baggage.

Comport means "to behave in a certain way."

A **report** is an account prepared in an organized form.

A. Read each vocabulary word. Find and underline two other words that mean almost the same thing.

1. comport	act	behave	compost
2. transport	tramp	carry	tote
3. aquarium	bowl	arrangement	tank
4. aqueduct	pipe	approve	channel
5. report	resort	retelling	account
6. aquatic	wet	watery	action
7. aquanaut	diver	alligator	explorer

B. Underline the root in each word.

1. aquatic   **2. portable**   **3. porter**

Scholastic

aquarium	aquamarine	aqueduct	transport	comport
aquatic	aquanaut	portable	porter	report

A. Use what you know. Write the best word to complete each sentence.

1. When Grandpa arrived at the airport, a _____ helped him with his suitcase.

2. Everyone in the class will write a _____ about the field trip.

3. An _____ brings water to the villages in the valley.

4. I use a laptop computer when traveling because it's so _____ .

5. The students took turns feeding the fish in their _____ .

6. Large trucks _____ food to supermarkets all over the country.

7. The movie is about an _____ who works in an underwater station.

8. Vicki wore an _____ sweater with her jeans.

9. We learned about _____ plants that grow in the pond.

10. Mom asked my brother to _____ himself quietly in the library.

B. Read each question. Choose the best answer.

1. Which one could be a crayon? ❏ aquanaut ❏ aquamarine

2. Which one is portable? ❏ tent ❏ tower

3. What does a train do? ❏ transport ❏ transform

4. What does a newspaper do? ❏ report ❏ repay

Scholastic

artisan	artistic	population	popular	corporal
artifact	artist	populous	corporation	corps

**MANY WORDS HAVE
LATIN ROOTS.**

A **corps** is a group of people with special training.

Root:

Art means "art."   An **artisan** is a craftsperson skilled in an industry or trade.

An **artifact** is something, such as a tool, made by human skill.

Artistic means "having to do with art or artists."

An **artist** is someone who paints or is skilled in other fine arts.

Pop means "people."   The **population** is the number of people living in a place.

When a place is **populous**, it has a lot of people.

If you are **popular**, you are well liked.

Corp means "body."   A **corporation** is an organization made up of a group of people who act as one.

Corporal means "having to do with the body."

A. Read the vocabulary word. Find and underline two other words that mean almost the same thing.

1. popular	favored	liked	detested
2. artist	arrow	painter	sculptor
3. populous	crowded	sparse	populated
4. artistic	creative	skilled	clumsy
5. corporation	corner	company	organization
6. population	people	popularity	inhabitants
7. artifact	tool	object	agent

B. Underline the root in each word.

1. artisan   **2. corps**   **3. corporal**

Scholastic

artisan	**art**istic	**popul**ation	**popul**ar	**corp**oral
artifact	**art**ist	**popul**ous	**corp**oration	**corp**s

A. Use what you know. Write the best word to complete each sentence.

1. Tokyo, Japan, is a crowded and _____ city.

2. The beautiful cabinets showed that the carpenter was a talented _____ .

3. Justin's feelings were hurt, but he suffered no _____ harm.

4. Monet was a famous _____ , and his paintings hang in museums.

5. While digging near a stream, the scientists found a very old _____ .

6. Tracy's mother works for a large _____ .

7. That radio program is very _____ with teens.

8. Leon works with a _____ of students who clean up the park.

9. In the last ten years, the _____ of our town has doubled.

10. Kyle decorated the room in an _____ way.

B. Read each question. Choose the best answer.

1. Which word is an adjective? ❑ population ❑ popular

2. Which word is a noun? ❑ artisan ❑ artistic

3. Which word is a homograph? ❑ corporal ❑ corporation

4. Which word is a homophone? ❑ car ❑ corps

Scholastic

geography	geometry	photogenic	telephoto	autobiography
geology	photograph	photocopier	autograph	automatic

MANY WORDS CONTAIN GREEK WORD PARTS.

Lily Brooks

When you sign your name, you write your **autograph**.

Word Part:

Geo means "earth."   The study of the earth's surface is called **geography**.
The science of how the earth was formed is called **geology**.
Geometry is the study of angles, lines, and figures.

Photo means "light."   A **photograph** is a picture taken by a camera.
Someone who is **photogenic** looks good in photographs.
A **photocopier** is a machine that makes copies.
A **telephoto** lens can take pictures at great distances.

Auto means "self."   If you write the story of your life, it's an **autobiography**.
Something that is **automatic** is self-propelled.

A. Draw a line to match each description with the correct vocabulary word.

1. a biography about yourself
2. a door that opens before you touch it
3. an image taken with the use of light
4. the study of rocks that make up the earth
5. a lens that receives light from far away
6. a signature that you write
7. a lesson in circles, squares, and triangles

a. **telephoto**
b. **geology**
c. **autograph**
d. **automatic**
e. **geometry**
f. **photograph**
g. **autobiography**

B. Underline the Greek word part in each vocabulary word.

1. **geography**   2. **photocopier**   3. **autograph**

Scholastic

geography	geometry	photogenic	telephoto	autobiography
geology	photograph	photocopier	autograph	automatic

A. Use what you know. Write the best word to complete each sentence.

1. The class learned about mountains and other landforms in their _____ class.

2. The movie star was very _____ and posed for many pictures.

3. The neighbors put in an _____ sprinkler system for their garden.

4. The students worked with cubes and spheres in _____ class.

5. These pictures of the countryside were taken with a _____ lens.

6. Bob asked the author to _____ her latest book.

7. Mr. Chee used the _____ to reproduce the minutes of the meeting.

8. A geologist is someone who studies _____ .

9. On the desk was a _____ of the whole family.

10. In his _____ , the singer told about his childhood.

B. Read each question. Choose the best answer.

1. Which one is a science?   ❏ geology   ❏ geometry

2. Which one is a book?   ❏ automatic   ❏ autobiography

3. Which one is a picture?   ❏ photogenic   ❏ photograph

4. Which one is a machine?   ❏ photocopy   ❏ photocopier

Scholastic

An **analogy** is a comparison of two sets of similar objects or things.

Think about how the first pair of words is related. Then write the word that completes the second part of the analogy. Use the words in the box or another word you know that fits.

conductor	cashier	custodian
astronaut	professor	paratrooper
geologist	architect	archaeologist
hairdresser	physician	astronomer

1. *Spade* is to *gardener* as *baton* is to _____.

2. *Athlete* is to *team* as ___teacher_____ is to *faculty*.

3. *Lawyer* is to *courtroom* as __hair dresser__ is to *salon*.

4. *Pattern* is to *seamstress* as *blueprint* is to _____.

5. *Cook* is to *chef* as *clean* is to ___custodian___.

6. *Scuba* is to *diver* as *parachute* is to _____.

7. *Mechanic* is to *garage* as ___astronaut_____ is to *space station*.

8. *Screwdriver* is to *carpenter* as *stethoscope* is to _____.

9. *Books* are to *librarian* as *rocks* are to __arch_____.

10. *Flight attendant* is to *airplane* as _____ is to *supermarket*.

11. *Collector* is to *taxes* as _____ is to *artifacts*.

12. *Lasso* is to *cowhand* as *telescope* is to _____.

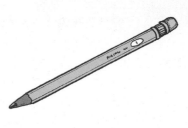

Find the word in each box that doesn't belong. Cross it out, then write it on the last line in the box where it does belong.

1.
fall
inform
swoop
drop
descend
tumble

_____

2.
osprey
heron
stamen
emu
petrel
kingfisher

_____

3.
teach
tell
notify
impart
instruct
pond

_____

4.
pollen
stigma
ovule
temple
pistil
petal

_____

5.
shrine
pagoda
mosque
cathedral
church
macaw

_____

6.
bay
lagoon
topple
inlet
lake
gulf

_____

Explain how the things in each pair are alike.

1. kite and balloon ___They Stay(fly) in the___

___air.___

2. watch and clock ___They tell time___

___

3. magazine and newspaper ___You read them___

___

4. piano and accordion ___~~Ŧ~~ Music ♀ Music~~ey~~ instruments___

___bodies.___

5. pond and lake ___Water___

___

6. highway and street ___Roadways___

___

7. bunk and hammock ___N/A types of bed___

___

8. bonnet and cap ___Lids___

___

Scholastic

Decide how the words in each group are alike. On the blank line write a word that names the group.

GREAT!

A+

1. __Animals__
poodle
collie
beagle

5. __Meat__
beef
ham
veal

2. __Weathers__
rainy
snowy
sunny

6. __Measurement__
pint
gallon (liquid)
quart

3. __Drinks__
cider
milk
juice

7. __Places landforms__
mountain
valley
plain

4. __Body parts in face.__
nose
lips
eyes

8. __Shapes__
rectangle
circle
triangle

Scholastic

Complete the analogies below.

> **Tip** ✓
>
> A *lobe* is to an *ear* as a *nostril* is to a *nose*.
>
> Say to yourself: A lobe is a part of an ear, and a nostril is a part of a nose.

1. A *statue* is to a *museum* as a *dictionary* is to a _____.

Ⓐ library   Ⓑ student   Ⓒ book ✓

2. A *lung* is to a *mammal* as a *gill* is to a _____.

Ⓐ breathe   Ⓑ bird   Ⓒ fish ✓

3. A *stanza* is to a *poem* as a *paragraph* is to a _____.

Ⓐ glossary   Ⓑ story   Ⓒ verse

4. A *paw* is to a *cat* as a *hoof* is to a _____.

Ⓐ dog   Ⓑ horse   Ⓒ claw

5. A *periscope* is to a *submarine* as a *speedometer* is to a _____.

Ⓐ highway   Ⓑ car   Ⓒ telescope

6. A *second* is to a *minute* as a *pint* is to a _____.

Ⓐ hour   Ⓑ quart   Ⓒ cream

7. A *rudder* is to a *boat* as a *handlebar* is to a _____.

Ⓐ bike   Ⓑ basket   Ⓒ ship

8. A *faucet* is to a *sink* as a *nozzle* is to a _____.

Ⓐ shower   Ⓑ bathroom   Ⓒ drain

Scholastic

Hit the books! *is an* **idiom**, *or expression. It means "study carefully," as for a class or a test, but knowing the ordinary meaning of the words does not necessarily help you understand the meaning of the idiom.*

What does the underlined expression in each sentence mean?
Circle the word that you think makes the most sense.

1. My suggestion to get a puppy <u>went over like a lead balloon</u>.

    succeeded   failed   spread

2. Jack tried to <u>butter up</u> his sister, but she knew what he was up to.

    flatter   tease   pester

3. My mother <u>chewed me out</u> for ruining my new jacket.

    praised   scolded   ignored

4. Winning the science prize was a <u>feather in my cap</u>.

    accomplishment   disappointment   monument

5. My brother was <u>green with envy</u> when he saw my new snowboard.

    furious   delighted   jealous

6. My father told me to clean up the mess I had made <u>on the double</u>.

    immediately   afterward   thoroughly

7. Are you still <u>on the fence</u> about what you are going to do?

    certain   undecided   uneasy

8. Why do you always <u>make a mountain out of a molehill</u>?

    underestimate   complain   exaggerate

9. The coach told me to <u>chill out</u> when I flung the bat after striking out.

    practice   shower   relax

10. Buying that old car was money <u>down the drain</u>.

    wasted   found   earned

11. I am <u>all thumbs</u> when it comes to sewing a button onto a shirt.

    skilled   clumsy   frightened

12. Tickets for the concert are <u>scarce as hen's teeth</u> because they were all sold out in an hour.

    available   expensive   nonexistent

A. Buzz, hiss, fizz, *and* hoot *imitate sounds. They are called* **onomatopoeic** *words. Below are more words. Think about their sounds as you say each one aloud. Then list other words you know that imitate sounds.*

sniffle	swish	rumble	crunch	whish	slurp
sizzle	crackle	clatter	hiccup	thud	screech
whir	zing	sputter	clomp	burp	splash

Complete each sentence with a word from the box.
Add *-ed* to the word when necessary.

1. It is not polite to _____ your soup.

2. As the storm approached, we could hear the _____ of thunder.

3. The steaks began to _____ on the grill.

4. The packed snow _____ under our feet.

5. The book fell from the shelf and hit the floor with a _____.

6. If you drink that soda pop too fast, you are sure to _____.

7. The burning logs _____ in the fireplace.

8. The child _____ across the floor in his father's boots.

9. The _____ of the owl startled me the first time I heard it.

10. As soon as I flipped the switch, the motor began to _____.

B. Now write original sentences using onomatopoeic words you listed.

1. _____

2. _____

3. _____

4. _____

5. _____

6. _____

Scholastic

*The phrase "Accidentally on purpose" is what's know as an **oxymoron** because words that make up the phrase contradict each other.*

Create an oxymoron by writing a word from the box next to the underlined word in each sentence.

random	inside
original	bitter
estimate	minor
whisper	sorrow
awfully	unfinished
serious	ugly
shrimp	half
misunderstood	

1. Mason ordered a plate of <u>jumbo</u> _____.

2. I bought a desk that was <u>completely</u> _____.

3. Meg sliced the sandwich and gave me the <u>larger</u> _____.

4. We made cookies with _____ <u>sweet</u> chocolate chips.

5. It is time for some _____ <u>fun</u>!

6. That shirt is <u>pretty</u> _____.

7. I <u>clearly</u> _____ what you were trying to say.

8. Who said that parting is <u>sweet</u> _____?

9. Speaking in a <u>loud</u> _____, we heard what he did not want us to hear.

10. My day was one _____ <u>disaster</u> after another.

11. Did you know that your shirt is _____ <u>out</u>?

12. I have an _____ <u>copy</u> of the letter.

13. Please make an <u>exact</u> _____ of what you will need.

14. The children arranged themselves in _____ <u>order</u>.

15. The soup tasted _____ <u>good</u>.

Many words in the English language have been adopted from other languages.

Chinese	Dutch	Russian	Hindi	Spanish	German
Arabic	Turkish	Japanese	Yiddish	Italian	French

What language do you think each of the following words comes from? Write your guess. Then use a dictionary to check. The dictionary entry for *mammoth* tells that it comes from the Russian language.

mammoth \'ma-məth\ *n* a large, extinct elephant that had long curved tusks and was covered with hair. (1706) [Russian *mamont, mamot*]

		Guess	Check
1.	delicatessen	_____	_____
2.	shampoo	_____	_____
3.	chow	_____	_____
4.	pickle	_____	_____
5.	bouquet	_____	_____
6.	macaroni	_____	_____
7.	borscht	_____	_____
8.	judo	_____	_____
9.	coyote	_____	_____
10.	sherbet	_____	_____
11.	pastrami	_____	_____
12	alfalfa	_____	_____
13.	pumpernickel	_____	_____
14.	bologna	_____	_____
15.	potato	_____	_____
16.	detour	_____	_____

Scholastic

gong	umbrella	opera	judo	depot
paddy	ravioli	trampoline	futon	corduroy

MANY WORDS IN ENGLISH COME FROM OTHER LANGUAGES.

Words From French   A **depot** is a station or storehouse.

Corduroy is a cotton cloth with ridges.

Trampoline is an Italian word.

Words From Malay   A **paddy** is a flooded field where rice grows.

A **gong** is a kind of bell that makes a deep sound when struck.

Words From Italian   An **umbrella** protects you from rain or sun.

Ravioli is a small pocket of pasta filled with meat or cheese.

An **opera** is a story performed in song and music.

Words From Japanese   **Judo** is a sport and form of self-defense using the body.

A **futon** is a kind of mattress.

A. Write *French, Malay, Italian,* or *Japanese* to tell where the word for each picture is from.

1. _____

2. _____

3. _____

4. _____

5. _____

6. _____

7. _____

8. _____

B. Write a vocabulary word for each clue.

1. Many people eat the grain that comes from me. _____

2. People wear pants and jackets made of me. _____

Scholastic

gong	umbrella	opera	judo	depot
paddy	ravioli	trampoline	futon	corduroy

A. Use what you know. Write the best word to complete each sentence.

1. Meg slept on a _____ when she visited Dale.

2. You'll need an _____ today because it's raining.

3. When the _____ was rung, the campers went to dinner.

4. The acrobats did flips while jumping on the _____ .

5. Jody showed us some of the moves she learned in _____ .

6. As the curtain rose, the audience settled in to watch the _____ .

7. Farmers build a low dirt wall to hold water in the rice _____ .

8. The little boy wore brown _____ overalls.

9. Uncle Pete was waiting at the _____ for our bus.

10. One of Janet's favorite foods is _____ .

B. Read each question. Choose the best answer.

1. Which sound does a gong make?   ❏ bing   ❏ bong

2. Which one is like a paddy?   ❏ puddle   ❏ paddle

3. Which one do you stop at?   ❏ depot   ❏ detour

4. What's a trampoline for?   ❏ trembling   ❏ tumbling

Scholastic

deli	disco	vet	gym	dorm
condo	mayo	gas	flu	drape

A CLIP IS A WORD THAT HAS BEEN
SHORTENED, OR CLIPPED.

A **deli** is a store that sells prepared foods.

A **disco** is a nightclub where people go to dance.

If your pet is sick, you take it to a **vet**.

A **gym** is a place for sports and exercise.

Students sleep in a **dorm** at school.

The **flu** is an illness that causes high temperatures and aches.

A **condo** is an apartment that is owned instead of rented.

Mayo is a sauce that people use on sandwiches and salads.

Gas is fuel that makes cars go. / You put a **drape** over a window.

A. Draw a line to match each clip to the word from which it comes.

1. **disco**   a. gasoline

2. **drape**   b. delicatessen

3. **gas**   c. condominium

4. **vet**   d. gymnasium

5. **condo**   e. drapery

6. **deli**   f. discotheque

7. **gym**   g. veterinarian

B. Write the clip for each word.

1. mayonnaise   2. dormitory   3. influenza

_____   _____   _____

deli	disco	vet	gym	dorm
condo	mayo	gas	flu	drape

A. Use what you know. Write the best word to complete each sentence.

1. Bill lives in a _____ at college.

2. Please add some _____ to that tuna fish sandwich.

3. Lewis pulled open the _____ so he could see the view.

4. The workers stopped at the _____ to pick up some lunch.

5. Many students play basketball in the school _____

6. Our teacher has been absent because she has the _____

7. Mr. Perez got out of his car to pump _____

8. The Tylers are buying a _____ in this building.

9. The _____, Dr. Singh, examined my cat.

10. Lily goes dancing at a _____ with friends.

B. Read each question. Choose the best answer.

1. Which one is a home?   ❑ disco   ❑ condo

2. Which one causes fever?   ❑ flue   ❑ flu

3. Which one is a doctor?   ❑ pet   ❑ vet

4. Which one is a deli?   ❑ shop   ❑ ship

Scholastic

astronaut	suburb	hatchback	jazz	laptop
skyscraper	nylon	takeout	monorail	infomercial

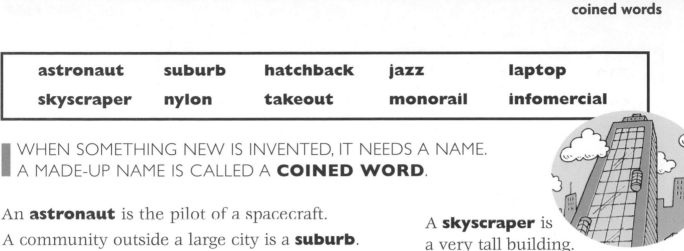

▌WHEN SOMETHING NEW IS INVENTED, IT NEEDS A NAME. A MADE-UP NAME IS CALLED A COINED WORD.

An **astronaut** is the pilot of a spacecraft.

A community outside a large city is a **suburb**.

A car with a hatch in the back is a **hatchback**.

A **skyscraper** is a very tall building.

Jazz is music with strong rhythm and an accented beat that falls in unusual places.

A **laptop** is a small portable computer. / **Nylon** is a material made from chemicals.

Prepared food that you take home to eat is called **takeout**.

A **monorail** is a train that runs on a single track.

An **infomercial** is a TV program that gives information and also sells a product.

A. Write the correct vocabulary word for each picture.

1. _____ 2. _____ 3. _____

4. _____ 5. _____ 6. _____

B. Read each group of words. Write the vocabulary word that goes best with each group.

1. homes, cars, schools _____   **2.** trumpet, piano, saxophone _____

3. pizza, sushi, hamburger _____   **4.** jewelry, clothes, housewares _____

Scholastic

astronaut	suburb	hatchback	jazz	laptop
skyscraper	nylon	takeout	monorail	infomercial

A. Use what you know. Write the best word to complete each sentence.

1. In the parking lot, Mom loaded the groceries into the _____ .

2. Penny wore a _____ jacket when she went out.

3. From his spaceship, the _____ could see Earth.

4. The trio played _____ at the concert.

5. Mr. Farro's company was on the twentieth floor of the _____ .

6. Tim took his _____ so he could work on the plane.

7. After she saw the _____ , Mrs. Ford wanted to place an order.

8. Let's get _____ for dinner tonight.

9. Many people leave the _____ each day to work in the city.

10. A _____ carried people from one terminal to the other.

B. Read each question. Choose the best answer.

1. Which one has stories? ❏ skyscraper ❏ skylight

2. Which one is a vehicle? ❏ hatchback ❏ astronaut

3. Which one is nylon? ❏ threat ❏ thread

4. Which one is food? ❏ takeover ❏ takeout

Scholastic

dummy	beat	bleed	widow	typo
masthead	scoop	crop	headline	stringer

The **headline** of a newspaper article is the title of the story.

▌ THE SPECIAL VOCABULARY USED BY PEOPLE WHO WORK AT CERTAIN JOBS IS CALLED **JARGON**.

A **dummy** is a model of how a page will look.

The area or subject that a reporter covers is called a **beat**.

When a picture goes to the edge of a page, it **bleeds**.

A **widow** is a word on a line by itself at the end of a paragraph.

A **typo** is a mistake in a printed word caused by hitting the wrong letter key.

The names of a newspaper's publishers and editors are listed on the **masthead**.

If a newspaper publishes a big story before anyone else, it's a **scoop**.

If you cut off part of a picture, you **crop** it.

A **stringer** is a reporter who is not on the newspaper staff but sends in stories.

A. Read the newspaper jargon word. Find and underline two other words that mean almost the same thing.

1. dummy	mock up	doll	model
2. bleed	injure	run	extend
3. scoop	first	precede	shovel
4. typo	error	compose	mistake
5. crop	plant	cut	trim
6. beat	assignment	specialty	attack
7. stringer	writer	journalist	twine

B. Write the newspaper jargon word for each clue.

1. a list of names _____   **2.** a word by itself _____

dummy	beat	bleed	widow	typo
masthead	scoop	crop	headline	stringer

A. Use what you know. Write the best word to complete each sentence.

1. The reporter's _____ was City Hall, and his story was about the mayor.

2. The editor wanted to focus on the boy's face so she decided to _____ the photo.

3. Clay's fingers flew over the keys, but he rarely made a _____ .

4. The _____ called to say she had a good story on a robbery.

5. Maya was so proud when her name was listed as an editor on the _____ .

6. The art director made up a _____ to show how the page would look.

7. The picture on this page will _____ across the margin.

8. Marie had some good contacts and got a _____ on a big story.

9. The _____ about the fire was in large bold type.

10. Cut a few words to get rid of the _____ at the end of the story.

B. Read each question. Choose the best answer.

1. Which one do you correct? ❏ typo ❏ type
2. Which one is first? ❏ scoop ❏ scope
3. Which one is alone? ❏ window ❏ widow
4. Which one is a stringer? ❏ reader ❏ reporter

Scholastic

Complete the chart. Write the jargon meaning for each word. Use a separate sheet of paper if necessary.

WORD	USUAL MEANING	NEWSPAPER JARGON
1. bleed	*lose blood*	_____
2. scoop	*a small shovel*	_____
3. crop	*plants grown by a farmer*	_____
4. stringer	*someone who hangs string*	_____
5. dummy	*a lifelike doll*	_____
6. beat	*hit*	_____
7. masthead	*a tall pole for a boat*	_____
8. widow	*a woman whose husband has died*	_____

poppycock	bamboozle	polliwog	dillydally	bonkers
slugabed	scalawag	ballyhoo	hobnob	gobbledygook

SOME WORDS ARE FUN TO KNOW BECAUSE THEY SOUND OR LOOK FUNNY.

If there is an uproar about something, there is a lot of **ballyhoo**.

Poppycock means "nonsense."

When you **bamboozle** someone, you trick that person.

A **polliwog** is a tadpole—a frog in a very young stage.

If you **dillydally**, you waste time. / **Bonkers** means "crazy" or "mad."

Someone who is lazy is a **slugabed**. / A **scalawag** is a rascal or mischievous person.

If you **hobnob** with someone, you are on familiar terms with that person.

Gobbledygook is writing or speaking that is long and windy and hard to understand.

A. Read the words in each row. Cross out the word that does not have a similar meaning to the vocabulary word.

1. bamboozle	fool	bamboo	deceive
2. dillydally	linger	dawdle	rush
3. poppycock	popcorn	foolishness	rubbish
4. bonkers	calm	nuts	wild
5. ballyhoo	commotion	ballroom	disturbance
6. scalawag	scarecrow	troublemaker	good-for-nothing
7. hobnob	associate	hobble	know
8. gobbledygook	confusing	wordy	clear

B. Write a vocabulary word for each picture.

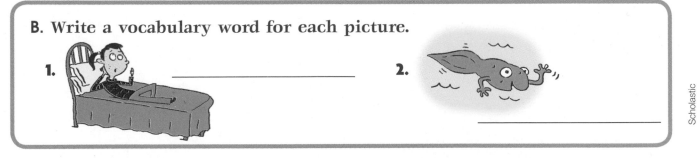

1. _____

2. _____

Scholastic

poppycock	bamboozle	polliwog	dillydally	bonkers
slugabed	scalawag	ballyhoo	hobnob	gobbledygook

A. Use what you know. Write the best word to complete each sentence.

1. The crowd went _____ when the home team won.

2. If you _____ over your meal, we'll miss the show.

3. Beware of salespeople that try to _____ you into parting with money.

4. A _____ has a tail but has not yet developed legs.

5. Gina waited by the stage door so she could _____ with the dancers.

6. The report was full of long, unclear sentences and _____ .

7. In the show, Arnie Piper plays a no-good character who is a _____ .

8. There was a _____ in town when the TV camera crew arrived.

9. Leah is a real _____ and has to be reminded of her chores.

10. Dina didn't believe the news and said it was a lot of _____ .

B. Read each question. Choose the best answer.

1. Which one is a slugabed?   ❐ sleepyhead   ❐ masthead

2. What happens when you dillydally?   ❐ you're early   ❐ you're late

3. Who might bamboozle?   ❐ scalawag   ❐ polliwog

4. If you go bonkers, what are you?   ❐ weary   ❐ excited

*An **abbreviation** is a letter or group of letters that stand for a longer word. Abbreviations for proper nouns begin with a capital letter and end with a period.*

A. Read and write each word. Look for the abbreviation that can stand for both an address and a person. Then organize the list words in the correct category.

List Words	month	address
1. Jan.	_____	_____
2. Feb.	_____	_____
3. Mar.	_____	_____
4. Apr.	_____	_____
5. Aug.	_____	**person**
6. Sept.	_____	_____
7. Oct.	_____	_____
8. Nov.	_____	
9. Dec.	_____	
10. Ave.	_____	
11. St.	_____	**address and person**
12. Rd.	_____	_____
13. Dr.	_____	
14. Gov.	_____	
15. Pres.	_____	

B. **Challenge Words**
Read and write each word.

16. government _____

17. capitol _____

18. senator _____

19. governor _____

20. president _____

Scholastic

A. Circle the letters for the abbreviation of a month found in each word. Then write the abbreviation using a capital letter and a period. The first one has been done for you.

1. (b)(e)n e(f)i c i a l   _Feb._

2. s p e c i a l t y   _____

3. r e p u t a t i o n   _____

4. e n v i r o n m e n t   _____

5. v a g u e   _____

6. s t o m a c h   _____

7. c o m m e n t a r y   _____

8. a d j u s t m e n t   _____

9. i n c r e d i b l e   _____

Rewrite each sentence using an abbreviation for the underlined word.

10. <u>President</u> Adams was the first president to live at 1600 Pennsylvania <u>Avenue</u>.

_____

11. <u>Governor</u> Shapp had to be evacuated from his home at 2035 North Front <u>Street</u> because of the flood in 1972.

_____

12. I bought a book about <u>Doctor</u> Martin Luther King, Jr., at the bookstore on Ballas <u>Road</u>.

_____

 *The **accented syllable** is the syllable that is spoken the most strongly. In a dictionary, it is marked with an accent mark (').*

B. Draw a line to connect the syllables of each challenge word. Then circle the accented syllable.

1. gov   a   dent

2. cap   er   ment

3. sen   em   tol

4. gov   i   tor

5. pres   i   nor

When you address an envelope, use the two-letter postal abbreviation for the name of the state followed by the ZIP code.

Alabama AL	Hawaii HI	Massachusetts MA	New Mexico NM	South Dakota SD
Alaska AK	Idaho ID	Michigan MI	New York NY	Tennessee TN
Arizona AZ	Illinois IL	Minnesota MN	North Carolina NC	Texas TX
Arkansas AR	Indiana IN	Mississippi MS	North Dakota ND	Utah UT
California CA	Iowa IA	Missouri MO	Ohio OH	Vermont VT
Colorado CO	Kansas KS	Montana MT	Oklahoma OK	Virginia VA
Connecticut CT	Kentucky KY	Nebraska NE	Oregon OR	Washington WA
Delaware DE	Louisiana LA	Nevada NV	Pennsylvania PA	West Virginia WV
Florida FL	Maine ME	New Hampshire NH	Rhode Island RI	Wisconsin WI
Georgia GA	Maryland MD	New Jersey NJ	South Carolina SC	Wyoming WY

The capital cities of all 50 states are listed below, but the names of the states are missing. Fill in the states using the two-letter postal abbreviation.

Oklahoma City, _____

Lincoln, _____

Little Rock, _____

Salem, _____

Hartford, _____

Dover, _____

Trenton, _____

Columbia, _____

Augusta, _____

Tallahassee, _____

Cheyenne, _____

Atlanta, _____

Boise, _____

Madison, _____

Springfield, _____

Des Moines, _____

Frankfort, _____

Denver, _____

Annapolis, _____

St. Paul, _____

Jackson, _____

Salt Lake City, _____

Richmond, _____

Charleston, _____

Nashville, _____

Boston, _____

Topeka, _____

Jefferson City, _____

Helena, _____

Carson City, _____

Concord, _____

Santa Fe, _____

Albany, _____

Raleigh, _____

Bismarck, _____

Columbus, _____

Montgomery, _____

Lansing, _____

Harrisburg, _____

Providence, _____

Sacramento, _____

Indianapolis, _____

Honolulu, _____

Pierre, _____

Juneau, _____

Austin, _____

Montpelier, _____

Olympia, _____

Phoenix, _____

Baton Rouge, _____

U.S. MAIL

111 OAK ST.
ELYRIA, OH.
44035

G. FRIEND
222 GROVE ST.
CENTERTON, AR.
72719

PICK UP
TIMES:
9AM

Scholastic

All the words are supposed to be synonyms, but one word in each group actually belongs in one of the other groups. Cross out the word and write it in the correct group.

1. clumsy awkward klutsy ordinary _____	**2.** glossy big-hearted shiny sparkling _____	**3.** weird bewildered confused puzzled _____
4. generous kind trustworthy giving _____	**5.** devoted loyal faithful graceless _____	**6.** average red regular typical _____
7. gleaming wobbly rickety shaky _____	**8.** eerie strange baffled mysterious _____	**9.** brisk unsteady rapid quick _____
10. sturdy durable strong alert _____	**11.** ruby swift crimson scarlet _____	**12.** cautious wary solid careful _____

Antonyms *are words that mean the opposite or nearly the opposite of each other.*

Use the words from the box to write an antonym for each word below. Use a dictionary for help. Then complete each sentence with the word that makes the most sense.

lower	minor	hustle	innocent	sloppy	dry
scarce	failure	darken	brand-new	narrow	

1. (moist, _____)

This chocolate cake is rich, _____, and the best I have ever tasted!

2. (guilty, _____)

The defendant was sentenced to prison after the jury found him _____.

3. (broad, _____)

One behind the other, the hikers made their way along the _____ trail.

4. (lighten, _____)

As the early dawn hour approached the sky began to _____.

5. (dawdle, _____)

Please do not _____, or you may miss the bus again.

6. (hoist, _____)

We used a pulley and rope to _____ everything up to our tree house.

7. (major, _____)

The man had only _____ injuries, so he was treated and released.

8. (success, _____)

It took a little luck and a lot of hard work to be a _____.

9. (plentiful, _____)

Food supplies were _____ after the harvest.

10. (neat, _____)

His handwriting is _____ and difficult to read.

11. (second-hand, _____)

I bought a _____ bike at the thrift store that looked as good as new.

Scholastic

boar	sweet	vein	metal	boulder
bore	suite	vain	mettle	bolder

A **HOMOPHONE** IS A WORD THAT SOUNDS LIKE ANOTHER WORD BUT HAS A DIFFERENT MEANING AND A DIFFERENT SPELLING.

A **boar** is a wild pig.

An uninteresting person can be a **bore**.

Sugar and honey taste **sweet**.

A **suite** is a group of rooms that are connected.

Someone who is **vain** is proud.

Mettle is courage. / A **metal** is a substance such as iron, copper, silver, lead, or brass.

A **boulder** is a big rock. / When you feel braver, you feel **bolder**.

A **vein** is a vessel that carries blood to your heart.

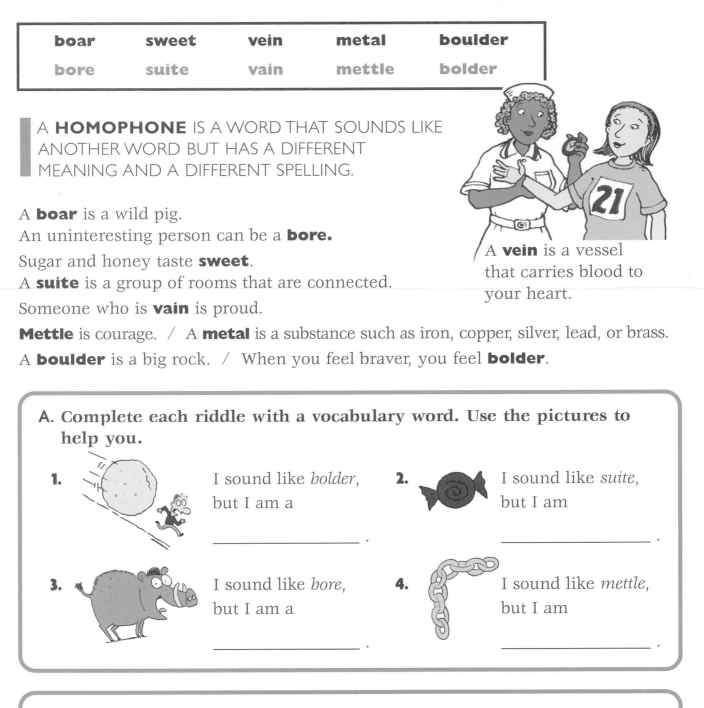

A. Complete each riddle with a vocabulary word. Use the pictures to help you.

1. I sound like *bolder*, but I am a

_____ .

2. I sound like *suite*, but I am

_____ .

3. I sound like *bore*, but I am a

_____ .

4. I sound like *mettle*, but I am

_____ .

B. Write a vocabulary word for each clue.

1. I am a part of the body.

_____

2. I am a prideful way of acting.

_____

boar	sweet	vein	metal	boulder
bore	suite	vain	mettle	bolder

A. Use what you know. Write the best word to complete each sentence.

1. Our family rented a _____ of rooms at the hotel.

2. We climbed over a huge _____ on the hike.

3. Greg really showed his _____ during the storm.

4. The singer was rather _____ about his fine voice.

5. Dad always likes something _____ for dessert.

6. After she improved, Delia felt _____ about speaking French.

7. Much of a car is made from _____ .

8. The speaker was such a _____ that Hal fell asleep.

9. The runner could feel the blood pumping through his _____ .

10. A _____ has bristles and lives in the woods.

B. Read each question. Choose the best answer.

1. Which one is sweet?   ❑ gumdrop   ❑ lemon

2. What's made of metal?   ❑ spoon   ❑ soup

3. Which one is dull?   ❑ boar   ❑ bore

4. Which one's a boulder?   ❑ rock   ❑ pebble

These book titles have errors in them. Rewrite each title so it is correct.

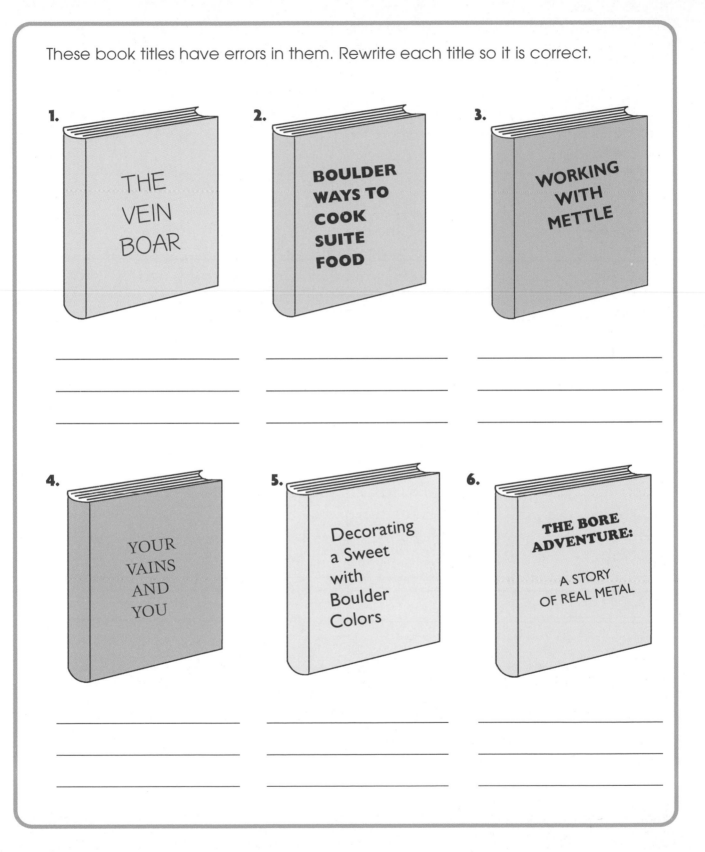

1.

THE
VEIN
BOAR

_____
_____
_____

2.

BOULDER
WAYS TO
COOK
SUITE
FOOD

_____
_____
_____

3.

WORKING
WITH
METTLE

_____
_____
_____

4.

YOUR
VAINS
AND
YOU

_____
_____
_____

5.

Decorating
a Sweet
with
Boulder
Colors

_____
_____
_____

6.

THE BORE
ADVENTURE:

A STORY
OF REAL METAL

_____
_____
_____

Each word below has a synonym, an antonym, and a homophone. See how many you know and can list without referring to the word box at the bottom of the page.

	Synonym	Antonym	Homophone
1. stationary			
2. taut			
3. current			
4. alter			
5. banned			
6. bolder			
7. coarse			
8. cruel			
9. sum			
10. sheer			
11. birth			
12. attendance			

Word Box:

loose   some   still   rough   origin   thin   total   prohibited
presence taught   altar   maintain   outdated   absence   up-to-date
death   meeker   thick   boulder   band   fight   attendants
berth   smooth   change   permitted course   difference
moving   shear   currant kind   hurtful   crewel   stationery

Scholastic

prune	desert	grouse	bass	sewer
prune	desert	grouse	bass	sewer

A **HOMOGRAPH** IS A WORD THAT IS SPELLED THE SAME AS ANOTHER WORD BUT HAS A DIFFERENT MEANING AND SOMETIMES A DIFFERENT PRONUNCIATION.

A **prune** is a dried plum.
When you **prune** something, you trim it.

If you **desert** someone, you leave that person.
A **desert** is a region with little rainfall.

A **grouse** is a kind of bird.

A **bass** is a kind of fish.
The low singing voice of a man is a **bass**.

If you **grouse**, you complain.

Someone who sews is a **sewer**. / A **sewer** is a pipe for carrying away waste.

A. Read each sentence. Then underline the correct phonetic spelling.

1. This lake has a lot of **bass**.   **a.** bas   **b.** bās
2. This cactus grows in the **desert**.   **a.** de´zert   **b.** di´zert
3. A **sewer** made this dress.   **a.** sō´er   **b.** soo´er
4. We hoped the guide wouldn't **desert** us.   **a.** dez´ert   **b.** di´zurt
5. The **sewer** in our town runs beneath the ground.   **a.** sō´er   **b.** soo´er
6. The **bass** singer in the chorus was good.   **a.** bas   **b.** bās

---

B. Write a vocabulary word for each underlined word or words.

1. The gardener will <u>clip</u> the bushes.   _____

2. We saw a <u>bird</u> flying overhead.   _____

3. The boys will <u>grumble</u> if they miss the show. _____

4. A <u>dried plum</u> is a good snack.   _____

prune	desert	grouse	bass	sewer
prune	desert	grouse	bass	sewer

A. Use what you know. Write the best word to complete each sentence.

1. It's not fair to _____ the team now.

2. If you _____ the tree, you'll have a better view.

3. No one wants to hear you _____ all the time.

4. It's usually very warm in the _____ during the day.

5. Every street has a _____ for waste.

6. Nelson caught a _____ in the river.

7. A musical instrument with low tones is the _____ fiddle.

8. Look at all the _____ on the branches of that tree.

9. Mom is a good _____ and will make my costume.

10. If you want some fruit, there is one _____ left in the box.

B. Read each question. Choose the best answer.

1. Can a grouse grouse?   ❏ yes   ❏ no

2. Does a bass sing bass?   ❏ yes   ❏ no

3. Can you desert a desert?   ❏ yes   ❏ no

Scholastic

Read each sentence and the question that follows. Then write the correct word to answer the question. Use a dictionary if you are unfamiliar with the meaning of a word.

1. Your homework is very difficult to read. Is it <u>illegible</u> or <u>eligible</u>?

   _____

2. Your ancestors came to live in America in 1840. Did they <u>emigrate</u> or <u>immigrate</u> to the United States? _____

3. Your grandfather tells an interesting story about his boyhood. Did he tell an <u>antidote</u> or <u>anecdote</u>? _____

4. Your mother insisted that you stop teasing your sister. Did she want you to <u>seize</u> or <u>cease</u> the teasing? _____

5. You showed that your friend's claim was not true. Did you <u>disprove</u> or <u>disapprove</u> it? _____

6. You faint suddenly and then awaken several minutes later. Are you <u>conscious</u> or <u>conscience</u> again? _____

7. Your family moved from New Jersey to Pennsylvania. Are you <u>formally</u> or <u>formerly</u> from New Jersey? _____

8. You brought home an orphaned kitten from the animal shelter. Did you <u>adapt</u> or <u>adopt</u> it? _____

9. You laughed at your sister's odd new hairdo. Did you think it was <u>bizarre</u> or <u>bazaar</u>? _____

10. You and your friends worked together on a project. Did you demonstrate <u>corporation</u> or <u>cooperation</u>? _____

11. You researched facts for a report on the Internet. Did you <u>access</u> or <u>excess</u> the information? _____

12. Your mom left a note asking you to walk the dog. Did she leave a <u>message</u> or a <u>massage</u> for you? _____

Scholastic

Add a letter to each word to create a word that
is very similar. Then say the words in each pair.
Notice how they are spelled. Use a dictionary
to look up the meaning of any unfamiliar words.

1. liter + t = _____

2. through + o = _____

3. father + r = _____

4. later + t = _____

5. envelop + e = _____

6. coma + m = _____

7. desert + s = _____

8. breath + e = _____

9. decent + s = _____

10. ally + e = _____

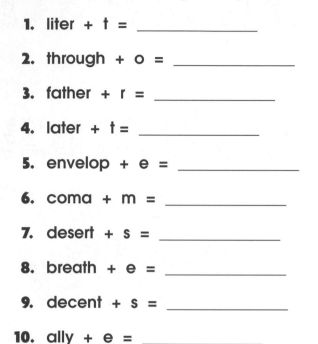

Write the correct word from each pair above to complete the sentences.

11. I took a deep _____ and dove into the water.

12. The _____ behind the building is not a good place to park.

13. The man was in a _____ for a week after the accident.

14. We observed the _____ of the jet as it neared the airport.

15. Alex made a _____ search of his room for the missing boot.

16. A thick fog began to _____ the valley.

17. The hikers went _____ along the trail than they had planned.

18. A surprising number of animals thrive in the _____.

19. If I had to choose between broccoli and spinach, I'd choose the _____.

20. We were so thirsty that we drank a _____ of water.

Scholastic

envious	suburb
custodian	monorail
corps	astronaut
aquatic	frailty
comport	artisan
photogenic	brood
depot	lagoon
populous	scoop

dillydally	seize
scalawag	swish
bonkers	access
bamboozle	conscious
gobbledygook	baffle
disprove	vain
bizarre	antidote
corporation	adapt

geology	durable
autograph	clumsy
conscience	cautious
anecdote	wary
cease	eerie
emigrate	crimson
grouse	scarce
mettle	suite

Vocabulary Practice Test

Fill in the bubble next to the correct answer.

1. Which word completes the following analogy?

   Gymnasium is to gym as gasoline is to _____.

   ○ **A**   station

   ○ **B**   gas

   ○ **C**   oil

   ○ **D**   car

2. Which of the following is an onomatopoeic word?

   ○ **F**   bamboozle

   ○ **G**   crash

   ○ **H**   dummy

   ○ **J**   deli

3. Which word is from a language other than English?

   ○ **A**   camper

   ○ **B**   scoop

   ○ **C**   depot

   ○ **D**   gas

4. Which word names a place where food is served?

   ○ **F**   disco

   ○ **G**   deli

   ○ **H**   gym

   ○ **J**   vet

Vocabulary Practice Test

Fill in the bubble next to the correct answer.

5. Which word describes someone who is lazy?

- **A** dillydally
- **B** poppycock
- **C** polliwog
- **D** slugabed

6. Which word is NOT a synonym for "clumsy"

- **F** awkward
- **G** klutzy
- **H** graceless
- **J** elegant

7. Which word is the opposite of "sloppy"?

- **A** neat
- **B** messy
- **C** untidy
- **D** chaotic

8. What does the word "dummy" mean in newspaper jargon?

- **F** you cut off part of a picture
- **G** a word on a line by itself
- **H** a model of how the page will look
- **J** a mistake in a printed word

Scholastic

Reading Comprehension Skills

Your child can become a strong reader by using key reading comprehension skills to make meaning out of what he or she reads. Good readers set a purpose when reading: to find the main idea, to discover important details, to find the sequence of the story, to compare and contrast story events or characters, to make inferences, predictions, or to draw conclusions. These key reading skills will help improve your child's comprehension of both fiction and nonfiction selections.

What to Do

Read the selections and directions, then have your child complete each activity. Check the work together. Answers, when needed, are provided at the back of the workbook.

Keep On Going!

Reading skills are very important when reading content area materials. You can help your child get more from reading an assigned chapter in a social studies or science textbook. Point out any subtitles in the chapter and explain that they give clues about what is to follow. Then, have your child set a purpose for reading: to find out the events that led to the Revolutionary War; to find out the parts of the flower, and so on. Ask your child questions such as: What caused that to happen? What happened as a result? Why did the colonists declare their independence from Great Britain? Find details that support your answer. These questions provide strategies that will help your child better understand and organize the information he or she reads.

*To **compare** and **contrast** ideas in a passage, determine how the ideas are alike and how they are different.*

Native Americans were the first people to live in America. They lived in many different areas of the United States including the Eastern Woodlands and the Southwest.

The Eastern Woodlands Native Americans had a much different lifestyle than those who lived in the Southwest. The Eastern Woodlands encompassed all of the area from what is now the Canadian border down to the Gulf Coast. The area also extended from the East Coast to the Mississippi River. The northern parts of this area had cold winters, and the whole region had warm summers.

The Southwest Native Americans lived in a large, warm, dry area. Today, Arizona, New Mexico, southern Colorado, and northern Mexico make up this area. In the northern part of this region, wind and water created steep-walled canyons, sandy areas, mesas, buttes, and other interesting landforms. In the southern part, the desert land was flat and dry.

The Iroquois, Wampanoag, Cherokee, and Chickasaw are just a few of the major tribes that made their home in the Eastern Woodlands. The Southwest was home to tribes such as the Apache, Navajo, and Pueblo.

Housing was very different for the Native Americans who lived in these two different regions. The Eastern Woodlands natives built a variety of homes, depending on their location. Northern dwellers lived in dome-shaped wigwams covered with sheets of bark or in longhouses. A longhouse was a large, rectangular shelter that was home to a number of related families, each living in its own section. Those in the southeastern area often built villages around a central public square where community events took place.

Many of the Native Americans of the Southwest lived in cliff houses or large, many-storied homes built from rock and a mud-like substance called adobe. These adobe dwellings could house many families.

All of the Native Americans living in both regions ate a lot of corn, beans, and squash. Hunting was important in both regions, but fishing was more significant in the Eastern Woodlands.

Scholastic

The tribes living in both regions were excellent craftspeople. Those in the Eastern Woodlands made pottery, wicker baskets, and deerskin clothing. Many tribes in the Southwest also made pottery and were very skilled at spinning cotton and weaving it into cloth. This cloth was made into breechcloths and cotton kilts for the men and a kind of dress for the women.

Learning about these fascinating people is important as they have played, and continue to play, a valuable role in our country's history.

1. **Fill in the Venn diagram using the descriptions below.**

wigwams and longhouses	excellent craftspeople
made pottery	cold winters, warm summers
hunting	buttes
many-storied homes	Arizona, New Mexico, and southern Colorado
steep-walled canyons	corn, beans, and squash
fishing	Iroquois and Cherokee
Apache and Navajo	bordered what is now Canada

Southwest   **Both**   **Eastern Woodlands**

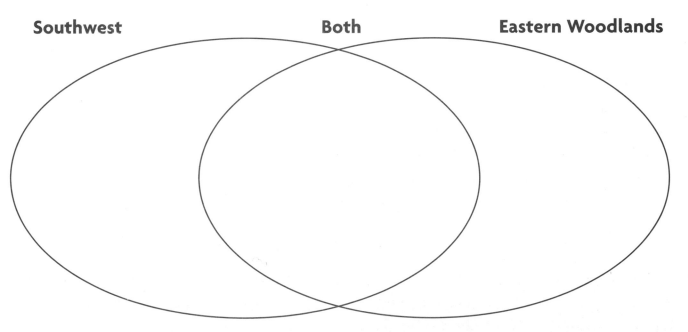

2. **Circle the ways longhouses and adobe houses were alike.**

large   one-family dwellings   fairly small   multiple-family dwellings

3. **How was the climate in certain parts of the Eastern Woodlands different from**

other parts in the same region? _____

Scholastic

The events in a story take place in a certain order. This is called the **sequence** of events.

Pecos Bill is a well-known character in American folklore. His legend developed from stories written by Edward O'Reilly in the early 1900's. This cowboy hero is often credited for being the creator of branding, roping, and other cowboy activities. It is also said that Pecos Bill taught broncos how to buck and cowboys how to ride.

Legend has it that Pecos Bill was born in the 1830s in Texas. He teethed on a bowie knife and had bears and other wild animals as friends. On a family trip to the West, little Bill fell out of the wagon near the Pecos River. He was found by coyotes that raised him.

Two famous natural landmarks are also amusingly traced back to Pecos Bill—the Grand Canyon and Death Valley. Supposedly, Pecos Bill once made a bet that he could ride an Oklahoma cyclone without a saddle. The cyclone was not able to throw him off, and it finally "rained out" under him in Arizona. This rain was so heavy that it created the Grand Canyon. When he reached California, Pecos Bill crashed. It was the force of his fall that is said to have created Death Valley. In actuality, some rocks in the deepest part of the Grand Canyon date back to about two billion years ago. The Colorado River began forming the Grand Canyon about six million years ago. Over centuries, the water eroded the layers of rock, and the walls of the canyon were created. More erosion occurred later as a result of wind, rain, and melting snow.

Death Valley is a desert in California and Nevada. It contains the lowest point in the Western Hemisphere at 282 feet below sea level.

No one is quite sure how Pecos Bill died. One version says he laughed himself to death after listening to silly questions a man from Boston asked him about the West.

Scholastic

1. Look at each picture. Number the events in the order in which they happened in the story. Write a sentence for each.

2. Four words from the story are hidden in the puzzle. The definition of each word is given below. Shade in the letters for each word. The letters go from left to right and top to bottom. The remaining letters will spell the name of a real cool cowboy two times.

a piece of writing

laughingly

attributed with

a particular form of something

a	p	r	t	e	i	c
c	o	l	e	s	a	b
m	u	s	i	i	n	l
g	l	y	l	c	p	r
e	d	e	i	t	c	e
o	d	v	s	e	b	r
i	s	l	l	i	o	n

Scholastic

Sequencing *is when events are arranged in the order in which they happened.*

A. Many linking words help a writer to move through the sequencing more smoothly. Words like *now, then, when, soon, next, later, while, before,* and *after* tie the sentences together.

There are sequencing words used in each sentence below. Underline the sequencing words in each sentence.

1. Before we went to the party, we wrapped our gifts.
2. Everyone jumped into the van then drove to Joe's house.
3. When we arrived, we saw all the beautiful decorations.
4. After greeting our host, we put our gifts on the table.
5. Soon other guests began to arrive.
6. Next, Joe thanked his friends for coming over.
7. While Joe opened his gifts, the guests were served cake and soda.
8. After, a comic told jokes.
9. Finally, it was time to leave.
10. Now, we will go back home.

B. Choose words from the word bank below to fill in the blanks.

then	next	after	at last	first

Colleen was thrilled; _____ the day of the big volleyball match was here!

_____ a brief morning practice, the team ate breakfast together and the coach

sent them home to rest. Colleen took a short nap and called a teammate to discuss strategy.

_____ it was time to return to the gym. _____ Colleen put on her

kneepads. _____ she put on her elbow pads. She was ready to go!

Scholastic

Sequencing *is when events are arranged in the order in which they happened.*

The sentences below belong together. Put them in proper order by writing the correct number (1, 2, 3, 4) in the blank beside each sentence.

Making a Pie Crust

_____ Next, cut in one-third a cup of shortening.

_____ First, sift and measure a cup of flour.

_____ Finally, shape this into a ball and roll it out.

_____ Then, mix two tablespoons of cold water into the flour–shortening mixture.

Changing a Tire

_____ Then, remove the tire and replace it with the spare.

_____ Next, remove the lug nuts.

_____ First, chock the wheels, loosen the lug nuts slightly,

and raise the car.

_____ Finally, tighten the lug nuts, lower the car, retighten the lug nuts.

Baking a Cake

_____ Finally, bake it in a hot oven.

_____ Next, you measure the dry ingredients.

_____ First, measure the liquid ingredients.

_____ Then, combine the liquid and dry ingredients and mix well.

Feeding the Cat

_____ Next, open the can and scoop the cat food into a dish.

_____ First, choose a can of cat food from the pantry.

_____ Then, find a can opener and a spoon from the drawer.

_____ Lastly, feed the cat.

Scholastic

The **main idea** *tells what a story or paragraph is mostly about.*

Read the letters Tyler wrote from camp and those he received. Write the main idea for each letter.

Dear Mom and Dad,   Saturday, June 7

Camp is great! I have met a lot of new friends. Jimmy is from California, Eric is from Iowa, and Tony is from Missouri. We have a great time together, swimming, canoeing, hiking, and playing tricks on other campers! Every night, we sneak over to another cabin. We then try to scare the other campers either by making scary noises or by throwing things at their cabin. It's so funny to see them run out screaming! Now don't worry, Mom. I'm not going to get caught like I did last year.

One thing that is different from last year is how many bugs there are! I know that scientists discover 10 to 20 thousand new kinds of insects each year, and I think they could discover even more here! I have at least 100 itchy mosquito bites and about 20 fire ant bites. Every time I go outside, horseflies chase me, too! Other than all these buggy bugs, I'm having the best time!

Love,
Tyler

Main idea _____

Dear Tyler,   Tuesday, June 10

Are you sure you are okay? All of those bugs sound awful! Have you used all of the "Itch-Be-Gone" cream I got you? You know how your feet swell if you don't use the cream! How about the "Ants 'R Awful" lotion for the ant bites? You and your Aunt Ethel have always seemed to attract those nasty fire ants.

Now Tyler, I am very happy that you have met some new friends and that you are having fun together. However, you MUST stop trying to scare other campers. Remember, honey, some campers may frighten easily. I want you to apologize for any anxiety you may have caused them and start being the nice, polite boy that I know you are. Do you hear me, Tyler? Please be careful. I want you home safely.

Love,
Mom

Main idea _____

Scholastic

Dear Steven,   Saturday, June 7

    Camp is amazing this year! Our guides help us do the coolest stuff. Like yesterday, we hiked for six miles until we found this awesome spring. Then we used a rope hanging on a tree to jump in the water. I went so high that I made a huge splash! Thursday, our guides took us rowing. We rowed to this little island where we made a bonfire. We roasted the fish we had caught. My fish was the biggest, of course!

    Last night, we collected a big bunch of frogs in a bag. Then we put the bag under a bed in another cabin while they were all at the campfire. When they got back, the frogs were all over their cabin. We laughed so hard! I know they're going to get us back. I've seen them planning. I can't wait to see what they try. Hey! How's the leg? Sure wish you were here!

Your friend,
Tyler

Main idea _____

Dear Tyler,   Tuesday, June 10

    That's great you're having so much fun! I wish I were there. All I do is sit around bumming out, thinking about all the fun you are having. I can't believe I broke my leg two days before camp started. My mom keeps renting me movies and video games, but I think I've seen everything and played everything. I just know I won't be happy again until this cast is off.

    Your new friends sound great! Sure wish I was there helping you guys play tricks on the other campers. Remember last year when we smeared honey all over another cabin and all those bees came? That was so funny—except the part where we had to scrub all the cabins clean wearing hot protective gear. I'm still surprised they let you come back this summer!

    Hey! What's up with all the bugs? Your mom called my mom all worried about a bunch of bugs or something. Have fun and write soon!

Your friend,
Steven

Main idea _____

Details *in a story provide the reader with information about the main idea and help the reader better understand the story.*

Washington, D.C., is the capital of the United States. It is located between Virginia and Maryland on the Potomac River. Washington, D.C., is also the headquarters of the federal government. This incredible city is a symbol of our country's history and the home of many important historical landmarks.

Many of Washington, D.C.'s, famous landmarks are located in the National Mall. The Mall is a long, narrow, park-like area that provides large open spaces in the middle of the city's many huge buildings. In addition to being home to the U.S. Capitol, where Congress meets, and the White House, the Mall is also dedicated to honoring the history of our nation. Memorials for presidents George Washington, Abraham Lincoln, Thomas Jefferson, and Franklin D. Roosevelt can all be found in the Mall. There are also memorials honoring Americans who fought in the Korean and Vietnam Wars.

Near the Lincoln Memorial is another memorial. It is the National World War II Memorial. This memorial honors Americans who fought and supported the United States during World War II. The U.S. fought in this war from 1941 to 1945.

The memorial features a Rainbow Pool, two giant arches, a ring of stone columns, and a wall covered with gold stars. Each star represents 100 Americans who died while fighting in World War II.

Bob Dole, a former senator and World War II veteran, worked tirelessly to get this memorial built. He said that the memorial would remind Americans of the value of freedom. "Freedom is not free," said Dole. "It must be earned. . . ."

More than $190 million was raised to build the memorial. Many businesses, private groups, and schools donated money to this cause. The memorial was completed in 2004.

Scholastic

1. **Where is Washington, D.C., located?** Located between Virgingia and Maryland on the Potomac river

2. **Write three facts about Washington, D.C.** Many of Washington D.C.'s landmarks are near the National mall. There is a National world war II memorial. Linconln memorial was finished by 2004

3. **Which four presidents are memorialized in the National Mall?** George.W Abraham Lincoln, Thomas Jefferson, Franklin.D

4. **Besides the four presidents, who else is honored in the Mall?** People who fought in the Korean and Vietnamese wars

5. **What is the name of the 2004 memorial?** National World War II Memorial

6. **Why was it built?** To honor Abe.Lincoln

7. **How long did the United States fight in World War II?** 1941-1945

8. **What are some features of the 2004 memorial?** Rainbow pool, large arches, a ring of stones raised build the Memorial

9. **Write what the stars represent.** Each star repesents a 100 people who died in the world war II

10. **What World War II veteran worked hard to get the memorial built?** Bob Dole

11. **What remembrance did Dole say the memorial would bring to the minds of people?** "Freedom is not free, It must earned"

12. **What were the sources of the over $190 million that was raised to build the memorial?** Businesses, private groups, and Schools.

March-10-23

Context clues *are words or sentences that can help determine the meaning of a new word.*

Jackson was excited! He and his family were on their way to the White House. Jackson could not wait to see the President's official **residence**. He had been reading all about it so that he might recognize some things he saw. After standing in a long line, Jackson, his sister, and their parents were allowed to enter the 132-room, six-floor **mansion**. They entered through the East **Wing**. Jackson knew that he and his family were only four of the 6,000 people who would visit this **incredible** house that day.

The first room they were shown by the **guide** was the State Dining Room. Jackson learned that 140 dinner guests could eat there at one time. "What a great place for a huge birthday party!" Jackson thought.

The Red Room was shown next. Red satin **adorned** its walls. The third room the **visitors** entered was the Blue Room. This room serves as the main **reception** room for the President's guests. Jackson wondered when the President would be out to greet him. After all, he was a guest, too.

The Green Room was the fourth room on the **tour**. Jackson and his family were not surprised to find green silk covering the walls in this room.

The last room was the biggest room in the White House. It is called the East Room. Here, guests are **entertained** after **formal** dinners. Jackson wondered if they could **vary** the entertainment by rolling in **huge** movie screens so they could all watch the latest movies. He wondered if kids were invited sometimes; maybe they had huge, bouncy boxes you could jump in. Perhaps they even set up huge ramps so all the kids could practice skateboarding and roller blading. How fun!

Jackson loved his tour of the White House. He was just sorry that he did not get to see the living quarters of the President's family. He wondered if the President had to make *his* bed every day!

Scholastic

Write one of the boldface words from the story to match each definition below. Use context clues to help. Then write each numbered letter in the matching blank below to answer the question and learn an interesting fact.

1. following the usual rules or customs in an exact way __ __ __ __ __ __ __ __ __
                                                                                    1

2. home __ __ __ __ __ __ __ __
              12   10

3. a gathering at which guests are received __ __ __ __ __ __ __ __ __
                                                  9   17

4. kept interested with something enjoyable __ __ __ __ __ __ __ __ __ __ __
                                                 15   16   8

5. decorated __ __ __ __ __ __ __ __
                            13

6. a leader of a tour __ __ __ __ __
                                      4

7. a part that sticks out from a main part __ __ __ __
                                                  2

8. a very large, stately house __ __ __ __ __ __ __
                                            7

9. a trip to inspect something __ __ __ __
                                       6

10. amazing __ __ __ __ __ __ __ __
                          11

11. very large __ __ __ __ __
                     5

12. guests __ __ __ __ __ __ __ __ __
                3

13. to change __ __ __ __
                   14   18

14. How many gallons of paint does it take to paint the outside of the White House?

__ __ __ __   __ __ __ __ __ __ __   __ __ __ __ __ __ __
1 2 3 4   5 6 7 8 9 10 11   12 13 14 15 16 17 18

Scholastic

To better understand a character, a reader needs to carefully study, or **analyze**, a character's traits, personality, motivations, relationships, and strengths and weaknesses.

One day, Lindsay and Erica were sitting at Lindsay's house working very diligently. Fourth grade was tough, and they were working on a science project about weather. Lindsay was a hard worker like Erica, so the two girls were happy to have each other as partners. They were currently writing about rain and were amazed to learn how much rain Hawaii gets. Lindsay found that Mount Waialeale, on the island of Kauai, gets about 420 inches of rain a year! In 1982, Mount Waialeale set a world record when it received 666 inches of rain. The girls knew that their classmates would find all these facts interesting.

The girls were enjoying the fun facts they were finding when all of a sudden, Lindsay saw Erica choking. Erica had been chewing on a pen cap and had accidentally swallowed it! Erica started pointing to her neck. Lindsay asked her if she was choking. When Erica nodded to say yes, Lindsay quickly got her mom to do the Heimlich maneuver to try to help Erica stop choking. (The Heimlich maneuver is a way to save someone from choking.  This method is named after the doctor who invented it, Henry Heimlich.)

Lindsay's mom did not want to hurt Erica, so the first time she tried the Heimlich maneuver, she did not do it very hard. She tried a second time, and nothing happened. After trying it a third time, the pen cap flew out of Erica's mouth!

Erica was very grateful to Lindsay and her mom. She had been terrified when she realized she had swallowed the pen cap and could not breathe. Lindsay's quick thinking saved her friend. This was one science project that both girls would never forget!

Scholastic

1. Circle each word that describes Lindsay.

   (hard worker)   boring   (brave)   (fast-thinking)

   (quick-acting)   selfish   timid   lazy

2. Circle each word that tells how Erica might have been feeling when she realized she was choking.

   (scared)   thankful   enthusiastic   (helpless)

   courageous   sick   (alarmed)   friendly

3. What do you think Lindsay might be when she grows up? _____
   _____

4. Write *L* for Lindsay, *E* for Erica, or *B* for both.

   _B_ good students   _E_ frightened   _E_ persistent

   _L_ dependable   _E_ grateful   _E_ appreciative

5. What is the name of the doctor who invented the lifesaving maneuver?
   Henry Hiemilch

6. What place gets about 420 inches of rain a year? Mount Waialeal

7. Circle the average amount of rain Mount Waialeale received each day in 1982.

   almost 3"   (just under 2")   just over 4"   about 1"

8. Why do you think this project will be one neither girl will ever forget? _____
   Because Lindsey Saved Ericas
   Life. And Erica was thankful
   _____

Dec -5-22

Scholastic

➤ **Making predictions** *is using information from a story to determine what will happen next.*

Hurray! Spring break is here! Tommy's mom and dad are also on vaction from work all week. They want to plan all kinds of fun things to do, like biking, hiking, fishing, swimming, and tennis. They are hoping for some warm, enjoyable weather. However, they just cannot decide which day to do each activity. So, they decided to check the weather forecast in the newspaper before making some final plans.

THE FIVE-DAY FORECAST

Monday	Tuesday	Wednesday	Thursday	Friday
a beauty with no clouds; high of 82	partly cloudy with a 40% chance of afternoon thunderstorms; high of 80	lingering showers until noon; then clearing and cooler with a high of 70	partly sunny with a high of 60	partly cloudy with a high of 65

1. Tommy and his dad want to spend one whole day fishing. On which day(s) might they not want to go fishing? _Tueseday, Wednesday._

2. What day would be the best day for swimming? _Monday_

Scholastic

3. What other activities could Tommy and his family do on Tuesday and Wednesday?

Play with their dog. Very lucky! I will never get one it seems. Play roblox. Playing with dog is waaaaaaay better than Roblox. I wonder when when when when when when will I get a puppy

4. On what days do you think the family might wear jeans and jackets? _____

Thursday, Friday

5. Do you think Tommy and his family are pleased with the forecast? Why or why not?

No because all the weathers are odd. Monday beautiful! Tuesday, Wednesday good temp but rainy. Thurs, Fri sunny but cooler 60-65.!!

6. To do the kinds of activities Tommy and his family want to do, which forecast do you think they would like to see every day of spring break? Why?

80's because they can go fishing.

7. Write the word from the forecast that means "staying." Tue, Wed

8. Circle the words that describe Tommy's family.

incompetent   athletic   (energetic)   listless

9. Circle the things Tommy and his family might want to take with them if they go swimming on Monday.

jacket   (goggles)   (sunglasses)

(cooler with drinks)   rain umbrella   (sunscreen)

10. Write a paragraph about what Tuesday might be like for Tommy.

_____

_____

_____

_____

_____

_____

Scholastic

*Every story has certain **story elements**. These elements include the characters, the setting, the problem, and the solution.*

In the 1500s, brave men and women and their children sailed from Europe across the Atlantic Ocean to America, looking for a better way of life. These people wanted better jobs than they had in their homelands, and many wanted the freedom to choose their own religion. Still others wanted the opportunity to be able to own land.

This period of time in America is known as the colonial period. It lasted about 170 years. During this time, many colonists worked very hard creating a new nation. The first English colony, Jamestown, was established in 1607. Between 1607 and 1733, 13 permanent colonies were established on the east coast of America. These colonies started to grow and prosper as more and more people from other countries began to immigrate. As the population of the colonies grew, trade and manufacturing developed quickly, especially in towns that had good harbors.

Despite the growth and the many successes of the colonies, the colonists also faced their fair share of problems. One very big problem was the friction between the colonies and Britain. The colonists wanted very much to control themselves and have more say in making decisions that affected them. However, the British Parliament would not allow it. This angered the colonists, so they often ignored British laws.

As Britain imposed more and more taxes on the colonists, the colonists grew angrier and angrier. Acts passed by Parliament, such as the Sugar Act and the Stamp Act, forced the colonists to take action against Britain.

In 1774, delegates from all the colonies except Georgia met to decide how to gain some independence from Britain. They met again in 1775. The delegates helped organize an army and a navy to fight the British soldiers. The colonists wanted freedom from Britain. They outlined this freedom on July 4, 1776, in the Declaration of Independence.

Circle ✓ ✗

A. List each story element.

main characters: Europeans

setting: USA

problem: No freedom

solution: ✓ Declaration of indipendence

B. Use words from the story to complete the puzzle.

Across

1. Britain __had__ many taxes on the colonists, which greatly angered them.

7. People from other countries, looking for better jobs or religious freedom, would __it be__ to America.

8. The colonies decided they wanted to gain __rules__ from Britain.

Down

2. Thirteen __Jamestown__ colonies were established in America between 1607 and 1733.

3. __Colonists__ from almost all of the colonies met to discuss how to gain independence from Britain.

4. The colonists tried to organize an army and a navy to fight the British __Soldiers__

5. The men, women, and children who left their countries to come to America were very __Sad happy__

6. There was __Atlantic ocean__ between the American colonies and Britain.

9. As people from other countries moved to America, the colonies started to grow and __live__ .

Dec-5-22

Scholastic

The **cause** is what makes something happen.
The **effect** is what happens as a result of the cause.

The day was beautiful! Janie and Jake's mom decided to take them to the beach. She even told them that since they had finshed their chores without complaining, they could each bring a friend. Janie and Jake were excited! They loved the beach.

Janie decided to ask Hayley to go since Hayley had just had her over to play last week. Jake asked his friend Charlie—they went everywhere together. Once both friends had arrived, it was time to load up the van. The kids packed some beach toys they might want—shovels, buckets, beach balls, and flippers. Mom packed a cooler with sandwiches and drinks, towels, sunscreen, and a chair for herself.

On the way to the beach, Jake and Charlie groaned. They had forgotten their boogie boards. Oh well! At least they had buckets and shovels they could use to build a huge sandcastle. Jake and Charlie loved to see how big they could make a sandcastle. They even liked to add roads and moats and lots of other details.

Once they reached the beach, everyone helped unload and set up. Then Mom put sunscreen on everyone. It was going to be a hot one—91° with no clouds! Everyone even put on hats.

Right away, the kids started playing. Jake and Charlie started working on their sandcastle, and Janie and Hayley went looking for shells. What a great day!

1. **By each cause, write the letter of the effect.**

Cause:

____ **It was a beautiful, hot day.**

____ **They forgot their boogie boards.**

____ **Jake and Charlie go everywhere together.**

Effect:

A. **Jake asked Charlie to go to the beach.**

B. **Mom put sunscreen on all the kids.**

C. **Jake and Charlie were disappointed.**

Scholastic

2. Write *C* for cause or *E* for effect for each pair of sentences.

   a. _E_ Mom decided to take the kids to the beach.

   _C_ The day was beautiful.

   b. _C_ They forgot their boogie boards.

   _E_ Jake and Charlie would be building sandcastles instead of
   boogie boarding.

   c. _E_ Janie and Jake each got to take a friend to the beach.

   _C_ The children finished their chores without complaining.

   d. ____ Janie asked Hayley to go with her to the beach.

   ____ Hayley had just had Janie over to play.

3. Circle the main idea of the first paragraph.

   Janie and Jake loved to go to the beach.

   Janie and Jake finished their chores without complaining.

   Since it was a beautiful day, Janie and Jake's mom was taking them to
   the beach.

4. Janie and Jake each asked a friend to go to the beach for a different reason.
   Write each child's reason on the correct sandcastle.

Janie   Jake

5. What might Hayley or Charlie have thought on the way home from the beach?

   _____

   _____

Scholastic

To make an **inference** is to figure out what is happening in a story from clues the author provides.

There are eight planets that travel around the sun. They are much smaller than the sun and stars, which are shining balls of hot gases. The sun and stars produce their own heat and light. The planets do not produce heat or light. They get almost all of their heat and light from the sun. Each planet has features that make it unique.

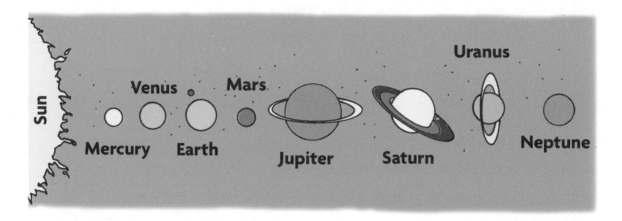

1. The largest planet, _____, is the fifth planet from the sun. It is about 1,000 times bigger than Earth. Saturn is next to this planet.

2. _____ rotates while lying on its side. It takes about 84 Earth years to orbit the sun. It is the seventh planet from the sun.

3. _____'s surface temperature is about 370° F below zero! Brrrrr! It is the eighth planet from the sun.

4. We live on _____, the third planet from the sun. It takes this planet 365 days to orbit the sun. It is often called the "living planet."

5. Many rings surround _____. It takes 10,759 Earth days to orbit the sun. It is located between Uranus and Jupiter.

6. _____ is the closest planet to the sun. It is next to Venus, the second planet from the sun. This planet only takes 88 Earth days to orbit the sun.

7. _____ is often called the "red planet." It lies between Earth and Jupiter, the largest planet. This planet has the largest volcano in the solar system—much higher than Mount Everest!

8. _____ was called the "mystery planet" for a long time because it is covered by thick clouds. It is the second planet from the sun.

Scholastic

Spencer, Jack, Grant, and Kara are new in Mrs. Steen's fourth-grade class. Each of these students came from one of the following states: Pennsylvania, Arizona, Washington, and Massachusetts. They are taking turns giving the class clues about the state from which they moved. The other children are trying to guess the state from the clues.

Use the following clues to help you determine which state was the home of each new student. Write each new student's name on the correct state outline below. Label the state in which all the students now live.

1. Spencer is not from the Keystone State.

2. Grant is not from the south or the east.

3. Kara is not from the south or the west.

4. Jack is not from the south or the west.

5. Grant and Spencer are both from states that border another country.

6. Jack and Kara lived the closest to each other before they moved.

7. Grant used to be able to visit the Space Needle.

8. Many of Spencer's old friends speak Spanish very well.

9. Kara used to live in "the birthplace of the United States."

10. Jack used to vacation on Cape Cod. He also loved strolling along the Freedom Trail.

11. All four children love their new state. It is located in the northeastern corner of the United States. It is the largest New England state. Its nickname is the Pine Tree State. Canada forms its northern boundary.

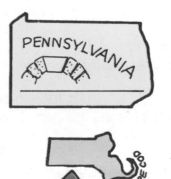

Scholastic

Classifying *means putting things into categories with other similar things.*

Katie knows that it is very important to eat right and to exercise in order to stay healthy. That is why she gets up every morning and has **oatmeal**, a **banana**, and a glass of **milk** for breakfast. Then Katie goes to play kickball.

Katie, Jimmy, Toni, and Anna always organize a two-on-two game of kickball. After playing all morning, the foursome usually sits down for lunch. Katie knows Toni's lunch by heart—**chicken nuggets**, **carrots** and dip, an **apple**, and two **chocolate chip cookies**. Jimmy's lunch varies a little. Some days it is **ham** on **wheat bread**, **grapes**, **yogurt**, and a **candy bar**. Other days his mom will make him come home to eat a good, hot meal of **peas** and **corn**, **rice**, a **hamburger**, **strawberries**, and homemade **ice cream**. Usually on those days, Jimmy has eaten **doughnuts** for breakfast.

The only meat Anna eats is fish, so she often has **fish sticks**, crunchy **broccoli**, a **pear**, **cheese** and **crackers,** and occasionally a piece of her mom's delicious

chocolate cake. Katie always wants a bite of the cake. Sometimes Anna shares, and sometimes she does not.

To finish off her day of trying to eat healthy, Katie usually goes home to one of her dad's magnificent meals. Tonight they are having **pork chops**, **pasta**, **cauliflower** with cheese sauce, and her choice of turtle **cheesecake** or a **vanilla milk shake**. Although Katie and her friends eat some sweets, they try not to eat a lot of them, and they exercise each day.

Scholastic

Write each boldface word from the story in the chart under the correct category.

Dairy	Vegetables	Grains	Fruits	Meat & Fish	Fats/Sweets
Milk	Carrots	Oatmeal	Banana	Chick Nugg	Choc cookies
Yougurt	Peas	Wheat bread	apple	ham	Candy Bar
Cheese	Corn	rice	grapes	hamburger	ice-cream
	brocoli	Crackers	Pear	Fish sticks	doughnuts
					Caker

1. What does Katie do to stay healthy? _____

2. Circle the foods Anna would NOT eat.

   hamburger   broccoli   apple   chicken   cheese   ribs   salmon

3. List four foods Katie might have had for a healthy lunch. _____

   _____

4. Write C for Cause and E for Effect.

   ___ Jimmy goes home to eat a good, hot meal.

   ___ Jimmy has probably eaten doughnuts for breakfast.

5. Write K for Katie, J for Jimmy, T for Toni, or A for Anna.

   ____ chocolate chip cookies   ____ fish sticks

   ____ candy bar   ____ chicken nuggets

   ____ banana   ____ ham

   ____ pear   ____ corn

   ____ carrots   ____ oatmeal

*To **draw conclusions** is to use the information in a story to make a logical assumption.*

Aaaaaahhhhh! It was that time of year again—time to plant flowers. Christina and her dad were trying to decide what kind of flowers to plant this year. Her dad showed her an ad in the morning paper. He wanted Christina to check it out so she could help him determine what they should buy. The two always like to surprise Christina's mom with beautiful flowers before her "big day" in May. Christina was surprised to see Flower Power was having a sale. She knew they had better hurry to the store.

FLOWER POWER SALE
Beautiful flowers of all kinds
— annuals and perennials—
are on sale — 25% OFF!
All pots and hanging baskets
are on sale, too.
Buy one, get one FREE!
Reg. $3.99 to $49.99
Hurry! Sale ends Tuesday!
Flower Power
2418 Harbor Ave.

1. **What time of year is it?** _____

2. **Underline the day in May on which Christina and her dad want her mother to enjoy beautiful flowers.**

   Father's Day   **Earth Day**   **Mother's Day**   **Easter**

3. **Underline why Christina and her dad will probably go to Flower Power today.**

   because they are having a sale

   because they want to plant today

   because the two always plant flowers together

4. **Why might Christina and her dad want to buy new pots or hanging baskets?**

   _____

5. **Why does the ad say to hurry?** _____

   _____

   _____

On the Move

Sam and Danny cannot believe that they have to move away from Florida. Florida is so awesome! They can play outside all day long—every day. It is almost always warm and sunny, and all of their friends live there. What will they do without Brendan, Bailey, John, Alexis, and Brian? They will never have such great friends again. Never!

However, Sam and Danny are very excited for their dad. He has a great new job. The only problem is that the job is in New Hampshire. Danny was not even sure where this state was located. After learning that it is way up north near Canada, both boys did get a little excited about playing in the snow. Danny has always wanted to learn to ski, and Sam thinks playing ice hockey sounds like fun.

Sam and Danny also like the location of New Hampshire. It is between Maine and Vermont and not far from Boston, Massachusetts. Quebec, Canada, borders this state on the north. Neither of the boys has ever visited this part of the country, so they are now looking forward to exploring a new area. If only their friends could come with them! Their parents have promised that they can visit their old friends over spring break and even go to Disney World. The boys think that moving to New Hampshire will not be so bad after all.

1. **How do Sam and Danny feel about Florida?** *They feel like they don't want to move.*

2. **Circle how Sam and Danny feel about leaving their friends.**

   They are sad.

   They do not know what they will do without their good friends.

   They know they will make a lot of new friends.

3. **Circle how the boys feel about moving to New Hampshire.**

   They think it sounds like a fun, interesting part of the country.

   They are excited about visiting their old friends on spring break.

   They are disappointed that it is next to Vermont.

4. **On the map above, label New Hampshire and the states that border it.**

Scholastic

A **summary** *tells the most important parts of a story.*

For each paragraph, circle the sentence that tells the most important part.

1. The largest animal that has ever lived is the blue whale. It can grow up to 100 feet long and weigh up to 200 tons. Whales, for the most part, are enormous creatures. However, some kinds only grow to be 10 to 15 feet long.

(The blue whale is the largest animal.)

Most whales are enormous creatures.

Some whales are only 10 to 15 feet long.

2. Whales look a lot like fish. However, whales differ from fish in many ways. For example, the tail fin of a fish is up and down; the tail fin of a whale is sideways. Fish breathe through gills. Whales have lungs and must come to the surface from time to time to breathe. Whales can hold their breath for a very long time. The sperm whale can hold its breath for longer than an hour.

(Whales and fish do not share similar breathing patterns.)

Whales can hold their breath for about an hour.

Whales might look a lot like fish, but the two are very different.

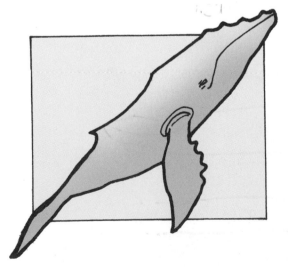

3. Baleen whales have no teeth. Toothed whales have teeth. Baleen whales have hundreds of thin plates in their mouth. They use these plates to strain out food from the water. Their diet consists of tiny animals. Toothed whales eat such foods as other fish, cuttlefish, and squid.

(Whales can be divided into two groups— baleen and toothed.)

Baleen whales have plates in their mouths; toothed whales do not.

Toothed whales use their teeth to chew their food.

Scholastic

4. Whales have a layer of fat called blubber. Blubber keeps them warm. Whales can live off their blubber for a long time if food is scarce. Blubber also helps whales float.

> Layers of fat are called blubber.
>
> Blubber is very important to whales and has many purposes.
>
> Blubber is what makes whales float.

5. Write the main idea of each paragraph to complete a summary about whales.

_____

_____

_____

_____

_____

6. Fill in the whale and the fish with the following descriptions. Write what the two have in common in the shared space. Write the descriptions that are specific to each on the spaces that don't overlap.

can hold breath for long time   people love to watch

gills   tail fin sideways

live in ponds   tail fin up and down

live in oceans   lungs

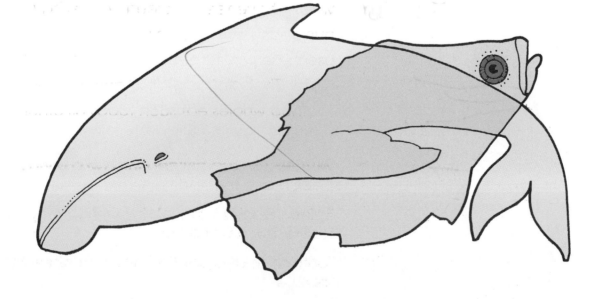

*A **fact** is information that can be proven.
(Example: Asia is a continent.)*

*An **opinion** is information that tells what someone thinks.
(Example: Asia is the most interesting continent in the
world.)*

Mount Everest is the highest mountain in the world. This mountain is located in Asia. Asia is home to all five of the world's highest mountains. Mount Everest's peak is five and one-half miles above sea level. That is very high!

Many climbers have tried to climb to the top of Mount Everest's approximately 29,028-foot peak. The first people to reach the peak were Sir Edmund Hillary and Tenzing Norgay. Since then, thousands of people have survived the climb to Mount Everest's top.

One of the successful climbers is Erik Weihenmayer. Like all who try to climb this huge mountain, Erik faced strong winds, snow, and avalanches. However, what really made Erik's climb unbelievable is the fact that he is blind. After losing his vision at age 13, Erik began climbing at age 16. He has climbed the tallest mountains on all seven continents. Erik became the first blind person to reach the peak of Mount Everest.

At the age of 32, Erik began his climb as part of a 19-member team. His team wore bells that he could follow during his climb, and fellow climbers were quick to warn him of such things as a big drop on the right or a boulder to the left. Erik also used long climbing poles and an ice ax to feel his way across the ice, rock, and snow on the mountain.

During his climb, Erik encountered many dangers. He struggled through 100 m.p.h. winds and sliding masses of snow, ice, and rock. Because the air became thinner the higher Erik climbed, he wore an oxygen mask, as do many who climb high mountains. This helped him breathe as he climbed higher and higher. It took Erik about two and a half months to reach the top of this incredible mountain.

Scholastic

1. Write F for fact or ○ for opinion.

    √ Erik is very courageous.

    ___ The bells made Erik's climb a lot easier.

    ___ Erik is blind.

    ___ All climbers should use climbing poles and ice axes.

    ___ Mount Everest is the world's tallest mountain.

    ___ Erik's oxygen mask helped him breathe.

    ___ Erik used tools to help him climb.

    ___ Erik is proud of his achievement.

2. List three interesting facts from the story. _____

    _____

    _____

3. Write your opinion of Erik's accomplishment. _____

    _____

    _____

4. Circle words that describe Erik.

    brave   foolish   cautious   strong   daring   athletic

5. What are some climbing tools Erik used? _____

    _____

    _____

6. Do you think bells are a good idea for all teams of climbers to use? Why or

    why not? _____

    _____

    _____

7. Why do you think Erik attempted this dangerous climb? _____

    _____

    _____

Scholastic

When you gather details, you must be able to tell facts from opinions. Each statement below is about cameras. Is the statement *fact* or *opinion*? Write *F* or *O* on the line next to each statement.

_____ **1.** Cameras bring happiness and pleasure.

_____ **2.** Joseph Niépce of France took the first photograph in 1827.

_____ **3.** He tried to photograph the view from his window.

_____ **4.** The quality of that first picture wasn't worth the hours he spent on it.

_____ **5.** But Niépce was the best photographer of his day.

_____ **6.** Niépce took on a young partner named Louis Daguerre.

_____ **7.** By 1837, Daguerre figured out how to make photos in far less time.

_____ **8.** Early photographs cost too much and were too hard to make.

_____ **9.** 1888 was the most important year in camera history.

_____ **10.** That's when George Eastman invented a simple camera that used film.

_____ **11.** Nowadays, everyone loves to take pictures.

_____ **12.** Almost anyone can learn to use a camera.

_____ **13.** Digital cameras are much better than film cameras.

_____ **14.** Being a photographer is one of the best jobs you could have.

Scholastic

Reading Comprehension Skills Practice Test

Fill in the bubble next to the correct answer.

1. What category would the words **Italian, Spanish, English,** and **Chinese** fit in?

   ○ **A**　countries

   ○ **B**　states

   ○ **C**　languages

   ○ **D**　peoples

2. Which of the following statements is opinion?

   ○ **F**　The math homework for today is on page 34.

   ○ **G**　Soccer is a great game.

   ○ **H**　The city council will meet next Monday.

   ○ **J**　We will be able to see the stars when it gets dark.

3. Which sentence comes **LAST** in the story?

   ○ **A**　We had a delicious desert for dinner.

   ○ **B**　Mom opened the cake mix.

   ○ **C**　Mom put the cake in the oven

   ○ **D**　I cut up fruit to put on top of the cake.

4. Read the riddle. Look for clues that will help you answer the question.
   How will I ever decide? Look at all the different kinds. There are red hots, chocolates, candy corn, and gummy worms. This is my favorite place in the mall! Where am I?

   ○ **F**　at a cookie shop

   ○ **G**　at a restaurant

   ○ **H**　at a soda fountain

   ○ **J**　at a candy store

Reading Comprehension Skills Practice Test

Fill in the bubble next to the correct answer.

5. Read the paragraph then answer the question.
Three brothers love to play sports. Jeff plays hockey, football, soccer, and baseball. Andy plays hockey, football, tennis, and golf. Seth plays hockey, tennis, soccer, and baseball.

Which sport do all three brothers play?

○ **A**   tennis

○ **B**   soccer

○ **C**   hockey

○ **D**   baseball

6. Read the paragraph and answer the question.
An elephant's trunk is probably the most useful nose in the world. It is used for breathing and smelling, like most noses. However, elephants also use their trunks like arms and hands to lift food to their mouths. They suck water into their trunks and pour it into their mouths. Sometimes they spray the water on their backs to cool off. Elephants also use their trunks to carry heavy things. I bet your nose can't do all that!

Which statement tells the main idea of the story?

○ **F**   Elephants use their trunks for breathing and smelling.

○ **G**   Elephants are clever animals.

○ **H**   Elephants have very useful trunks.

○ **J**   Some people like to ride on elephants.

7. Use the words in the sentence to figure out the meaning of the underlined word.
<u>Donations</u> for the rebuilding fund can be left at the bank.

○ **A**   contributions

○ **B**   forms

○ **C**   plans

○ **D**   lumber

Reading Comprehension Skills Practice Test

Fill in the bubble next to the correct answer.

8. Which of the following events came **FIRST**?

◯ **A**   Last night, I sat down to watch television.

◯ **B**   The television came on.

◯ **C**   Suddenly, the screen went blank.

◯ **D**   I grabbed the remote control and pressed the "on" button.

9. Which event was the result of the explosion?

◯ **F**   Simon placed the dynamite in the old building.

◯ **G**   The old building broke up into hundreds of pieces.

◯ **H**   Marcos lit the fuse.

◯ **J**   People watched the explosion.

10. Mom ordered egg rolls. Dad ordered lo mein. I ordered fried rice. My sister ordered walnut chicken. Where were we?

◯ **A**   at Aunt Karen's house

◯ **B**   in the school lunchroom

◯ **C**   at a Chinese restaurant

◯ **D**   at an Italian restaurant

11. Read the story and tell what you think happened next.
We were walking home from the movies. It was late at night. There wasn't much traffic in the streets. We were talking and laughing. The air was brisk. We could see the warmth of our breath in the air. All of a sudden we looked up and we saw:

◯ **F**   the sun shining on the trees.

◯ **G**   flakes of snow beginning to fall.

◯ **H**   it was starting to rain cats and dogs

◯ **J**   flowers falling from the sky

Scholastic

Reading Passages

Now is the time for your child to use the reading skills he or she practiced in the previous section to help him or her comprehend the selections in this part of the workbook.

What to Do
Have your child read each selection and answer the questions at the end of the selection. Review your child's answers. Remember, answers can be found at the back of the workbook.

Keep On Going!
Encourage your child to rate each selection—four stars for a favorite selection and one star for a least favorite. Be sure he or she gives reasons for the ratings.

A Soccer Superstar

The United States and China were tied 4–4 in the final game of the Women's World Cup soccer match. More than 90,000 fans packed the Rose Bowl in California, where the game was being played. Another forty million people were watching on TV. All eyes were on Brandi Chastain, who was about to take her turn in the penalty kick shoot-out that would decide the winner. The ball flew into the upper right corner of the net. She had scored a goal! The U.S. team won 5–4!

Making that final goal to win the 1999 World Cup may well have been the highlight of Chastain's career as a soccer player. But it was not her only triumph. She had been a soccer star in high school and college. She played on a winning World Cup team in 1991. At the 1996 Olympic games, when the U.S. women's team won the gold medal, Chastain played every minute of every game. Soccer was at the center of her life.

Unfortunately, there were no women's professional teams in the United States for this talented athlete to join. In 1993, Chastain played for one season on a professional team in Japan. She was voted the team's most valuable player. But when she returned home, she could not continue playing soccer as a professional.

Then at last, in May 2000, a United States professional league for women was formed. The Women's United Soccer Association (WUSA) set up eight teams. Women from the 1999 World Cup team were assigned to different teams in the new league. Brandi Chastain was assigned to play for San Francisco. Would she mind playing against her former teammates? Not likely! As usual, Brandi Chastain welcomed the chance to play against tough opponents— and win.

1. **When Brandi Chastain made the most famous goal of her career, she was playing against _____.**

    (A) China.

    (B) her former teammates.

    (C) Japan.

    (D) San Francisco.

2. **What can you tell about the 1999 U.S. World Cup team from this article?**

    (F) Members of the team had been playing together for many years.

    (G) Everyone expected the team to win.

    (H) The players were not professionals.

    (J) It was the first U.S. team to win the Women's World Cup.

Scholastic

Where Did We Get That Word?

The dancer put a cardigan sweater over her leotard. Then she sat down to eat a sandwich. *Cardigan, leotard, sandwich*—where did these words come from? Did you know that each of them was a person's name? Words that come from proper names are called *eponyms*, and there are many eponyms in English.

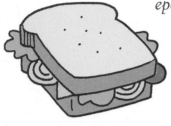

The sandwich, for example, was named for John Montagu, the Earl of Sandwich. He lived from 1718 to 1792. He loved to play cards and did not want to stop a game even to eat. By putting cold meat between two pieces of bread, he could eat while he played.

The cardigan sweater was named for an officer in the British army. In the 1800s, James Thomas Brudenell, the Earl of Cardigan, spent his own money to buy special knitted jackets for the men in his regiment. Knitted jackets with buttons soon came to be called *cardigans*.

Jules Leotard was a French circus performer. In 1859, at the age of twenty-one, Leotard performed the first mid-air somersault. He became known as the "daring young man on the flying trapeze." Leotard invented a close-fitting one-piece suit to wear when he performed. Dancers and acrobats still call their close-fitting garments *leotards*.

Another person who gave her name to a style of clothing was Amelia Bloomer. Bloomer was the editor of a magazine called *The Lily*. American women in her day were expected to wear heavy skirts that dragged on the floor. In 1851, a young woman named Elizabeth Smith Miller introduced a new kind of clothing that was much easier to move around in. She wore a dress that came only to the knees. Under it she wore baggy pants that fitted close at the ankles. Amelia Bloomer published a picture of the outfit in *The Lily*. She hoped women would adopt the new style. In news stories, reporters called the pants "bloomers." A hundred years later, people were still using the word *bloomers* for pants worn under a dress.

Scholastic

There are many other words that come from people's names. The *diesel* engine was named for its inventor, Rudolf Diesel. The word *boycott* comes from the name of an English landlord named Charles Boycott. Where each word came from is a story in itself. Who knows, maybe your name will become a word someday.

1. **Which of these word stories would best fit in this article?**

Ⓐ *Armadillo* comes from a Spanish word meaning "armed." The animal's hard shell looks like armor.

Ⓑ *Braille* is a system of writing for the blind that was developed by Louis Braille.

Ⓒ *Cricket* is a word that imitates the sound a cricket makes.

Ⓓ *Dynamite* comes from a Greek word meaning "power." Alfred Nobel, the inventor of dynamite, created the word.

2. **Which of these words came from a person's name?**

Ⓕ trapeze

Ⓖ editor

Ⓗ boycott

Ⓙ acrobat

3. **What is this article mainly about?**

_____

_____

4. **Why did the Earl of Sandwich invent the "sandwich"?**

_____

_____

5. **What are "bloomers," and where did the word *bloomers* come from?**

_____

_____

_____

A Park in Danger

Everglades National Park is the most endangered national park in America. The purpose of making a national park is to protect the plants and animals that live there. But things that happen outside the park also affect the life within it.

Everglades National Park is part of a much larger area known as the Everglades. At one time, water flowed freely in the Everglades. During the rainy season, water would fill the Kissimmee River. Then it flowed into Lake Okeechobee. Once the lake became full, water spilled over onto the flatland. From there a shallow sheet of water moved slowly down the Florida Peninsula. Then it emptied into Florida Bay. This shallow sheet of water was the Everglades River. It was only a few inches deep in some spots. But it was up to 50 miles wide and over 100 miles long.

The Everglades are home to many plants and animals found nowhere else in the world. Today, some of these plants and animals are in danger of disappearing forever.

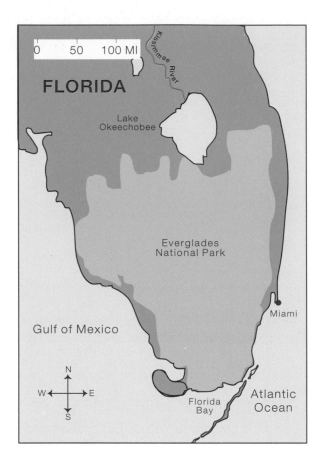

The main reason is that the Everglades is no longer a free-flowing river. Canals have been built to drain most of the shallow river. People have also built a dam to hold back water from Lake Okeechobee. Most of the water from the Everglades is trapped in manmade lakes. Cutting off the flow of water into Everglades National Park has done more harm than good. Now it threatens the wildlife in the park.

Scholastic

Water pollution is another reason some plants and animals are disappearing. Years ago, large areas of the Everglades were drained and turned into farmland. Today the fertilizers used on crops are polluting the water. The "river of grass" is slowly disappearing. The tall sawgrass that once grew in the Everglades River is being replaced by cattails. Many other kinds of plants are disappearing. Animals that depend on these plants for food no longer have anything to eat.

The problems facing Everglades National Park are very serious. But there is still hope. Work is already underway to save the Everglades. The federal government, the state of Florida, and several other groups are all working together to try to undo the damage. But can they do it? Can they save the Everglades before it is too late?

1. **What is another good title for this article?**
   A "Saving the Everglades"
   C "Following the River"
   B "Rare Plants and Animals"
   D "Canals, Dams, and Lakes"

2. **What is the main source of problems in the Everglades?**
   F The rainy season is too short.
   G There are too many plants and animals.
   H Water is no longer allowed to flow freely.
   J Water spills out of Lake Okeechobee.

3. **Give an example of how things that happen outside the Everglades National Park affect the plants and animals within it.**

   _____

   _____

4. **How do you think the author of this article feels about the ways people have changed the Everglades? Tell why you think so.**

   _____

   _____

A Hero for the World

When baseball player Sammy Sosa steps up to the plate, he hits home runs, and lots of them.

Born in 1968 in the Dominican Republic, Sammy Sosa learned early the value of hard work. When Sosa was only seven, his father died, leaving the family extremely poor. Everyone pitched in to help support the family. Sammy shined shoes every day and gave every penny he earned to his mother.

Young Sosa was so busy working, he did not have much time to play. Every once in a while, though, he would join some of the other neighborhood boys in a game of baseball. Too poor to own real equipment, the boys used tree branches or scraps of wood for bats and milk cartons for baseball gloves. The baseball was a piece of cloth wrapped with tape.

When he was fourteen, Sosa got to play on a real baseball team in his hometown. It was the first time he'd ever played using a real glove. He worked hard, and he had a lot of natural talent. When he hit the ball, he hit it hard.

Shortly after Sosa turned sixteen, he was noticed by a scout for the Texas Rangers. The Rangers offered him a contract to play baseball in the United States. Sosa signed the contract on July 30, 1985, becoming a professional baseball player at age sixteen.

Sosa was not an instant success. He still had a lot to learn about the game of baseball. Even though he could hit a fastball hard for a home run, he struck out a lot. Then he also started making more mistakes in the field.

Finally, in 1989, the Rangers traded Sosa to the Chicago White Sox. The White Sox were excited about having him. This helped restore Sosa's confidence, and he began to play well again. Unfortunately, his success did not last. Part of Sosa's problem was that he was trying too hard. He was thinking too much. He ended up making more and more mistakes. In 1992, the White Sox traded Sosa to the Chicago Cubs.

The Cubs believed Sosa could become a great player. They began to work with him to improve his batting. Sosa worked harder than ever before. Soon he was hitting more and more home runs, and he continued to improve. By 1998, he had become baseball's best all-around player. He was voted the National League's Most Valuable Player that year.

Scholastic

On the playing field or off, Sammy Sosa is, indeed, a hero for the world. In 1997, he created the Sammy Sosa Foundation to help people less fortunate than himself. "I want to be known as a good person more than a baseball player," Sosa said. He has donated money to worthy causes in both the Dominican Republic and in Chicago. When Hurricane Georges hit the Dominican Republic in 1998, Sosa arranged to have food, blankets, and other supplies sent there. Sosa's foundation also raised $700,000 to help his country.

For his outstanding service to the community, Sosa received the Roberto Clemente Award in 1998. Mrs. Vera Clemente was present, and she had this to say about Sosa: "He's not just a good baseball player, but a great human being." These words most likely meant more to Sosa than any award he received that year.

1. **Which of these events happened first?**
   - Ⓐ The Texas Rangers traded Sosa to the White Sox.
   - Ⓑ Sosa played on a baseball team in the Dominican Republic.
   - Ⓒ Sosa signed a contract to play baseball in the United States.
   - Ⓓ A scout for the Texas Rangers noticed Sosa.

2. **What is the most important thing in the world for Sammy Sosa?**
   - Ⓕ being a good baseball player
   - Ⓖ living in the United States
   - Ⓗ helping others
   - Ⓙ being voted the Most Valuable Player

3. **Why was Sosa most likely traded by the Rangers?**

   _____

   _____

4. **In what way is Sammy Sosa a "hero for the world"? Give one or two examples.**

   _____

   _____

   _____

Scholastic

Whales and Dolphins

There are more than 80 different kinds of whales and dolphins around the world. Even though they live in water, whales and dolphins are not fish. They are warm-blooded mammals, like cats, dogs, and humans. Like other mammals, their babies are born alive and feed on mother's milk. Mammals breathe air and cannot breathe underwater as fish do. Most whales and dolphins must come up for air after several minutes, or they would drown. A few, though, can stay under for an hour or more.

All whales and dolphins belong to the group of mammals called *cetaceans*. There are two main kinds of cetaceans: those with teeth and those without. *Toothed* whales have sharp teeth that they use to catch, bite, and kill their prey. *Baleen* whales, on the other hand, do not have teeth. Instead, they have mouths full of hanging plates called baleen, which look like big brushes or combs. These are used to filter bits of food from the water. The baleen whales are the real giants of the sea. One kind of baleen whale, the blue whale, is the largest living thing on earth.

All dolphins are whales, and they have teeth. Names can be confusing, though, especially when some dolphins are called *dolphins* and some others are called *whales*. Killer whales, for example, are really dolphins.

The killer whale is one of the most handsome beasts in the sea. It doesn't look much like other dolphins, which are a dull gray or all black. The killer whale is marked with a clear pattern of black and white, and it is the largest of the dolphins. But it is still much smaller than the baleen whales.

Scholastic

Bottlenose dolphins are probably the best known dolphins. They are the ones most often seen on TV and in marine parks. They can be trained to perform jumps, flips, and other exciting moves. Killer whales, too, can be trained to perform jumps and flips. Sea World's Shamu® is one example. During their training and while they are performing, the dolphins are rewarded often, usually with a fish, for carrying out certain behaviors. However, since these are all natural behaviors to begin with, the question is, who's training whom? Dolphins and whales are very intelligent creatures.

1. **The killer whale is really a _____.**
- Ⓐ dolphin
- Ⓑ fish
- Ⓒ porpoise
- Ⓓ baleen whale

2. **Which of these statements is an opinion?**
- Ⓕ All dolphins are whales.
- Ⓖ The killer whale is one of the most handsome beasts in the sea.
- Ⓗ Most dolphins are dull gray or all black.
- Ⓙ The blue whale is the largest living thing on earth.

3. **What are the two main kinds of cetaceans? Tell how they differ.**

_____

_____

_____

4. **All dolphins are whales, but not all whales are dolphins. Explain.**

_____

_____

_____

Scholastic

"I Will Fight No More Forever"

The Nez Percé people lived for many centuries in the part of America we now call Oregon. In the 1800s, white settlers began pouring into that rich and beautiful land. The settlers wanted the land for themselves, and they had the United States Army to help them take it. A band of Nez Percé, led by Chief Joseph, fought hard for the right to stay on their land, but in the end they were defeated. In 1877, Chief Joseph surrendered to General Howard of the United States Army. His speech ended with these famous words:

Hear me, my chiefs! I am tired. My heart is sick and sad. From where the sun now stands I will fight no more forever.

Chief Joseph and the other survivors of his band were forced to leave their homeland. They were sent far away to reservations in Kansas and Oklahoma. Many died of sickness. Those who lived wanted desperately to go back home. In January 1878, Chief Joseph delivered a speech to a large gathering of United States officials and congressmen. He spoke through an interpreter.

There has been too much talking by men who had no right to talk. Too many misrepresentations have been made, too many misunderstandings have come up between the white men about the Indians. If the white man wants to live in peace with the Indian he can live in peace. There need be no trouble.

Treat all men alike. Give them all the same law. Give them all an even chance to live and grow. All men were made by the same Great Spirit Chief. They are all brothers. . . .

You might as well expect the rivers to run backward as that any man who was born free should be contented penned up and denied liberty to go where he pleases. . . .

Let me be a free man—free to travel, free to stop, free to work, free to trade, where I choose, free to choose my own teachers, free to follow the religion of my fathers, free to think and talk and act for myself—and I will obey every law, or submit to the penalty.

Scholastic

1. **The main purpose of Chief Joseph's speech in January 1878 was to _____.**
   - Ⓐ create misunderstandings between whites and Indians
   - Ⓑ make the American people feel sorry for him
   - Ⓒ persuade the U.S. government to let him return to his homeland
   - Ⓓ teach white people about Indian religious beliefs

2. **Which sentence best expresses the main theme of Chief Joseph's speech?**
   - Ⓕ People who break laws cannot expect freedom.
   - Ⓖ Whites can live in peace with Indians if they respect them as equals.
   - Ⓗ A country's laws are more important than individual people.
   - Ⓙ People with freedom to travel and work where they choose will obey the law.

3. **What clue do you have that the U.S. government did not believe Chief Joseph when he said he would "fight no more forever"?**

   _____

   _____

   _____

4. **Reread the sentence that begins, "You might as well expect the rivers . . ." What does Chief Joseph mean? Rewrite the sentence, using your own words to express the same idea.**

   _____

   _____

   _____

5. **Reread the last paragraph of Chief Joseph's speech. Do you think that what he is asking for is reasonable? Why or why not?**

   _____

   _____

   _____

Scholastic

Read each story. Then fill in the circle that best completes each sentence or answers each question.

SAMPLE

Many people like to glide along the sidewalk on roller skates. They owe a vote of thanks to Joseph Merlin of Belgium. He invented a kind of roller skate back in 1760. His skates **provided** a pretty bumpy ride, however.

1. What is the best title for this story?
○ **A.** "Inventors"
○ **B.** "Famous Inventions"
○ **C.** "Belgium"
● **D.** "Early Roller Skates"

2. In this story, the word **provided** means
○ **F.** scraped.
○ **G.** invented.
● **H.** gave.
○ **J.** took.

A. Boston Post Road is the oldest road in the United States. It is more than 300 years old! Colonists made the road in the 1670s, more than 100 years before the American Revolution. They needed a way to carry mail and messages between two growing cities—Boston and New York. The road followed old Native American trails.

1. What is the best title for this story?
○ **A.** "Building Roads"
○ **B.** "U.S. Mail"
○ **C.** "Two Colonial Cities"
○ **D.** "America's First Road"

2. You can guess that
○ **F.** Boston Post Road is still around.
○ **G.** Boston is a small city.
○ **H.** Boston Post Road is short.
○ **J.** New York is older than Boston.

3. You would probably find this story in a book about
○ **A.** fairy tales.
○ **B.** current events.
○ **C.** how to build roads.
○ **D.** American history.

Scholastic

B. In 1271, Marco Polo left Italy and set out for China. He was just 17 years old! Polo's trip took three and a half years. In China, he discovered a black stone that burned and gave heat. It was coal. Polo also learned about paper-making and the compass. When he got home, he wrote a book about his **journey**.

1. Marco Polo traveled to
○ **A.** Greece.
○ **B.** the United States.
○ **C.** China.
○ **D.** Africa.

2. In this story, the word **journey** means
○ **F.** trip.
○ **G.** findings.
○ **H.** sailboat.
○ **J.** country.

3. Which of these is an *opinion* about Marco Polo?
○ **A.** He lived in the 1200s.
○ **B.** He traveled to China.
○ **C.** He was the greatest explorer of all time.
○ **D.** He wrote a book.

C. When you're hungry, or even just thinking about food, you often hear your stomach growl. Sometimes, your stomach also growls when you're nervous or excited. What you are actually hearing is your stomach muscles pushing air around inside your stomach.

Your stomach also makes noises right after you eat. That's because your stomach muscles move around to mix the food you've eaten with special juices. When they do this, they also move around the air that you swallowed with your food. This causes your stomach to growl, though not as loudly as when your stomach is empty.

1. This story is mainly about
○ **A.** how you digest food.
○ **B.** muscles of the human body.
○ **C.** why your stomach growls.
○ **D.** why people get hungry.

2. You can guess that your stomach growls the loudest when you
○ **F.** are eating.
○ **G.** are at school.
○ **H.** yell loudly.
○ **J.** need food.

3. Which of the following statements is an *opinion*?
○ **A.** Stomach noises are gross.
○ **B.** Your stomach growls when its muscles push air around in your stomach.
○ **C.** Your stomach can growl when it's full.
○ **D.** Sometimes your stomach growls when you're nervous.

4. Your stomach growls because
○ **F.** you have eaten too much.
○ **G.** there is air in your stomach.
○ **H.** you feel sick to your stomach.
○ **J.** you are tired.

Scholastic

D.   Hundreds of fish produce electricity. The most dangerous is the electric eel, a long slimy fish that lives in South America. This snakelike fish gives off electric signals to "see" in the dark water where it lives. These signals bounce off underwater objects and help the eel find fish and frogs to eat.

   Once the electric eel locates its prey, it fills the water with an electric shock. The organs that produce electricity are in the eel's body. The shock stuns or kills any small animals in the area around the eel. The electric charge is so strong it could also stun a person or knock over a full-grown horse!

1. The electric eel looks like a
   ○ **A.** snake.
   ○ **B.** fish.
   ○ **C.** turtle.
   ○ **D.** bird.

2. The author wrote this story to
   ○ **F.** tell about different kinds of eels.
   ○ **G.** tell about electric eels.
   ○ **H.** ask people to protect fish.
   ○ **J.** explain electricity.

3. In this story, the word **locates** means
   ○ **A.** swims.
   ○ **B.** eats.
   ○ **C.** slides.
   ○ **D.** finds.

E.   Popcorn is one of the oldest American snack foods. By the time European explorers arrived here in the 1400s, Native Americans were already growing about 700 types of corn. They used popcorn for both food and decoration. Some tribes used it in their headdresses and necklaces.

   These early popcorn lovers couldn't plug in the electric popper or zap the popcorn in the microwave. Instead, they popped the kernels in clay pots over an open fire. Some kinds of popcorn were even popped right on the cob.

   English colonists got a taste of popcorn at the first Thanksgiving feast in 1621. A Native American named Quadequina brought a deerskin bag filled with popcorn to the dinner. It was a hit!

1. What is the best title for this story?
   ○ **A.** "The History of Popcorn"
   ○ **B.** "Native Americans"
   ○ **C.** "The First Thanksgiving"
   ○ **D.** "Snack Foods"

2. Which happened first?
   ○ **F.** Colonists ate popcorn.
   ○ **G.** Electric-poppers were invented.
   ○ **H.** Movie theaters served popcorn.
   ○ **J.** Native Americans grew corn.

3. Popcorn has been used for
   ○ **A.** sewing.
   ○ **B.** making paint.
   ○ **C.** heating homes.
   ○ **D.** making jewelry.

4. This story would probably go on to talk about
   ○ **F.** how microwaves work.
   ○ **G.** the popularity of popcorn today.
   ○ **H.** Native American customs.
   ○ **J.** snacks of the world.

Scholastic

Reading Passages Practice Test

Read the selection. Fill in the bubble next to the correct answer.

Courtney's father is a doctor. His name is Dr. Goodwin. Everyone in our community thinks he is a great doctor. I think so, too. Whenever I don't feel well, my mother calls Dr. Goodwin. When we get to his office, he checks my temperature and asks me what is wrong. He always gives me something that makes me feel much better. It is easy to see that Dr. Goodwin really cares about his patients. He always calls later in the day to make sure that I'm feeling better.

1. The main idea of this story is:

   ○ **A**   Dr. Goodwin is my friend.

   ○ **B**   Courtney's father is my doctor.

   ○ **C**   Our community has a great doctor.

   ○ **D**   Dr. Goodwin had children, too.

2. Another word for community is:

   ○ **F**   town

   ○ **G**   state

   ○ **H**   country

   ○ **J**   school

3. Which sentence shows that Dr. Goodwin cares about his patients?

   ○ **A**   Dr. Goodwin is an excellent physician.

   ○ **B**   Wherever I don't feel well, my mother calls Dr. Goodwin.

   ○ **C**   Dr. Goodwin always takes my temperature.

   ○ **D**   Dr. Goodwin always calls to check up on his patients.

Scholastic

Reading Passages Practice Test

Choose a sticker to place here.

Read the selection. Fill in the bubble next to the correct answer.

Crayons were not always so colorful. Two hundred years ago, all crayons were black. They were used in factories to label crates and lumber. Children could not use crayons because they were poisonous. Then a company called Binney & Smith came up with an idea. They invented a safe formula for crayons so that teachers and children could use them. They also added colors. These new crayons were named "Crayola crayons." The first box of Crayola crayons included eight colors: black, brown, blue, red, purple, orange, yellow, and green. A box of crayons sold for five cents.

4. What is the main idea of the story?

○ **A** Crayons have changed a lot over the last two hundred years.

○ **B** You should not eat crayons.

○ **C** Each box of Crayola crayons has eight colors.

○ **D** The first crayon was black.

5. Which color was not one of the original eight?

○ **F** brown

○ **G** yellow

○ **H** pink

○ **J** purple

6. How were the Crayola crayons different from the original black crayon?

○ **A** They were only used in factories.

○ **B** They were not poisonous.

○ **C** They were used to label crates.

○ **D** They did not contain the color black.

Scholastic

Grammar/Writing

To be a successful writer, you have to understand the rules of the game. Grammar provides the rules your child needs to write clear and interesting selections in a variety of writing modes: expository, persuasive, and narrative.

The activities in this section review the rules for good writing. Those rules include knowing parts of speech (nouns, pronouns, adjectives, verbs, adverbs) and how to use them to build clear, interesting, and well-developed sentences and paragraphs.

What to Do

Each new skill starts with a definition or explanation. Have your child read the definitions or explanations on the activity page. Then have your child complete the activity. Review his or her work together. Let your child know that he or she is doing a great job!

Keep On Going!

Read your child's writing assignments. Prompt your child with suggestions such as: Can you give a clearer explanation? How does that idea relate to the next idea? What is the main idea? Do you have details to support it? Why not compare the actions of the main characters?

noun

adjective

verb

A **noun** names a person, place, thing, or idea.

Fill in the letter beneath the word in each sentence that is a noun.

1. The world's first toothbrushes weren't brushes at all.
   (A)   (B)   (C)   (D)

2. They were pencil-sized twigs that were frayed at one end.
   (A)   (B) (C)   (D)

3. These "chew sticks" were found in many ancient Egyptian tombs!
   (A)   (B) (C)   (D)

4. The oldest bristle toothbrush was made in China over 500 years ago.
   (A)   (B) (C)   (D)

5. The stiff bristles came from the necks of hogs.
   (A)   (B)   (C)   (D)

6. They were attached to handles carved out of bone or bamboo.
   (A)   (B)   (C)   (D)

7. The early Chinese toothbrushes were known for having hard bristles.
   (A)   (B)   (C)   (D)

8. Europeans who brushed at all used softer toothbrushes made of horsehair.
   (A)   (B)   (C)   (D)

9. A 1723 French medical book said to clean teeth with a natural sponge.
        (A)   (B)   (C)   (D)

10. But any natural animal hair could introduce germs to the mouth.
   (A)   (B)   (C)   (D)

11. In 1938, Americans could buy the very first nylon-bristled toothbrush.
   (A)   (B)   (C)   (D)

12. Nylon was a new fiber that was considered safer and cleaner to use.
   (A)   (B)   (C)   (D)

13. Today, you can get toothbrushes in any size, stiffness, shape, and color.
        (A) (B)   (C)   (D)

14. You can also get electric toothbrushes to help keep your mouth healthy.
   (A)   (B)   (C)   (D)

Scholastic

Dec-5-22

A **proper noun** names a particular person, place, or thing. A **common noun** names any person, place, or thing.

Write a proper noun that is an example of each common noun.
The first one has been done for you.

1.	state	Arizona
2.	singer	Michael Jackson
3.	river	Patapsco (psco)
4.	artist	keth harin
5.	woman	Pallavi
6.	mountain	Everest
7.	athlete	Lebron James
8.	game	Roblox Soccer
9.	shampoo	Dove
10.	song	Calm Down
11.	medicine	Allout drops
12.	doctor	Eye doctor

Write a common noun to name the group that includes each proper noun.
The first one has been done for you.

13.	Brazil	country
14.	Harry Potter	Show
15.	New York Mets	Game
16.	Asia	Continent
17.	Britney Spears	Singer
18.	Honda	car
19.	*Lord of the Rings*	Movie (Book)
20.	Indiana	state
21.	Superior	word
22.	April	Month
23.	Tuesday	day
24.	Abe Lincoln	President

Dec-5-22

Scholastic

➡ A *and* an *are* **articles**. *They are noun signals. They let you know a noun is coming up in a sentence.*

Use *a* when the word following it begins with a consonant sound. Use *an* when the word following it begins with a vowel sound.

Write the correct article in the blank.

1. There was _____*an*_____ opening in the cave.

2. Michael hid in _____*a*_____ hollow tree.

3. I looked under the water and saw _____*a*_____ big red crab.

4. _____*An*_____ umbrella was lying open on the floor.

5. Judy stood by _____*an*_____ odd-looking structure.

6. Matthew was being followed by _____*an*_____ animal.

7. The treasure was buried on _____*a*_____ piece of property.

8. Joshua did _____*a*_____ good trick with the cards.

9. Julie was sailing on _____*a*_____ rickety old boat.

10. Peggy wants to be _____*a*_____ pilot when she grows up.

11. Frankenstein was _____*a*_____ friendly monster.

12. Ms. Betty broke her crown when she fell down on _____*a*_____ clown.

13. _____*An*_____ apple a day will keep the doctor away.

14. The girls were three peas in _____*a*_____ pod.

15. The girl took _____*an*_____ order for the yearbook.

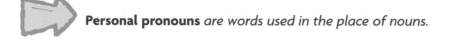

Personal pronouns *are words used in the place of nouns.*

Example: (Katie) went out to finish her chores and then **she** went out to play.
"She" (pronoun) takes the place of "Katie" (proper noun).

Listed below are some personal pronouns.

| I | me | you | he | him | she | her | it | we | us | they | them |

Underline the personal pronouns in the following sentences.

1. Greg read the book and returned it to the library.

2. The teacher chose Lisa and me to hand out the papers.

3. You will represent the school at the spelling bee.

4. Did I receive a phone call?

5. Steven, please help him with the math homework.

6. All of us will be attending the football game.

7. Who will help them finish the decorations?

8. Tell her that she won the prize.

9. We will have to drive them to the party.

10. Please hang it up on the back wall.

11. How many of you will be able to attend?

12. Only four of us ate lunch in the cafeteria.

Scholastic

Possessive pronouns *come before nouns and show ownership. Some possessive pronouns are:* **my, his, her, its, your, our,** *and* **their.**

Example: Lisa has a pet **frog**. **His** name is Hopper.
His (possessive pronoun) takes the place of **frog** (noun).

Fill in the blanks with one of the possessive pronouns listed above.

1. The firemen showed _____ class how to climb a ladder.

2. Peter cleaned _____ room.

3. Kate loves to play soccer. _____ favorite position is goalie.

4. The students planned a surprise party for _____ teacher.

5. "Mrs. Ruiz, please take _____ students through the museum."

6. _____ team won the game.

7. "_____ dog just had puppies," said Karen.

8. The boy thanked _____ teacher for helping him with his French homework.

9. Bobby, Joel, and Jack helped _____ coach put away the baseball equipment.

10. The spider spun _____ web near the door.

11. Julie came into the room and asked, "Why are _____ papers all over

    the floor?"

12. Why can't you put _____ things away neatly?

13. After Vernon saw the movie, he got into _____ car and drove away.

14. The girls said a few words and then put _____ coats on and went home.

15. _____ mom was so tired that we cooked dinner for her.

Scholastic

A **subject pronoun**—**I, you, he, she, it, they,** or **we**—can replace the subject of a sentence. An **object pronoun**—**me, you, him, her, it, us,** or **them**—can replace a noun that is the object of an action verb or that follows a preposition.

A. Choose the pronoun in parentheses ( ) that completes each sentence, and write it on the line. Then identify the kind of pronoun in the sentence by writing *S* for *subject* or *O* for *object*.

1. _____ took a boat trip through the Everglades. (We, Us) _____

2. The boat's captain gave _____ a special tour. (we, us) _____

3. The captain said, " _____ will love the wildlife here!" (You, Us) _____

4. _____ brought a camera in my backpack. (I, M__) _____

5. I used _____ to photograph birds, turtles, and alligators. (he, it) _____

6. My sister Kit carried paper and pencils with _____ (she, her) _____

7. Kit used _____ to sketch scenes of the Everglades. (t__, them) _____

8. _____ is an excellent artist. (She, Her) _____

B. Rewrite each sentence. Replace the underlined words with the correct subject or object pronoun.

1. <u>Our grandparents</u> sent a postcard to <u>my sister, my brother, and me</u>.

_____

2. The <u>postcard</u> was addressed to <u>my older brother</u>.

_____

C. Write two sentences. In the first, use a subject pronoun. In the second, use an object pronoun.

1. _____

2. _____

Scholastic

Circle the correct *antecedent* (the noun that matches the meaning) of each underlined pronoun.

1. Checkers is a very old game; <u>it</u> was played in Egypt over 4,000 years ago!

   Ⓐ **board game**   Ⓒ **checkers**

   Ⓑ **Egypt**   Ⓓ **years**

2. Players then were neither children nor old folks; <u>they</u> were warriors and rulers.

   Ⓕ **players**   Ⓗ **folks**

   Ⓖ **children**   Ⓙ **warriors**

3. What proof do we have for checkers in Egypt? <u>It</u> appears in ancient paintings.

   Ⓐ **ancient**   Ⓒ **paintings**

   Ⓑ **proof**   Ⓓ **Egypt**

4. "Enemy" pieces were "captured" by opponents <u>who</u> tried to defeat each other.

   Ⓕ **enemy**   Ⓗ **opponents**

   Ⓖ **pieces**   Ⓙ **other**

5. Another name for checkers is "draughts." <u>This</u> is pronounced *drafts*.

   Ⓐ **name**   Ⓒ **drafts**

   Ⓑ **draughts**   Ⓓ **checkers**

6. Many famous people through history loved to play checkers. <u>One</u> was Ulysses S. Grant—the Civil War general who later became president.

   Ⓕ **general**   Ⓗ **famous person**

   Ⓖ **president**   Ⓙ **history**

7. The oldest known book about checkers (draughts) was published in Spain in 1547. <u>Its</u> author was Antonio Torquemada.

   Ⓐ **the book's**   Ⓒ **the game's**

   Ⓑ **the author's**   Ⓓ **Spain's**

8. The world's largest checkerboard, <u>which</u> uses big round pillows for playing pieces, is in Petal, Mississippi.

   Ⓕ **pieces**   Ⓗ **pillows**

   Ⓖ **Mississippi**   Ⓙ **checkerboard**

Scholastic

Prepositions *show the relationship between a noun or pronoun and another word or group of words in a sentence such as* **in, on, of, for,** *or* **at.** *Groups of words introduced by a preposition are called* **prepositional phrases.**

A. Read each sentence. Underline each group of words that begins with a preposition, and circle the preposition. Some sentences have more than one prepositional phrase.

1. The boy cut out pictures of mountains, rivers, and lakes.

2. He enjoyed pasting them on the walls of his room.

3. His father responded to the scenes in the pictures.

4. He decided that he would take his son on a camping trip.

5. They carried supplies in a backpack and knapsack.

6. The boy drank a hot drink from his father's mug.

7. That afternoon they hiked in the mountains for hours.

8. They were disappointed when they found many campers at the Lost Lake.

9. The boy and his father continued on their journey.

10. Finally, they stopped at a quiet place for the night.

11. The boy and his father ate and slept in a tent.

12. The tent kept them safe from the wind and rain.

13. Will this trip make the boy feel closer to his father?

14. What else will they see on their camping trip?

B. Complete each sentence with a prepositional phrase.

1. Let's go to the store _____.

2. I just received a letter _____.

3. Eduardo found his missing sneaker _____.

4. Tanya always plays soccer _____.

A **verb** *tells the action in a sentence.*

Fill in the letter beneath the word that is a verb.

1. Did you know that bats are the only mammals
     Ⓐ   Ⓑ   Ⓒ

that can fly?
    Ⓓ

2. Many people fear bats, but bats are really
      Ⓐ Ⓑ   Ⓒ

very important to us.
    Ⓓ

3. Bats eat half their body weight in bugs every night.
    Ⓐ   Ⓑ   Ⓒ Ⓓ

4. Fear and ignorance give people the wrong ideas about bats.
    Ⓐ   Ⓑ Ⓒ   Ⓓ

5. Most bats are harmless to humans and valuable to nature's balance.
     Ⓐ   Ⓑ   Ⓒ   Ⓓ

6. Bat mothers generally produce only one baby (called a pup) each year.
    Ⓐ   Ⓑ   Ⓒ Ⓓ

7. Bats usually live in large colonies, often in caves or other dark places.
    Ⓐ Ⓑ   Ⓒ   Ⓓ

8. Each year, vandals destroy thousands of bats by blocking cave entrances.
     Ⓐ   Ⓑ   Ⓒ   Ⓓ

9. Bats are not really blind, but they do have that reputation.
    Ⓐ   Ⓑ Ⓒ   Ⓓ

10. As for the belief that bats carry rabies, this idea has been exaggerated.
 Ⓐ   Ⓑ   Ⓒ   Ⓓ

11. You're more likely to be hit by a falling star than to get rabies from a bat.
     Ⓐ   Ⓑ Ⓒ Ⓓ

12. All the people who misunderstand bats keep science educators busy!
     Ⓐ   Ⓑ Ⓒ Ⓓ

The most common linking verb is *be*. *Am, is, are, was,* and *were* are forms of the verb. Circle the correct form of *be* for each sentence.

1. Last spring, my brother and I _____ helping Uncle Rusty, who is a rancher.

   Ⓐ **are**   Ⓒ **were**

   Ⓑ **was**   Ⓓ **have been**

2. The first day we got there—it _____ a Friday—one of his mares had a new foal.

   Ⓐ **has been**   Ⓒ **may be**

   Ⓑ **was**   Ⓓ **was being**

3. That was the first time I _____ so close to such a big newborn animal.

   Ⓐ **being**   Ⓒ **were**

   Ⓑ **have been**   Ⓓ **had been**

4. Just before the birth, the mother horse _____ quietly pacing in her stall.

   Ⓐ **had been**   Ⓒ **were**

   Ⓑ **has been**   Ⓓ **would be**

5. The newborn's wobbly legs _____ longer than its body, yet the baby stood right up.

   Ⓐ **are**   Ⓒ **were**

   Ⓑ **was**   Ⓓ **have been**

6. "That's always the way it _____ with newborn foals," said Uncle Rusty with a smile.

   Ⓐ **should be**   Ⓒ **might**

   Ⓑ **have been**   Ⓓ **were**

7. "By summer, that foal _____ a frisky young horse racing its mom," he added.

   Ⓐ **was**   Ⓒ **were**

   Ⓑ **will be**   Ⓓ **have been**

8. We had such a great time on the ranch, Uncle Rusty predicted that we _____ back soon.

   Ⓐ **was**   Ⓒ **were**

   Ⓑ **would be**   Ⓓ **have been**

Adjectives *describe or tell more about things.*

Fill in the letter beneath the word in each sentence that is an adjective.

1. The world's tropical rain forests are
 A   B

amazing places.
 C   D

2. Rain forests grow so lush because
 A   B

of plentiful rain and warm sun.
 C   D

3. They are home to exotic creatures that live
 A   B   C

nowhere else on earth.
 D

4. Rain forests also play an important role in the world's weather.
 A   B   C   D

5. The highest part of the rain forest is called the canopy.
 A   B C   D

6. The canopy contains the most colorful layer of rain-forest life.
 A   B   C   D

7. There are brilliant flowers and fruits of every color.
 A   B   C   D

8. Many rain-forest plants reach enormous sizes that may seem unbelievable.
 A   B   C   D

9. The most spectacular of the rain forest's creatures are its birds.
 A   B   C   D

10. But insects win the grand prize—there are millions of insects in rain forests.
 A   B   C   D

11. Some of the world's most valuable medicines come from rain-forest plants.
 A   B   C   D

12. The rosy periwinkle is a plant used to make cancer medicines.
 A   B   C   D

13. Let's save the rain forests so that future generations can benefit from them.
 A   B   C   D

Scholastic

> **Comparative adjectives** *compare two things by adding* **–er** *to the adjective or by using the word* **more**. **Superlative adjectives** *compare three or more things by adding* **–est** *or by using the word* **most**.

A. In each sentence, underline the adjective that compares.

1. Anna is older than her brother Caleb.

2. That was the loudest thunderstorm of the entire summer.

3. Seal is the biggest cat that I have ever seen.

4. Papa is quieter than Sarah.

5. The roof of the barn is higher than the top of the haystack.

6. The kitten's fur was softer than lamb's wool.

7. Sarah pointed to the brightest star in the sky.

8. What is the saddest moment in the story?

B. Underline the adjective in parentheses ( ) that completes each sentence correctly. On the line write *two* or *more than two* to show how many things are being compared.

1. On the (hotter, hottest) day in July, we went swimming. _____

2. Today is (warmer, warmest) than last Tuesday. _____

3. Is winter (colder, coldest) on the prairie or by the sea? _____

4. This is the (taller, tallest) tree in the entire state. _____

5. Sarah's hair is (longer, longest) than Maggie's. _____

6. Of the three dogs, Nick was the (friendlier, friendliest). _____

7. Caleb's horse is (younger, youngest) than Anna's pony. _____

8. The new foal is the (livelier, liveliest) animal on the farm. _____

Adverbs can tell *when, where, how,* or *how much*. Answer each question using one or more of the adverbs in the box below. Write in full sentences.

always
eagerly
loudly
rarely
slowly
occasionally
usually
very

1. When does it rain in the desert?

_____

_____

_____

2. How do most animals move in the heat?

_____

_____

_____

3. How does a cactus grow? _____

_____

_____

4. How do thirsty creatures drink? _____

_____

_____

5. How often should you drink water when you are in the desert?

_____

_____

Scholastic

Circle the letter of the answer that best completes each sentence.

1. That is the _____ of the two rocks to climb.

    a. hard   **b.** harder   **c.** hardest   **d.** more harder

2. It has the _____ face of all the beginner's rocks in the area.

    a. smooth   **b.** smoother   **c.** smoothest   **d.** most smoothest

3. Rock climbing is _____ nowadays thanks to high-tech gear.

    a. safer   **c.** most safe

    b. more safer   **d.** safest

4. Climbers wear special shoes that have the _____ grip and give.

    a. great   **c.** greatest

    b. greater   **d.** more greater

5. Beginning climbers _____ retrace their steps to build confidence and skill.

    a. often   **b.** more often   **c.** most often   **d.** oftenest

6. They are told not to go _____ than their trainers tell them to.

    a. farther   **b.** more far   **c.** farthest   **d.** more farthest

7. Some cities have indoor climbing walls that are _____ than actual rocks.

    a. difficult **b.** more difficulter **c.** difficulter **d.** more difficult

8. The _____ my local indoor climbing wall opens is 6:00 A.M.

    a. early   **b.** earlier   **c.** most early   **d.** earliest

Scholastic

There are four kinds of sentences. Each one does something different.

A **declarative sentence** tells something.
It is a **statement** and ends with a period.
   My grandparents grew up during the 1960s.

An **interrogative sentence** asks something.
It is a **question** and ends with a question mark.
   Do you know who the hippies were?

An **imperative sentence** tells someone to do something.
It is a **command** and ends with a period.
   Check out this photo of my grandmother.

An **exclamatory sentence** shows strong feeling.
It is an **exclamation** and ends with an exclamation mark.
   Now that's one strange-looking outfit she has on!

Read the following sentences. Identify what kind of sentence each one is. Write *S* for statement, *Q* for question, *C* for command, and *E* for exclamation.

_____ 1. Grandma says there was a fashion revolution in the 1960s.

_____ 2. What an amazing time it must have been!

_____ 3. Here's a photo of my grandfather in his teens.

_____ 4. How do you like those sideburns and the long hair?

_____ 5. Take a look at what he's wearing.

_____ 6. I don't believe those bell-bottoms and sandals!

_____ 7. Please tell me he's not wearing beads.

_____ 8. I'm glad these fashions are no longer in style!

_____ 9. Have you ever seen anything so funny?

_____ 10. Try not to laugh too hard.

_____ 11. One day our grandchildren may laugh at us.

_____ 12. What's so funny about what we're wearing?

Scholastic

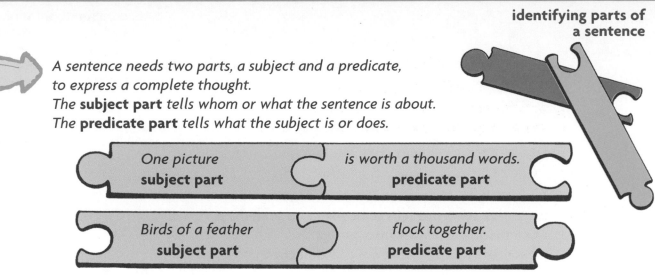

A sentence needs two parts, a subject and a predicate,
to express a complete thought.
The **subject part** tells whom or what the sentence is about.
The **predicate part** tells what the subject is or does.

One picture	is worth a thousand words.
subject part	**predicate part**

Birds of a feather	flock together.
subject part	**predicate part**

A. Read the subject and predicate parts from some other famous sayings.
Write *S* next to each subject part. Write *P* next to each predicate part.

_____half a loaf

_____one good turn

_____spoils the whole barrel

_____the show

_____every cloud

_____deserves another

_____catches the worm

_____the early bird

_____ must go on

_____ gathers no moss

_____ has a silver lining

_____ makes waste

_____ one rotten apple

_____ a rolling stone

_____ is better than none

_____ haste

B. Now combine the subject and predicate parts to create famous sayings.

1. _____

2. _____

3. _____

4. _____

5. _____

6. _____

7. _____

8. _____

If two sentences share the same subject, information about the subject can be written as a phrase after the subject in the new sentence. Be sure to use commas to set apart the phrase from the rest of the sentence.

Sentence 1: **The Gateway Arch is America's tallest human-made monument.**

Sentence 2: **The monument rises 630 feet above the ground.**

Combined: **The Gateway Arch, America's tallest human-made monument, rises 630 feet above the ground.**

Read the sentences. Combine the ideas in each pair into one sentence by including information in a phrase after the subject in the sentence.

1. The Caspian Sea is the world's largest lake.
The lake covers an area about the same size as Montana.

_____

2. The Komodo dragon is a member of the monitor family.
It can grow to a length of 10 feet.

_____

3. Our closest star is the sun.
It is estimated to be more than 27,000,000°F.

_____

4. Ronald W. Reagan was our nation's 40th president.
He worked as a Hollywood actor for almost 30 years.

_____

5. Georgia is the state that grows the most peanuts.
It harvests over 2 billion pounds each year.

_____

6. Jackie Robinson was the first African American to play in the major leagues.
He played for the Brooklyn Dodgers.

_____

Scholastic

When you write about something, try to include interesting details. Sometimes you can take the important details from several related sentences and add them to the main sentence.

Kyle and Jim had a great plan.
They're my brothers.
The plan was for a tree house.

Now here's a sentence that combines all the important details.
My brothers Kyle and Jim had a great plan for a tree house.

Read each group of sentences. Take the important details from the two related sentences and add them to the main sentence to make one sentence.

1. My brothers built a tree house. They built it in the old oak tree. It's in our backyard.

_____

2. Jim made a ladder for the tree house. He made it out of rope. It is sturdy.

_____

3. Kyle bought paint. The paint was brown. He bought a gallon.

_____

4. Kyle and Jim finished painting. They painted the walls. It took an hour.

_____

5. Jim painted a sign. He painted "no trespassing." The sign is on the tree house door.

_____

6. A squirrel leaped into their tree house. It leaped from a branch. It was curious.

_____

7. The visitor startled my brothers. It was unexpected. My brothers were unsuspecting.

_____

8. The squirrel leaped out of the tree house. It was frightened. It was in a big hurry.

_____

Scholastic

Using the conjunction and, shows you are joining ideas of the same kind.
Using the conjunction but, shows the difference between two clauses.
Using the conjunction or, is usually showing a choice.

Write the correct conjunction in the blank.

1. Shelly loves seashells, _____ her collection
   is of coins.

2. My mother went on strike _____ she quit
   cleaning up after us.

3. Mrs. Goodwin gave us a choice of behaving _____
   losing our recess.

4. Apple, oranges, _____ grapes are on the table for a snack.

5. I cannot decide if I want to go to summer camp _____ to go stay with my best
   friend.

6. I know I have been well behaved, _____ I wonder if Santa saw me when I was
   acting up?

7. Sponge Bob is square _____ he absorbs everything.

8. Mary loves summer vacation, _____ she is always ready to get back to school.

9. Jada can eat a big lunch _____ she can wait and eat a big dinner.

10. Fred wants to be in the band and play tennis after school, _____ he cannot
    do both.

11. I like both Ted _____ Jim equally.

12. Did you want chicken _____ fish for dinner?

13. I thought she said "three," _____ she really said "tree."

14. Polly wants to go, _____ I want to stay.

Scholastic

Sometimes you can use words such as when, because, while, *and* before *to combine two sentences with related ideas into one sentence with a main clause and a dependent clause. A* **clause** *is a group of words with a subject and a predicate. A* **dependent clause** *cannot stand alone. An* **independent clause** *can stand alone.*

Lee woke up late today. He realized he hadn't set the alarm last night.
When Lee woke up late today, he realized he hadn't set his alarm last night.

              ↑   ↑

This is a dependent clause.   *This is an independent clause.*

When the dependent clause comes before the main clause as in the above sentence, add a comma after the dependent clause. If the dependent clause follows the main clause, you do not need a comma. Here's an example.

Lee was upset. He was going to be late for school.
Lee was upset because **he was going to be late for school.**

Use the word inside the parentheses to combine each pair of sentences into one.

1. I waited for my parents to get home. I watched a movie. **(while)**

_____

2. My brother was in his room. He had homework to do. **(because)**

_____

3. The movie was over. The power went out. **(before)**

_____

4. This happens all the time. I wasn't concerned. **(since)**

_____

5. I didn't mind the dark at first. I heard a scratching sound. **(until)**

_____

6. I found my flashlight. I started to look around. **(when)**

_____

7. I was checking the living room. I caught Alex trying to hide. **(when)**

_____

Scholastic

When you write, you may want to show how the ideas in two simple sentences are related. You can combine the two sentences by using a comma and the conjunctions and, but, *or* or *to show the connection. And shows a link between the ideas,* but *shows a contrast, and* or *shows a choice. The new sentence is called a* **compound sentence**.

My sister wants to join a football team. My parents aren't so happy about it.
My sister wants to join a football team, but **my parents aren't so happy about it.**

Annie is determined. Her friends think she'd make a great place kicker.
Annie is determined, and **her friends think she'd make a great place kicker.**

Should Annie play football? Should she try something else?
Should Annie play football, or **should she try something else?**

Combine each pair of sentences. Use *and, but,* or *or* to show the connection between the ideas and make a compound sentence.

1. My sister Annie has always participated in sports. Many say she's a natural

athlete.

_____

_____

2. Soccer, basketball, and softball are fun. She wanted a new challenge.

_____

_____

3. My sister talked to my brother and me. We were honest with her.

_____

_____

4. I told Annie to go for it. My brother told her to stick with soccer or basketball.

_____

_____

5. Will Dad convince her to try skiing? Will he suggest ice skating?

_____

_____

Scholastic

Sometimes a writer can change the order of the words in a sentence to make it more interesting.

The telephone rang just as the girls were about to leave.
Just as the girls were about to leave, the phone rang.

Gina decided to answer it in spite of the time.
In spite of the time, Gina decided to answer it.

Do not forget to add a comma when you begin a sentence with a clause or a phrase that cannot stand alone, as in the second and last sentences.

Rewrite each sentence by changing the order of the words.

1. Marta watched for the bus while Gina answered the phone.

_____

2. The caller hung up just as Gina said, "Hello."

_____

3. The girls were going to miss the one o'clock show unless they hurried.

_____

4. The bus had already come and gone by the time they got to the corner.

_____

5. The next bus to town finally showed up after the girls had waited a half hour.

_____

6. The girls decided to catch the four o'clock show since they missed the earlier

show.

_____

7. They wouldn't have to stand in line later since Gina bought the tickets first.

_____

8. Gina and Marta were at the theater by three o'clock even though it was early.

_____

9. They bought a tub of popcorn and drinks once they were inside.

_____

Scholastic

You know that you must use commas in a series of three or more items.
Max, Sam, and Alex ordered burgers, fries, and milkshakes for lunch.

Here are some additional rules you need to know about commas.
Use commas

— *to set off the name of the person or group you are addressing.*
Here's your order, boys.

— *after words like* yes, no, *and* well.
Well, what do you want to do now?

— *before a conjunction that joins two sentences.*
The boys finished lunch, and then they went to a movie.

Read the sentences below. Decide which ones need commas and which ones do not. Use this symbol ∧ to show where commas belong.

1. I'd like a bike a pair of in-line skates and a snowboard for my birthday.

2. Well my friend you can't always have what you want when you want it.

3. No but I can always hope!

4. My friends and I skate all year long and we snowboard during the winter.

5. I used to like skateboarding but now I prefer snowboarding and in-line skating.

6. What sports games or hobbies do you enjoy most Jody?

7. I learned to ski last year and now I'm taking ice-skating lessons.

8. Skiing ice skating and skateboarding are all fun things to do.

Review the four rules above for using commas. Then write an original sentence for each rule. Begin and end each sentence correctly. Remember to check your spelling.

9. _____

10. _____

11. _____

12. _____

Scholastic

Some stories may include dialogue, or the exact words of story characters. Dialogue lets readers know something about the characters, plot, setting, and problem or conflict in a story. Use quotation marks around a speaker's exact words and commas to set off quotations. Remember to put periods, question marks, exclamation points, and commas inside the quotation marks.

"Get away from my bowl!" yelled Little Miss Muffet when she saw the approaching spider.

"Please don't get so excited," replied the startled spider. "I just wanted a little taste. I've never tried curds and whey before."

Use your imagination to complete the dialogue between the fairy tale or nursery rhyme characters. Include quotation marks and commas where they belong and the correct end punctuation.

1. When Baby Bear saw the strange girl asleep in his bed, he asked his parents,

_____

His mother replied, _____

2. Humpty Dumpty was sitting on the wall when he suddenly fell off. On the way

down he shouted, _____

Two of the king's men approached. One whispered nervously to the other,

_____

3. When Jack realized he was about to fall down the hill with a pail of water, he

yelled, _____

cried Jill, as she went tumbling down the hill after Jack.

4. The wolf knocked on the door of the third little pig's house. When there was no

answer, the wolf bellowed, _____

Knowing that he and his brother were safe inside his sturdy brick house, the

third little pig replied, _____

_____

You can compare two things that are not alike in order to give your readers a clearer and more colorful picture. When you use like *or* as *to make a comparison, it is called a* **simile**.

Max is as slow as molasses when he doesn't want to do something.
My sister leaped over the puddles like a frog to avoid getting her shoes wet.
The angry man erupted like a volcano.

When you make a comparison without like *or* as, *it is called a* **metaphor**. *You compare things directly, saying the subject is something else.*

The disturbed anthill was a whirlwind of activity.
The oak trees, silent sentries around the cabin, stood guard.
Jenny and I were all ears as we listened to the latest gossip.

Finish the metaphors and similes.

1. Crowds of commuters piled into the subway cars like _____

_____

2. Chirping crickets on warm summer night are _____

_____

3. After rolling in the mud, our dog looked like _____

4. Happiness is _____

5. Just learning to walk, the toddler was as wobbly as _____

_____

6. After scoring the winning point, I felt as _____

_____

7. Having a tooth filled is about as much fun as _____

_____

8. A summer thunderstorm is _____

_____

9. _____ is _____

10. _____ is like _____

Scholastic

Sometimes you can spice up your writing by giving human characteristics and qualities to non-human things such as animals and objects. This is called **personification**.

**The sagging roof groaned under the weight of all the snow.
The falling leaves danced in the wind.**

You can also use **hyperbole**, *or deliberate exaggeration, to make a point clearer or to add drama to your writing.*

**The lost hiker is so hungry he could eat a bear.
Yesterday was so hot, we could have fried eggs on the sidewalk.**

Personify the animal or object in each sentence by giving it human qualities.

1. The rusted hinges on the old wooden door _____

_____

_____

2. As several birds began feasting on the farmer's corn, the scarecrow _____

_____

3. A gentle summer breeze _____

_____

4. Just as I walked past the statue of Ben Franklin, it _____

_____

Complete each sentence with an example of a hyperbole.

5. The salsa was so spicy hot _____

_____

6. The pumpkin grew so large _____

_____

7. If we placed all the books in the library end to end, they _____

_____

8. My room was so cold last night that by morning _____

_____

If your topic is too broad, it will be hard for you to treat it well. Examine this example of narrowing a topic:

Broad Topic: Movies
Narrow Topic: Adventure movies
Narrower Topic: Movies about adventures in space

Complete the chart by narrowing the given topics.

BROAD	NARROW	NARROWER
1. team sports	indoor team sports	
2. foods	desserts	
3. ocean creatures	sharks	
4. instruments		playing the harp
5. South America	jungles of South America	
6. lakes	The Great Lakes	
7. careers	careers in medicine	
8. transportation	one-person vehicles	
9. planets		Is there life on Mars?
10. dinosaurs	meat-eating dinosaurs	

Scholastic

A **paragraph** *is a group of sentences that tells about one main
idea. The* **topic sentence** *tells the main idea and is usually the
first sentence.* **Supporting sentences** *tell more about the main idea.
The* **closing sentence** *of a paragraph often retells the main idea
in a different way. Here are the parts for one paragraph.*

Paragraph Title: **Starting Over**

Topic Sentence: **Today started off badly and only got worse.**

Supporting Sentences: 1. **Everyone in my family woke up late this morning.**

2. **I had only 15 minutes to get ready and catch the bus.**

3. **I dressed as fast as I could, grabbed an apple and my
    backpack, and raced to get to the bus stop on time.**

4. **Fortunately, I just made it.**

5. **Unfortunately, the bus was pulling away when several
    kids pointed out that I had on two different shoes.**

Closing Sentence: **At that moment, I wanted to start the day over.**

When you write a paragraph, remember these rules:

• **Indent** *the first line to let readers know that you are beginning a paragraph.*
• **Capitalize** *the first word of each sentence.*
• **Punctuate** *each sentence correctly (? ! . ,).*

Use all the information above to write the paragraph. Be sure to follow the rules.

_____
paragraph title

_____

_____

_____

_____

_____

_____

_____

Scholastic

Every paragraph has a topic sentence that tells the main idea of the paragraph, or what it is about. It usually answers several of these questions:

Who?   What?   Where?   When?   Why?   How?

Here are some examples.

The doe and her fawn faced many dangers in the forest.
We were amazed by our guest's rude behavior.
Baking bread from scratch is really not so difficult, or so I thought.
Getting up in the morning is the hardest thing to do.

Did these topic sentences grab your attention? A good topic sentence should.

Here are some topics. Write a topic sentence for each one.

1. convincing someone to try octopus soup

_____

2. an important person in your life

_____

3. an embarrassing moment

_____

4. the importance of Independence Day

_____

_____

5. lunchtime at the school cafeteria

_____

Now list some topics of your own. Then write a topic sentence for each one.

Topic #1

_____

Topic #2   **Topic #3**

_____   _____

_____
        Topic sentence #1

_____
        Topic sentence #2

_____
        Topic sentence #3

Scholastic

Read each topic sentence. Then read the three sentences that follow it.
Circle the letter next to the sentence that best supports the topic sentence.

1. Topic sentence: A gas well in Oklahoma is one of the deepest wells in America.

    a. Natural gas is used for heating and cooking in homes and businesses.

    b. The Bertha Rogers well goes down 31,441 feet into the earth—nearly six miles!

    c. Oklahoma became a state in 1907.

2. Topic sentence: The community of Climax, Colorado, held an unusual record.

    a. It is located west of the capital city of Denver.

    b. Mining has been important to the area for nearly a century.

    c. Perched at 11,360 feet above sea level, it was the highest settlement in America.

3. Topic sentence: Yellowstone is the oldest national park in the world.

    a. President Grant established it on March 1, 1872.

    b. It includes parts of Wyoming, Montana, and Idaho.

    c. Old Faithful is one of the most famous geysers in Yellowstone.

4. Topic sentence: Mt. Waialeale in Hawaii is one of the wettest places on Earth!

    a. It is located on the small island of Kauai.

    b. Records dating back from 1912 show that this soggy spot gets about
       420 inches of rain every year.

    c. In the Hawaiian language, the word *waialeale* means "rippling water."

5. Topic sentence: The exact geographic center of Connecticut is a town called
Berlin in Hartford County.

    a. Hartford is the capital of Connecticut.

    b. Connecticut is one of the New England states.

    c. The town of Berlin has a total area of 27 square miles.

6. Topic sentence: The United States and Canada share a long and friendly border.

    a. Canada, to our north, is America's largest neighbor.

    b. The border between Mexico and the United States is about 1,933 miles long.

    c. The U.S.–Canada border runs a total length of about 5,525 miles.

Scholastic

There are many kinds of paragraphs. When you write a **compare-and-contrast paragraph**, you compare by telling how things are similar and contrast by telling how things are different. You can use a Venn diagram to help organize your ideas. Here is an example.

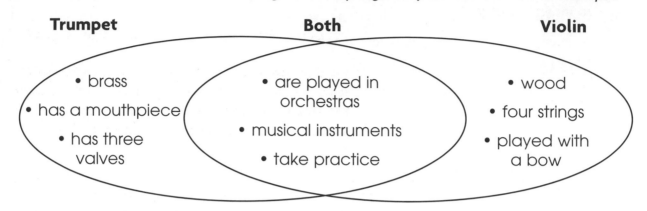

Trumpet
- brass
- has a mouthpiece
- has three valves

Both
- are played in orchestras
- musical instruments
- take practice

Violin
- wood
- four strings
- played with a bow

Complete the paragraph using details to compare and contrast the trumpet and violin. Remember to capitalize and punctuate correctly.

Trumpet Versus Violin

The trumpet and violin are both musical instruments that are _____

_____. However, there are some

important differences. The trumpet _____

_____

_____

_____

On the other hand, the violin _____

_____

_____

_____

Both instruments_____

_____

Scholastic

A **descriptive paragraph** *creates a vivid image or picture for readers. By choosing just the right adjectives, you can reveal how something looks, sounds, smells, tastes, and feels. Compare the sentences from two different paragraphs. Which one creates a more vivid picture?*

The pizza with sausage and onions tasted so good.

The smooth, sweet sauce and bubbly mozzarella topped with bite-sized chunks of extra-hot sausage and thin slivers of sweet onion on a perfectly baked, thin crust delighted my taste buds.

Cut out a picture of something interesting and paste it in the box. Then brainstorm a list of adjectives and descriptive phrases to tell about it.

_____   _____

_____   _____

_____   _____

_____   _____

_____   _____

Now, write a paragraph about the picture. Begin your paragraph with a topic sentence that will grab readers. Add supporting sentences that include the adjectives and descriptive phrases listed to create a vivid picture.

_____

_____

_____

_____

_____

_____

Scholastic

You can write a paragraph using a cause and effect relationship. One way to begin is to state a cause. Then you write about the effects that happen as a result of that cause.

The piercing sound of the smoke alarm reminded Max that he had forgotten to check the pot of stew heating up on the stove. The stew had boiled over, the bottom of the pot was scorched, and smoke was filling the kitchen. Dinner was obviously ruined, and Max was in big trouble. What a mess!

Answer each question about the paragraph above.

1. What is the cause? _____

_____

2. What were the effects? List them. _____

_____

_____

Read the first sentence of the following paragraph. It states a cause. What might happen as a result? Continue the paragraph. Write what you think the effects will be.

I walked into my room just as Sebastian, our very inquisitive cat,

managed to tip over the goldfish bowl that had been on my desk.

_____

_____

_____

_____

_____

_____

_____

_____

*When you write an **expository paragraph**, you give facts and information, explain ideas, or give directions. An expository paragraph can also include opinions. Here are some topic ideas for an expository paragraph.*

Explain how to play the flute.
Tell why you do not like brussels sprouts.
Give facts about yourself.

Explain how to bathe a dog.
Tell what skills you need to skateboard.
Give the facts about your favorite band.

Here is an example of an expository paragraph. It explains how to fry an egg.

     Frying an egg is not all that difficult. After melting a little bit of butter in a frying pan, just crack the eggshell along the rim of the pan and let the egg drop into the pan. Do it gently so the yolk does not break. Let the egg fry over a low heat for about a minute or so. That is all it takes.

Complete the following topics for expository paragraphs with your own ideas.

Explain how to	Give facts about	Tell why
_____	_____	_____
_____	_____	_____
_____	_____	_____

Use the form below to develop one of your ideas for an expository paragraph.

Paragraph Title: _____

Topic Sentence: _____

_____

_____

Details/Facts/Steps: _____

_____

_____

_____

_____

Closing Sentence: _____

_____

_____

_____

Scholastic

In a **persuasive paragraph,** *you give an opinion about something and try to convince readers to think or feel the way you do. A convincing persuasive paragraph includes*

— **a topic sentence that clearly states your opinion.**
— **reasons that support your opinion.**
— **facts to back up your opinion.**
— **a strong closing sentence that summarizes your opinion.**

Pretend you are a world famous chef who prepares dishes that include edible insects—insects that you can eat. You want to persuade people to include insects in their diet. Here is a topic sentence for a persuasive paragraph.

Everyone should try cooking with insects.

Here are some reasons and facts.
• Many insects like mealworms, crickets, and weevils are edible.
• People in many cultures around the world eat insects.
• Many insects are low in fat and rich in vitamins.
• Lots of tasty recipes include insects.
• Insects are really quite delicious.

Now put it all together. Write a persuasive paragraph that includes a title and a strong closing sentence. Remember the rules for writing a paragraph.

Paragraph Title: _____

Topic Sentence: _____

_____

Reasons/Facts: _____

_____

_____

_____

_____

_____

_____

_____

Closing Sentence: _____

_____

Scholastic

*A **news story** reports just the facts about an event and answers the questions* who, what, when, where, why, *and* how. *The most important information is included at the beginning of the article in a paragraph called the **lead**.*

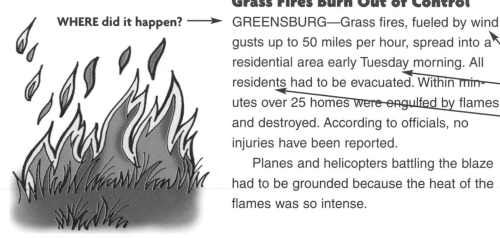

Grass Fires Burn Out of Control   headline

WHERE did it happen? ➔ GREENSBURG—Grass fires, fueled by wind gusts up to 50 miles per hour, spread into a residential area early Tuesday morning. All residents had to be evacuated. Within minutes over 25 homes were engulfed by flames and destroyed. According to officials, no injuries have been reported.

WHY did it happen?

WHEN did it happen?

WHO was affected?

Planes and helicopters battling the blaze had to be grounded because the heat of the flames was so intense.

Write a news story using the information below. Remember to write about the facts and events in the order they occurred. Follow the model lead above.

Who: Roseville Emergency Rescue Team
When: April 10, 2003; 5 A.M.
Where: Slate Run River
What: team and rescue vehicles sent;
    worked for three hours; rescued residents
How: used helicopter and boats
Why: residents along river stranded by flash flood after storm

_____

_____ — _____

_____

_____

_____

_____

_____

_____

Scholastic

When you keep a journal, you can record the facts and details about events that happen in your life and your feelings or opinions about them. Your journal entries can be a valuable resource when you are looking for writing ideas.

3/9 We had to take Fuzzer to his new home today. Our new landlord said he could not stay with us at our apartment anymore. I know Fuzzer will be much happier at the farm where he can run and play, but I still felt so sad. I tried not to cry, but I could not help it. Fuzzer has been part of our family for nine years. We grew up together. I will miss him very much!

3/15 I had to go to my sister's dance recital at the Palace Theater last night. She performed in three numbers. At first I didn't want to go because I thought it would be boring, but it wasn't. I actually felt really proud of my sister! She was fantastic. I guess I really should tell her.

3/19 Today, the entire fourth grade went on a field trip to the state capital. It was incredible! We met a state senator. She showed us around the capitol building. We even got to listen to the senators discuss a new law. Later, we toured the governor's mansion. Boy, is that a big house!

Think about the events that have happened in your life over the last several days. Did anything of special importance happen at home, on the way to or from school, or in your community, the country, or the world? Record the facts, details, and your feelings or opinions about two events on the journal page below. Write the date for each entry.

_____/_____/_____

_____

_____

_____

_____

_____/_____/_____

_____

_____

_____

_____

Scholastic

Each sentence below contains one kind of error—or no error at all. Choose the best answer.

1. So, are you sure you know all your times tables.

   A capitalization error
   B spelling error
   C punctuation error
   D no error

2. Which is the top number in a fraction—the numerator or the denominator?

   F capitalization error
   G spelling error
   H punctuation error
   J no error

3. Geometry, the study of lines angles and shapes is my favorite topic in math.

   A capitalization error
   B spelling error
   C punctuation error
   D no error

4. Our math teacher told us why the equil sign is made of two lines.

   F capitalization error
   G spelling error
   H punctuation error
   J no error

5. Our Principal says that he is more than two yards tall.

   A capitalization error
   B spelling error
   C punctuation error
   D no error

6. My ruller is marked in inches along one edge and in centimeters along the other.

   F capitalization error
   G spelling error
   H punctuation error
   J no error

7. We won't study percents until next year, but I know what it means to get 100% on a test!

   A capitalization error
   B spelling error
   C punctuation error
   D no error

8. Most Americans do not use Metric Measurements in their daily lives.

   F capitalization error
   G spelling error
   H punctuation error
   J no error

Capitalization and end punctuation help show where one sentence ends and the next one begins. Whenever you write, proofread to make sure each sentence begins with a capital letter and ends correctly. Here's an example of how to mark the letters that should be capitalized.

have you ever heard of a Goliath birdeater? it is the world's largest spider. this giant tarantula can grow to 11 inches in length and weigh about 6 ounces. now that's a big spider! although it is called a birdeater, it usually eats small reptiles and insects. these spiders are mostly found in rain forests.

Read the passage below. It is about another amazing animal, but it is not so easy to read because the writer forgot to add end punctuation and to use capital letters at the beginning of sentences. Proofread the passage. Mark the letters that should be capitals with the capital letter symbol. Put the correct punctuation marks at the ends of sentences. Then reread the passage.

think about the fastest car you've ever seen in the Indianapolis 500 race that's about how fast a peregrine falcon dives it actually reaches speeds over 200 miles an hour how incredibly fast they are peregrine falcons are also very powerful birds did you know that they can catch and kill their prey in the air using their sharp claws what's really amazing is that peregrine falcons live in both the country and in the city keep on the lookout if you're ever in New York City believe it or not, it is home to several falcons

Have you ever accidentally left out words when you write? Whenever you write, it is always a good idea to proofread for words that may be missing. Here is an example of what to do when you want to add a missing word as you proofread.

e-mail
I got an ∧ from my friend last night.

met
We ∧ last summer when my family was in Japan.

Read the passage below about school in Japan. Twenty-one words are missing. Figure out what they are and add them to the sentences. Use the ∧ symbol to show where each missing word belongs. Then write each missing word above the sentence. Hint: Every sentence has at least one missing word.

How would like to go to school on Saturdays? If you lived in the of

Japan, that's just where you could be each Saturday morning. I have a

who lives in Japan. Yuichi explained that attend classes five and one-half a

week. The day is on Saturday. I was also surprised to that the Japanese

school is one of the longest in the world—over 240 days. It begins in the of

April. While we have over two months off each, students in Japan get their

in late July and August. School then again in fall and ends in March. The

people of believe that a good is very important. Children are required to

attend school from the age of six to the of fifteen. They have elementary

and middle just like we do. Then most go on to school for another three

years. Yuichi says that students work very because the standards are so

high. He and some of his friends even extra classes after school. They all

want to get into a good someday.

An **idiom** *is a phrase or expression whose meaning can't be understood from the ordinary meanings of the words in it. For example, "Get off my back!" is an idiom meaning "Stop bothering me!" The idiom "You hit the nail on the head" means "You're exactly right."*

Here are some other idioms you might use in your writing.

Idiom	Meaning
We're in hot water.	We're in trouble.
Drop me a line.	Write me a short letter or call me sometime.
She gave him a dirty look.	She looked at him angrily.
The traffic was heavy.	There was a lot of traffic.
We don't see eye to eye.	We don't agree.
We're all in the same boat.	We all have the same problem.
The boss just gave him the ax.	The boss just fired him.
You really put your foot in your mouth.	You really said the wrong thing.
The judge threw the book at her.	The judge gave her a severe penalty.
This car can stop on a dime.	This car can stop very quickly.
I'm hung up on this problem.	I can't figure out this problem.
It's in the bag.	It will surely happen.
I'm stumped.	I can't figure this out.
He passed the test by the skin of his teeth.	He barely passed the test.
Let's see which way the wind blows.	Let's see what happens.
She let the cat out of the bag.	She told the secret.
You can't pull the wool over my eyes.	You can't fool me.
He gave me a leg up.	He helped me when I was in need.
Give me a hand with this assignment.	Help me with this assignment.
He thinks he's hot stuff.	He's conceited.
She's full of herself.	She's conceited.
I gave the assignment my all.	I worked very hard on the assignment.
Let's face the music.	Let's admit we're in a difficult situation.
The story really got to me.	The story affected me strongly.

Scholastic

Mark the best answer to each question about library materials.

1. In which section of the library would you find a book about rockets?

- A fiction
- B biography
- C nonfiction
- D sports

2. Which book would give information about Egyptian painting?

- F an atlas
- G a book on deserts
- H an art book
- J a dictionary

3. If you know the name of a book you want to borrow, which part of the card catalog should you check?

- A subject card
- B index card
- C author card
- D title card

4. You want to know who won the first World Cup Soccer tournament. Which resource would you choose?

- F an encyclopedia
- G an almanac
- H a soccer Web site
- J an interview with a soccer coach

5. To know if a book on submarines tells of the sinking of the *Kursk*, check

- A Chapter 7.
- B the index.
- C the book jacket.
- D a review.

6. Every book tells the year in which it was published. This fact is called

- F the spine.
- G the dedication.
- H the call number.
- J the copyright date.

7. Where in a book will you find the name of its author?

- A in the glossary
- B in the index
- C on the title page
- D in the table of contents

8. To find the capital of Kenya, which resource would you check?

- F an almanac
- G an encyclopedia
- H an atlas
- J all of the above

Mark the best answer to each question.

1. Sadie wants to know about Sir Arthur Conan Doyle. In which volume of the encyclopedia should she look?
- A A
- B C
- C D
- D S

2. Al is writing a report on passenger helicopters. Which book probably won't help?
- F *Into Deep Space*
- G *Modern Aircraft*
- H *The 'Copter Chronicles*
- J *Heliports and Helipads*

3. Penny wants to see a map of Easter Island. Which is the best source for her to check?
- A an atlas
- B a thesaurus
- C a dictionary
- D a holiday magazine

4. Gabe wants to find the definition of the word *dulcet*. To which part of the dictionary should he turn?
- F the beginning
- G the middle
- H the end
- J cannot tell

5. Rasheed wants to know the meaning of parody. It will be on the dictionary page that has which guide words?
- A parrot / partial
- B parlor / parole
- C parent / parochial
- D parallel / pardon

6. Jen wants to see pictures of ancient rock art. Which might be the best place for her to look?
- F a rock video
- G a filmstrip about ancestors
- H a Web site on caves
- J a Web site on Alaska

7. To learn the symptoms of a skin condition called *psoriasis*, which of these sources probably won't help?
- A a thesaurus
- B a medical dictionary
- C a home health-care book
- D an interview with a doctor

8. You want to know which albums won Grammy awards in 2002. Which resource would be your best choice?
- F an almanac
- G a music Web site
- H an encyclopedia
- J an interview with a guitarist

Grammar/Writing Practice Test

Fill in the bubble next to the correct answer.

1. Which common noun names the group that contains: New York, California, Nevada, Mississippi?

    ◯ **A**   provinces

    ◯ **B**   countries

    ◯ **C**   states

    ◯ **D**   cities

2. Which word in the following sentence is a possessive pronoun?
   The students planned a surprise party for their teacher.

    ◯ **F**   The

    ◯ **G**   students

    ◯ **H**   surprise

    ◯ **J**   their

3. Which sentence has NO punctuation mistake?

    ◯ **A**   The main ingredients are flour, butter, eggs, and milk.

    ◯ **B**   The frame's he makes are made of natural twigs.

    ◯ **C**   The kittens were born on January 9 1999.

    ◯ **D**   How late is the post office opened tonight.

4. Which word is the correct antecedent (the noun that matches the meaning) of the underlined pronoun in the following sentence?
   I read a book about the plants and animals that live in the rain forest. <u>Its</u> author was a well-known scientist.

    ◯ **F**   the plants'

    ◯ **G**   the animals'

    ◯ **H**   the book's

    ◯ **J**   the rain forest's

Grammar/Writing Practice Test

Fill in the bubble next to the correct answer.

5. Which sentence best supports the topic sentence "Adopting a Pet?"

    ◯ **A**   We won a huge stuffed animal at the fair.

    ◯ **B**   He went straight to the food.

    ◯ **C**   It's always best to know the animal's previous owner.

    ◯ **D**   The basket can safely hold three or four people.

6. Which word best completes the following sentence?
It was the annual barbecue, _____ our entire family gathers for a picnic.

    ◯ **F**   with

    ◯ **G**   although

    ◯ **H**   because

    ◯ **J**   when

7. Which best explains the underlined idiom in the following sentence?
We must never <u>cut corners </u>on safety.

    ◯ **A**   be foolish

    ◯ **B**   disagree

    ◯ **C**   take shortcuts

    ◯ **D**   get excited

8. Which word means the opposite of the underlined word in the following sentence?
The mayor's <u>loyal</u> aide takes care of every assignment.

    ◯ **F**   unfaithful

    ◯ **G**   tardy

    ◯ **H**   part-time

    ◯ **J**   reliable

Grammar/Writing Practice Test

Fill in the bubble next to the correct answer.

9. Which word would you use to combine the following short sentences?
The coach blew her whistle. The game stopped.

- ◯ **A**   because
- ◯ **B**   for
- ◯ **C**   and
- ◯ **D**   since

10. Write the correct form of the verb in parentheses ( ) to complete the following sentence.
Yesterday I (to feed) the cat tuna.

- ◯ **F**   feed
- ◯ **G**   feeds
- ◯ **H**   fed
- ◯ **J**   will feed

11. Look at the underlined noun in the following sentence and tell whether it names a person, place, thing, or idea.
Scientists look at small objects under a <u>microscope</u>.

- ◯ **A**   person
- ◯ **B**   place
- ◯ **C**   thing
- ◯ **D**   idea

12. Read the following sentence. Which linking verb correctly completes the sentence?
From 1860 to 1945, Denver _____ a mining and agricultural community.

- ◯ **F**   were
- ◯ **G**   was
- ◯ **H**   is
- ◯ **J**   will be

Addition & Subtraction

Understanding basic addition and subtraction facts is an important real-life skill. When you buy things you need to know how to add up the cost of the items and how to figure out the change you will receive when you pay for them. We probably add and/or subtract things several times every day.

What to Do

These activity pages provide many opportunities for your child to practice addition and subtraction with and without regrouping. Check your child's work when he or she finishes each activity page.

Keep On Going!

Encourage your child to become an addition and subtraction pro. Create addition and subtraction problems based on your child's activities for the day. For example: If you need to be at practice at 3:45 and get out of school at 2:30, how much time do you have to get to practice? Or, you want to buy your best friend flowers. You have $12.00. The flowers costs $18.00. How much more money will you need to purchase the flowers?

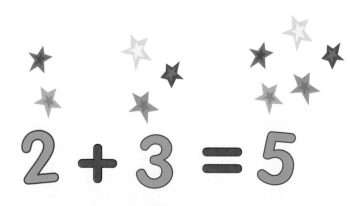

Add the numbers.

1. $\begin{array}{r} \overset{1\ \ 1}{3,827} \\ +\ \ 903 \\ \hline 4730 \end{array}$

2. $\begin{array}{r} \overset{1\ 1}{1,562} \\ +\ \ 843 \\ \hline 2,405 \end{array}$

3. $\begin{array}{r} \overset{1\ 1}{2,148} \\ +\ \ 674 \\ \hline 3822 \end{array}$

4. $\begin{array}{r} 7,291 \\ +\ \ 629 \\ \hline \end{array}$

5. $\begin{array}{r} 4,023 \\ +\ \ 721 \\ \hline \end{array}$

6. $\begin{array}{r} 5,484 \\ +\ \ 648 \\ \hline \end{array}$

7. $\begin{array}{r} 1,326 \\ +\ \ 984 \\ \hline \end{array}$

8. $\begin{array}{r} 6,423 \\ +\ \ 422 \\ \hline \end{array}$

9. $\begin{array}{r} 1,846 \\ +\ \ 221 \\ \hline \end{array}$

10. $\begin{array}{r} 9,016 \\ +\ \ 112 \\ \hline \end{array}$

11. $\begin{array}{r} 4,536 \\ +\ \ 119 \\ \hline \end{array}$

12. $\begin{array}{r} 2,349 \\ +\ \ 824 \\ \hline \end{array}$

13. $\begin{array}{r} 8,461 \\ +\ \ 714 \\ \hline \end{array}$

14. $\begin{array}{r} 3,654 \\ +\ \ 582 \\ \hline \end{array}$

15. $\begin{array}{r} 1,672 \\ +\ \ 432 \\ \hline \end{array}$

16. $\begin{array}{r} 5,184 \\ +\ \ 686 \\ \hline \end{array}$

17. $\begin{array}{r} 1,592 \\ +\ \ 768 \\ \hline \end{array}$

18. $\begin{array}{r} 4,394 \\ +\ \ 184 \\ \hline \end{array}$

19. $\begin{array}{r} 7,143 \\ +\ \ 527 \\ \hline \end{array}$

20. $\begin{array}{r} 1,489 \\ +\ \ 368 \\ \hline \end{array}$

Scholastic

To add multiple-digit numbers with regrouping, follow these steps.
1. Add the ones column.
2. If the sum is greater than 9, regroup to the tens column.
3. Add the tens column.
4. If the sum is greater than 9, regroup to the hundreds column.
5. Continue working through each column in order.

Which of these mountains is the tallest? To find out add. The sum with the greatest number in each row shows the height of the mountain in feet. Circle the height for each mountain.

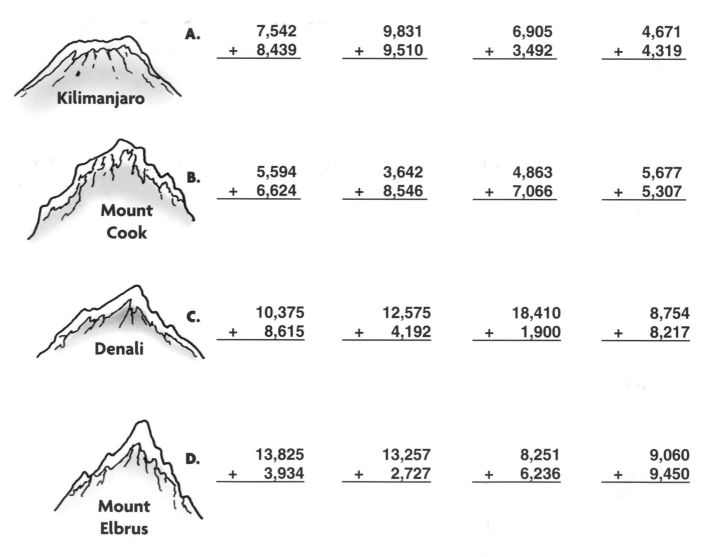

Kilimanjaro

A.
$$7,542 + 8,439$$ $$9,831 + 9,510$$ $$6,905 + 3,492$$ $$4,671 + 4,319$$

Mount Cook

B.
$$5,594 + 6,624$$ $$3,642 + 8,546$$ $$4,863 + 7,066$$ $$5,677 + 5,307$$

Denali

C.
$$10,375 + 8,615$$ $$12,575 + 4,192$$ $$18,410 + 1,900$$ $$8,754 + 8,217$$

Mount Elbrus

D.
$$13,825 + 3,934$$ $$13,257 + 2,727$$ $$8,251 + 6,236$$ $$9,060 + 9,450$$

Find the total height of the two mountains with the greatest heights.

Scholastic

Some addition problems will require regrouping several times. The steps look like this.

1. Add the ones column. Regroup if needed.

$$\begin{array}{r} 1 \\ 37{,}462 \\ + \quad 22{,}798 \\ \hline 0 \end{array}$$

2. Add the tens column. Regroup if needed.

$$\begin{array}{r} 11 \\ 37{,}462 \\ + \quad 22{,}798 \\ \hline 60 \end{array}$$

3. Add the hundreds column. Regroup if needed.

$$\begin{array}{r} 111 \\ 37{,}462 \\ + \quad 22{,}798 \\ \hline 260 \end{array}$$

4. Continue working through each column in order.

$$\begin{array}{r} 111 \\ 37{,}462 \\ + \quad 22{,}798 \\ \hline 60{,}260 \end{array}$$

Add. Then use the code to finish the fun fact below.

1.

bald eagle

Z.	B.	R.	Q.	S.	X.
953 + 418	295 + 337	418 + 793	565 + 957	862 + 339	478 + 283

2.

falcon

I.	C.	Y.	A.	Y.
2,428 + 6,679	1,566 + 2,487	3,737 + 6,418	9,289 + 4,735	8,754 + 368

3.

vulture

L.	P.	E.	F.
57,854 + 45,614	29,484 + 46,592	36,238 + 46,135	67,139 + 25,089

4.

owl

D.	O.	R.
240,669 + 298,727	476,381 + 175,570	882,948 + 176,524

What do all of these birds have in common?

They are ___ ___ ___ ___ ___   ___ ___
632   9,107   1,211   539,396   1,201   651,951   92,228

___ ___ ___ ___ .
76,076   1,059,472   82,373   10,155

Scholastic

To add numbers that require regrouping in more than one column, follow these steps.
1. Add the ones column. Regroup if needed.
2. Add the tens column. Regroup if needed.
4. Add the hundreds column. Regroup if needed.
5. Continue working through each column in order.

Add. Then use the code to finish the fun fact below.

H.   8,754
   +   368

L.   7,789
   +   4,759

I.   8,997
   +   9,978

A.   8,599
   +   8,932

E.   5,476
   +   4,846

O.   9,475
   +   7,725

C.   8,838
   +   9,668

T.   6,867
   +   7,256

M.   9,891
   +   3,699

N.   92,854
   +   37,898

U.   25,748
   +   85,362

Y.   99,977
   +   82,943

R.   57,544
   +   78,587

The bald eagle is found _____ _____ _____ _____   _____ _____
                              17,200 130,752 12,548 182,920   17,200 130,752

_____ _____ _____   _____ _____ _____ _____ _____
14,123   9,122   10,322   130,752 17,200 136,131 14,123   9,122

_____ _____ _____ _____ _____ _____ _____ _____
17,531   13,590 10,322 136,131 18,975 18,506 17,531 130,752

_____ _____ _____ _____ _____ _____ _____ _____ _____ .
18,506   17,200 130,752 14,123 18,975 130,752 10,322 130,752 14,123

Use the same steps to add several addends. Some columns will require regrouping, and some will not.

Add. Then use the code to find the answer to the riddle below.

W.	T.	P.	N.	O.	E.
1,233	6,314	2,305	1,238	3,541	3,525
1,442	3,380	2,404	6,281	309	2,213
+ 5,226	+ 2,606	+ 2,439	+ 5,366	+ 7,845	+ 9,281
1.	**2.**	**3.**	**4.**	**5.**	**6.**

H.	R.	S.	!	A.	U.
444	4,327	4,024	5,441	2,653	5,560
7,283	4,331	678	421	3,338	4,202
+ 8,217	+ 1,746	+ 4,505	+ 3,954	+ 2,924	+ 1,541
7.	**8.**	**9.**	**10.**	**11.**	**12.**

What is the difference between a man and a running dog?

| 11,695 | 12,885 | 15,019 | | |

| 7,901 | 15,019 | 8,915 | 10,404 | 9,207 |

| 12,300 | 10,404 | 11,695 | 11,303 | 9,207 | 15,019 | 10,404 | 9,207 |

| 12,300 | 15,944 | 15,019 |

| 11,695 | 12,300 | 15,944 | 15,019 | 10,404 |

| 7,148 | 8,915 | 12,885 | 12,300 | 9,207 | 9,816 |

Scholastic

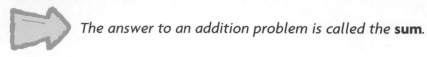 *The answer to an addition problem is called the **sum**.*

Find the path that leads from the mouse to the cheese by following the sums of eighteen. Add.

(5 + 4) + (3 + 6)	(7 + 6) + 5	(5 + 6) + (4 + 2)	(7 + 5) + 7	3 + (7 + 5)
1.	**2.**	**3.**	**4.**	**5.**
4 + (6 + 6)	3 + (8 + 7)	(5 + 3) + (3 + 4)	(4 + 6) + 5	(5 + 9) + 3
6.	**7.**	**8.**	**9.**	**10.**
(9 + 2) + 6	(5 + 3) + (6 + 4)	2 + (8 + 8)	8 + (6+ 2)	(4 + 5) + (2 + 5)
11.	**12.**	**13.**	**14.**	**15.**
5 + (6 + 6)	(6 + 6) + (4 + 6)	(2 + 3) + (9 + 4)	3 + (7 + 5)	(6 + 7) + 6
16.	**17.**	**18.**	**19.**	**20.**
(7 + 8) + 2	5 + (4 + 6)	7 + (4 + 7)	(5 + 6) + (4 + 3)	(8 + 4) + 6
21.	**22.**	**23.**	**24.**	**25.**

Always complete the operation inside the parentheses ( ) first.
Then complete the rest of the problem.

$$7 + (3 + 6) =$$
$$7 + 9 = 16$$

$$(4 + 4) + 8 =$$
$$8 + 8 = 16$$

Add.

A. (7 + 2) + 4 = _____

B. (5 + 4) + 9 = _____

C. 8 + (3 + 5) = _____

D. (2 + 6) + (5 + 2) = _____

E. (3 + 3) + (5 + 4) = _____

F. (6 + 6) + 3 = _____

G. 5 + (4 + 8) = _____

H. (2 + 9) + 8 = _____

I. (8 + 5) + 4 = _____

J. (8 + 2) + (3 + 2) = _____

K. (2 + 5) + (5 + 8) = _____

L. (3 + 4) + 7 = _____

M. 9 + (2 + 3) = _____

N. 6 + (2 + 4) = _____

O. (5 + 1) + (4 + 4) = _____

P. (4 + 3) + (6 + 2) = _____

Q. 4 + (5 + 4) = _____

R. (3 + 7) + 7 = _____

S. 5 + (5 + 5) = _____

T. (9 + 3) + 2 = _____

U. (5 + 7) + (4 + 4) = _____

V. (6 + 5) + (7 + 4) = _____

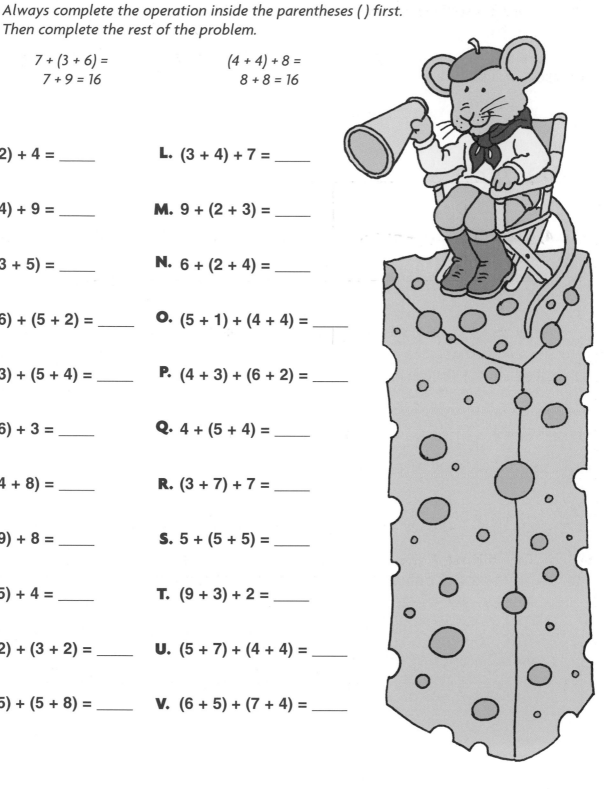

Write a number sentence for each problem. Solve.

A. Aimee and her 2 sisters are saving to buy a camera. Aimee has $12.89. Each of her sisters has $28.53. How much money do all the girls have combined?	**B.** Katie has $23.95 in her purse, $17.23 in her bank, and $76.82 in her savings account. What is the total amount of Katie's money?

(handwritten work in problem A:)

```
  1                        40        10
 53 2.89  +12    +28    +1.06
+53 8.5   +28          89
          40     68    1.95
1.06
    + 1.0  (41.95)
      8
```

C. Jonah worked in the yard for 3 days. The first day he earned $7.96. The second day he earned $2.00 more than the first day. The third day he earned $2.00 less than the first day. How much did Jonah earn altogether?	**D.** Jack has $9.29. He also has 79 dimes and 139 pennies. How much money does he have altogether?

E. Kelsey has 478 coins in her collection. The silver dollars equal $79.00, and the quarters equal $99.75. How much is Kelsey's collection worth in all?	**F.** Claire bought lemonade for herself and two friends. Each cup costs $1.75. How much did Claire spend in all?

Scholastic

To subtract multiple-digit numbers without regrouping, follow these steps.

1. Subtract the ones column.

$$
\begin{array}{r}
6,48\boxed{9} \\
-\ 2,16\boxed{5} \\
\hline
\boxed{4}
\end{array}
$$

2. Subtract the tens column.

$$
\begin{array}{r}
6,4\boxed{8}9 \\
-\ 2,1\boxed{6}5 \\
\hline
\boxed{2}4
\end{array}
$$

3. Subtract the hundreds column.

$$
\begin{array}{r}
6,\boxed{4}89 \\
-\ 2\boxed{1}65 \\
\hline
\boxed{3}24
\end{array}
$$

4. Subtract the thousands column.

$$
\begin{array}{r}
\boxed{6},489 \\
-\ \boxed{2},165 \\
\hline
\boxed{4},324
\end{array}
$$

Subtract.

1.
$$
\begin{array}{r}
6,518 \\
-\ 1,414 \\
\hline
5,104
\end{array}
$$

2.
$$
\begin{array}{r}
9,842 \\
-\ 621 \\
\hline
\end{array}
$$

3.
$$
\begin{array}{r}
7,966 \\
-\ 3,234 \\
\hline
\end{array}
$$

4.
$$
\begin{array}{r}
6,549 \\
-\ 21 \\
\hline
\end{array}
$$

5.
$$
\begin{array}{r}
4,916 \\
-\ 4,113 \\
\hline
\end{array}
$$

6.
$$
\begin{array}{r}
8,385 \\
-\ 7,224 \\
\hline
1,161
\end{array}
$$

7.
$$
\begin{array}{r}
3,309 \\
-\ 203 \\
\hline
\end{array}
$$

8.
$$
\begin{array}{r}
5,977 \\
-\ 2,863 \\
\hline
\end{array}
$$

9.
$$
\begin{array}{r}
9,459 \\
-\ 300 \\
\hline
9,159
\end{array}
$$

10.
$$
\begin{array}{r}
7,749 \\
-\ 7,637 \\
\hline
\end{array}
$$

11.
$$
\begin{array}{r}
4,969 \\
-\ 2,863 \\
\hline
3,106
\end{array}
$$

12.
$$
\begin{array}{r}
3,496 \\
-\ 3,260 \\
\hline
\end{array}
$$

13.
$$
\begin{array}{r}
6,839 \\
-\ 5,324 \\
\hline
\end{array}
$$

14.
$$
\begin{array}{r}
1,578 \\
-\ 1,241 \\
\hline
337
\end{array}
$$

15.
$$
\begin{array}{r}
8,659 \\
-\ 46 \\
\hline
8,613
\end{array}
$$

16.
$$
\begin{array}{r}
9,481 \\
-\ 9,240 \\
\hline
0,240
\end{array}
$$

Scholastic

To subtract with regrouping, follow these steps.

1. Subtract the ones column. Regroup if needed.

```
  2 11
  4 ⌿3 ⌿7
-  2 6 6
_____
        5
```

2. Subtract the tens column. Regroup if needed.

```
    12
  3 ⌿2 11
  4 ⌿3 ⌿7
-  2 6 6
_____
      6 5
```

3. Subtract the hundreds column. Regroup if needed.

```
    12
  3 ⌿2 11
  4 ⌿3 ⌿7
-  2 6 6
_____
    1 6 5
```

Subtract. Cross out the chess piece with the matching difference. The last piece standing is the winner of the match.

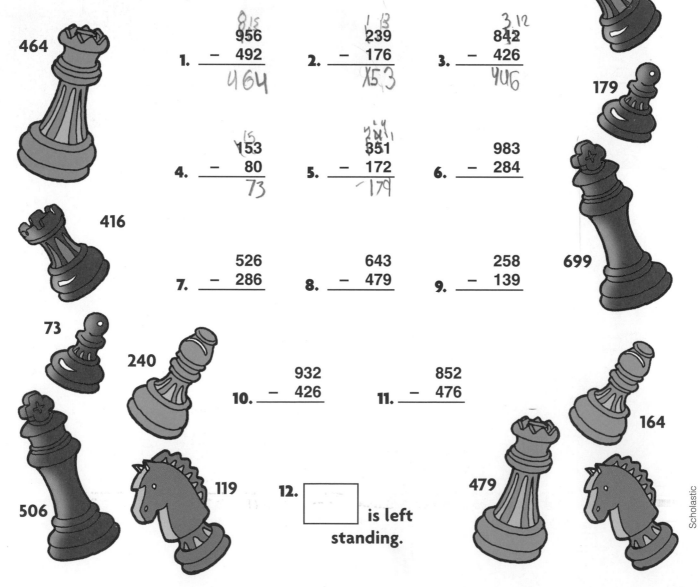

63

464

179

1.
```
  8 15
  956
- 492
_____
  464
```

2.
```
  1 3
  239
- 176
_____
  X5 3
```

3.
```
  3 12
  842
- 426
_____
  406
```

4.
```
  15
  153
-  80
_____
   73
```

5.
```
  2 4 1
  351
- 172
_____
 -179
```

6.
```
  983
- 284
_____
```

416

699

7.
```
  526
- 286
_____
```

8.
```
  643
- 479
_____
```

9.
```
  258
- 139
_____
```

73

240

10.
```
  932
- 426
_____
```

11.
```
  852
- 476
_____
```

164

506

119

479

12. [ ] is left standing.

Scholastic

To subtract with regrouping, follow these steps.

1.
```
        5 10
   3 , 4 6̶ 0̶
 −    8 7 6
 _____
            4
```

2.
```
           15
        3 5̶ 10
   3 , 4̶ 6̶ 0̶
 −     8 7 6
 _____
          8 4
```

3.
```
        13 15
     2 3̶ 5̶ 10
   3̶ , 4̶ 6̶ 0̶
 −      8 7 6
 _____
         5 8 4
```

4.
```
        13 15
     2 3̶ 5̶ 10
   3̶ , 4̶ 6̶ 0̶
 −      8 7 6
 _____
       2 , 5 8 4
```

Subtract. Then use the code to solve the riddle below.

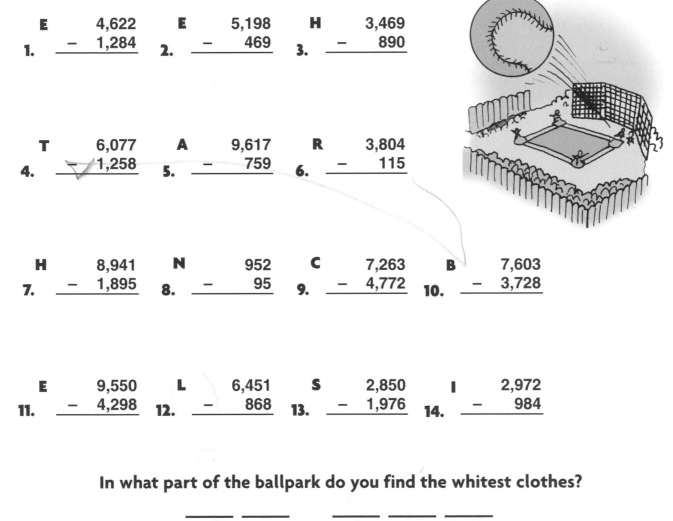

E 1. 4,622 − 1,284

E 2. 5,198 − 469

H 3. 3,469 − 890

T 4. 6,077 − 1,258

A 5. 9,617 − 759

R 6. 3,804 − 115

H 7. 8,941 − 1,895

N 8. 952 − 95

C 9. 7,263 − 4,772

B 10. 7,603 − 3,728

E 11. 9,550 − 4,298

L 12. 6,451 − 868

S 13. 2,850 − 1,976

I 14. 2,972 − 984

In what part of the ballpark do you find the whitest clothes?

___ ___   ___ ___ ___
1,988 857   4,819 2,579 5,252

___ ___ ___ ___ ___ ___ ___ ___ ___!
3,875 5,583 4,729 8,858 2,491 7,046 3,338 3,689 874

Scholastic

Subtract. The final score of the game will be written in the footballs at the bottom of the page.

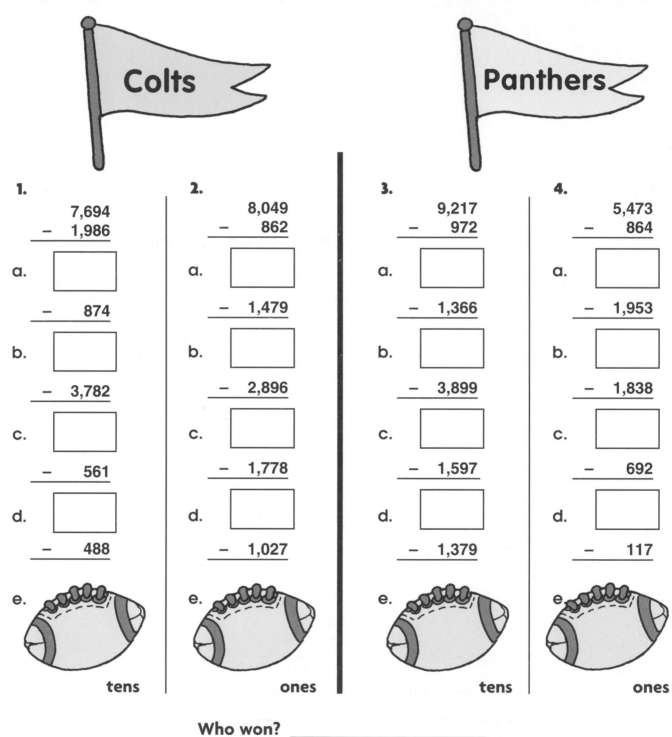

Colts

1.
```
    7,694
  − 1,986
```
a. ☐
```
  −   874
```
b. ☐
```
  − 3,782
```
c. ☐
```
  −   561
```
d. ☐
```
  −   488
```
e.

tens

2.
```
    8,049
  −   862
```
a. ☐
```
  − 1,479
```
b. ☐
```
  − 2,896
```
c. ☐
```
  − 1,778
```
d. ☐
```
  − 1,027
```
e.

ones

Panthers

3.
```
    9,217
  −   972
```
a. ☐
```
  − 1,366
```
b. ☐
```
  − 3,899
```
c. ☐
```
  − 1,597
```
d. ☐
```
  − 1,379
```
e.

tens

4.
```
    5,473
  −   864
```
a. ☐
```
  − 1,953
```
b. ☐
```
  − 1,838
```
c. ☐
```
  −   692
```
d. ☐
```
  −   117
```
e.

ones

Who won? _____

Scholastic

Always complete the operation inside the parentheses ( ) first.
Then complete the rest of the problem.

$(18 - 9) - 3 =$ _____ $18 - (9 - 3) =$ _____
$9 - 3 = 6$ $18 - 6 = 12$

Subtract. Then use the code to answer the question below.

1. **N** $(16 - 8) - 5 =$ _____   10. **T** $(18 - 6) - 2 =$ _____

2. **B** $17 - (12 - 4) =$ _____   11. **L** $19 - (10 - 6) =$ _____

3. **U** $(23 - 4) - 5 =$ _____   12. **E** $(13 - 5) - (10 - 9) =$ _____

4. **D** $(12 - 3) - (16 - 7) =$ _____   13. **O** $(14 - 7) - (12 - 6) =$ _____

5. **L** $(17 - 5) - (12 - 8) =$ _____   14. **I** $(16 - 8) - (11 - 9) =$ _____

6. **W** $13 - (11 - 3) =$ _____   15. **D** $17 - (14 - 9) =$ _____

7. **R** $(22 - 6) - 5 =$ _____   16. **N** $(21 - 2) - (15 - 9) =$ _____

8. **I** $(21 - 1) - (16 - 12) =$ _____   17. **O** $(10 - 3) - (11 - 6) =$ _____

9. **H** $(11 - 3) - 4 =$ _____

About how many stars are in the Milky Way Galaxy?

___ ___ ___   ___ ___ ___ ___ ___ ___ ___   ___ ___ ___ ___ ___ ___ ___
10 5   1   4   14 13 0   11 7   12   9   16 8   15 6   2   3

Scholastic

The answer to a subtraction problem is called the **difference**.

Subtract. Then write the differences in order to answer the fun fact.

How fast does the moon travel in its orbit? ____ ____ ____ ____ m.p.h.

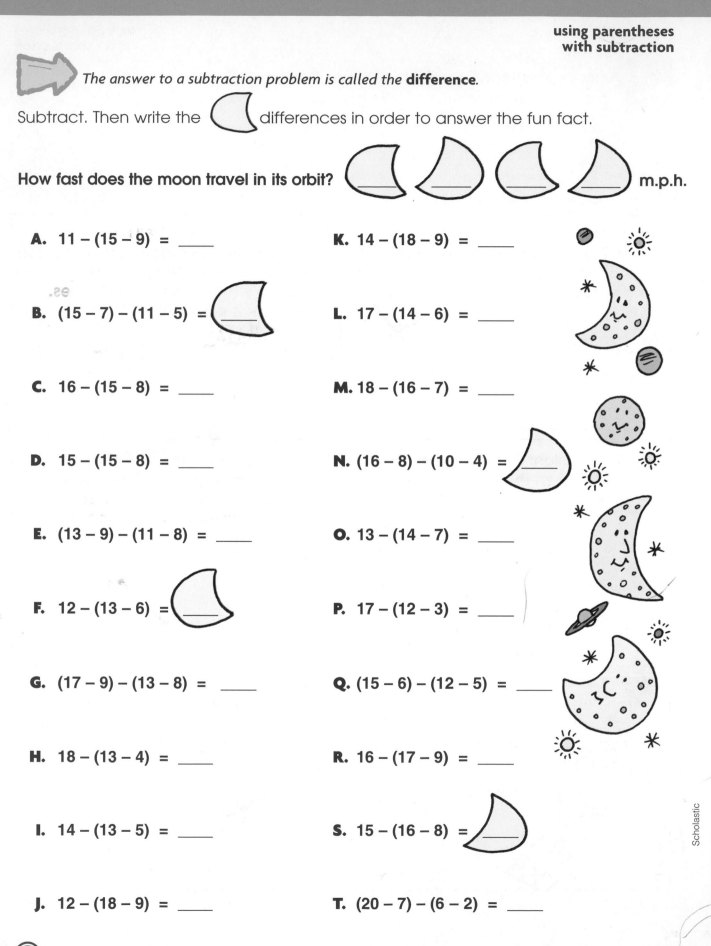

A. $11 - (15 - 9) =$ ____

B. $(15 - 7) - (11 - 5) =$ ____

C. $16 - (15 - 8) =$ ____

D. $15 - (15 - 8) =$ ____

E. $(13 - 9) - (11 - 8) =$ ____

F. $12 - (13 - 6) =$ ____

G. $(17 - 9) - (13 - 8) =$ ____

H. $18 - (13 - 4) =$ ____

I. $14 - (13 - 5) =$ ____

J. $12 - (18 - 9) =$ ____

K. $14 - (18 - 9) =$ ____

L. $17 - (14 - 6) =$ ____

M. $18 - (16 - 7) =$ ____

N. $(16 - 8) - (10 - 4) =$ ____

O. $13 - (14 - 7) =$ ____

P. $17 - (12 - 3) =$ ____

Q. $(15 - 6) - (12 - 5) =$ ____

R. $16 - (17 - 9) =$ ____

S. $15 - (16 - 8) =$ ____

T. $(20 - 7) - (6 - 2) =$ ____

Scholastic

Write a number sentence for each problem. Solve.

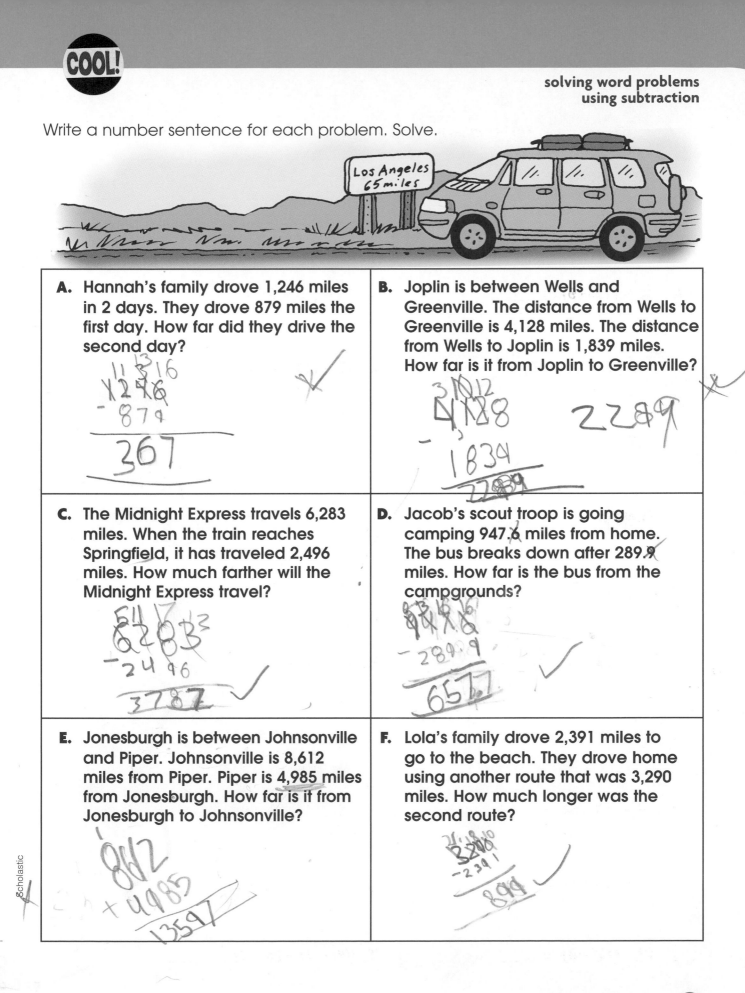

A. Hannah's family drove 1,246 miles in 2 days. They drove 879 miles the first day. How far did they drive the second day?

$$\begin{array}{r} 1\,246 \\ -\;879 \\ \hline 367 \end{array}$$

B. Joplin is between Wells and Greenville. The distance from Wells to Greenville is 4,128 miles. The distance from Wells to Joplin is 1,839 miles. How far is it from Joplin to Greenville?

$$\begin{array}{r} 4\,128 \\ -1\,839 \\ \hline 2289 \end{array}$$

2289

C. The Midnight Express travels 6,283 miles. When the train reaches Springfield, it has traveled 2,496 miles. How much farther will the Midnight Express travel?

$$\begin{array}{r} 6\,283 \\ -2\,496 \\ \hline 3787 \end{array}$$

D. Jacob's scout troop is going camping 947.6 miles from home. The bus breaks down after 289.9 miles. How far is the bus from the campgrounds?

$$\begin{array}{r} 947.6 \\ -289.9 \\ \hline 657.7 \end{array}$$

E. Jonesburgh is between Johnsonville and Piper. Johnsonville is 8,612 miles from Piper. Piper is 4,985 miles from Jonesburgh. How far is it from Jonesburgh to Johnsonville?

$$\begin{array}{r} 8\,612 \\ +4\,985 \\ \hline 13597 \end{array}$$

F. Lola's family drove 2,391 miles to go to the beach. They drove home using another route that was 3,290 miles. How much longer was the second route?

$$\begin{array}{r} 3\,290 \\ -2\,391 \\ \hline 899 \end{array}$$

Addition & Subtraction Practice Test

Fill in the bubble next to the correct answer.

1.

$$\begin{array}{r} 564 \\ +\ 399 \\ \hline 963 \end{array}$$

- A 963
- B 763
- C 937
- D 890

2.

$$\begin{array}{r} 4{,}912 \\ -\ 1999 \\ \hline \end{array}$$

- F 2913
- G 2391
- H 3211
- J 3929

3.

$$\begin{array}{r} 3434 \\ +\ 2876 \\ \hline \end{array}$$

- A 6340
- B 5580
- C 5797
- D 6310

4.

$$\begin{array}{r} 3867 \\ -\ 545 \\ \hline \end{array}$$

- F 3232
- G 3322
- H 2342
- J 3002

Scholastic

Addition & Subtraction Practice Test

Choose a sticker to place here.

Fill in the bubble next to the correct answer.

5. 155 + _____ = 444

⦿ **A**   289

⦿ **B**   189

⦿ **C**   309

⦿ **D**   389

7. 193 + 367 + 491 = _____

⦿ **A**   931

⦿ **B**   979

⦿ **C**   1051

⦿ **D**   1531

6. _____ + 1234 = 5678

⦿ **F**   4440

⦿ **G**   4444

⦿ **H**   4343

⦿ **J**   4040

8. 678 + 1988 = _____

⦿ **F**   2666

⦿ **G**   2676

⦿ **H**   2356

⦿ **J**   2777

Scholastic

Multiplication & Division

When you multiply, you add a number to itself a number of times. For example: $5 + 5 + 5 + 5 + 5 = 25$ or $5 \times 5 = 25$. Multiplying is a quick way to add things up.

When you divide, you group numbers into equal parts. In the example $20 \div 10 = 2$, you group 20 into 2 equal parts of 10. To check your answer, you do the opposite of division—you multiply $10 \times 2 = 20$.

Sometimes you can't group all the numbers into equal parts. In those cases you will have a remainder, a number left over. For example: $29 \div 6 = 4$, remainder 5.

What to Do

Have your child solve the multiplication and division problems on the activity pages. Review the answers with your child. Remind your child that he or she can check the division problems by multiplying. In the example $29 \div 6 = 4$ remainder 5, $(6 \times 4) + 5 = 29$. Your answer is correct! An answer key is provided at the back of the book for your convenience.

Keep On Going!

Show your child that math can be fun! Play a multiplication/division game with your child. Give your child a multiplication problem and have him or her solve it and then turn it into a division problem to check the answer. For example:

$$9 \times 4 = 36$$
$$36 \div 4 = 9 \quad \text{or} \quad 36 \div 9 = 4$$

To multiply with a 2-digit factor that requires regrouping, follow these steps.

1. Multiply the ones.
   Regroup if needed.

   7 x 3 = 21

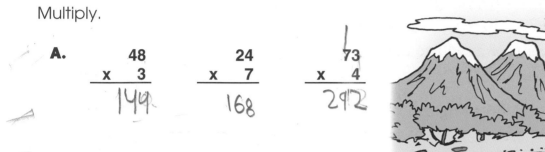

2. Multiply the bottom factor in the ones column with the top factor in the tens column. Add the extra tens.

   6 x 3 = 18   18 + 2 = 20

```
  292
+ 144
+ 168
─────
  604
```

Multiply.

A.

```
   48        24        73
 x  3      x  7      x  4
  144       168       292
```

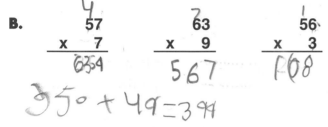

B.

```
    4
   57        63        56
 x  7      x  9      x  3
  634       567       f08
```

350 + 49 = 399

C.

```
   1         3         5         4         2         1
   98        64        57        35        23        82
 x  2      x  8      x  8      x  9      x  8      x  6
 196       512       456       315       184       492
```

D.

```
   4         4         2         4         3         3
   95        77        83        96        28        96
 x  9      x  6      x  9      x  8      x  4      x  5
  855       462       747       768       112       480
```

Switzerland is famous for the magnificent Swiss Alps. Waterfalls are formed by many of the mountain streams. To find out how many meters high one waterfall is, add the products in Row A.

Scholastic

6·7·8
100108

To multiply with zeros, follow these steps.

9 0	9 x 2 = 18
x 2	Add a zero in the ones place to make 180.

9 0	9 x 2 = 18
x 20	Add 2 zeros—one in the ones place and one in the tens place.

9 0 0	9 x 2 = 18
x 20	Add 3 zeros—one in the ones place, one in the tens place, and one in the hundreds place.

Multiply.

A.

80	60	900	40	120	200
x 7	x 50	x 30	x 11	x 2	x 60
560	3000	27000	440	240	12000

B.

70	120	60	700	50	30
x 7	x 300	x 90	x 60	x 70	x 12
490	36000	00		1004	

540
5400

112 = 10 + 2
100

C.

600	40	30	90	200	50
x 80	x 12	x 8	x 50	x 120	x 8

80
400
480

Which of these landmarks is the tallest? Multiply. Write the ones digit of each product, in order, to find the height of each landmark. Circle the tallest landmark.

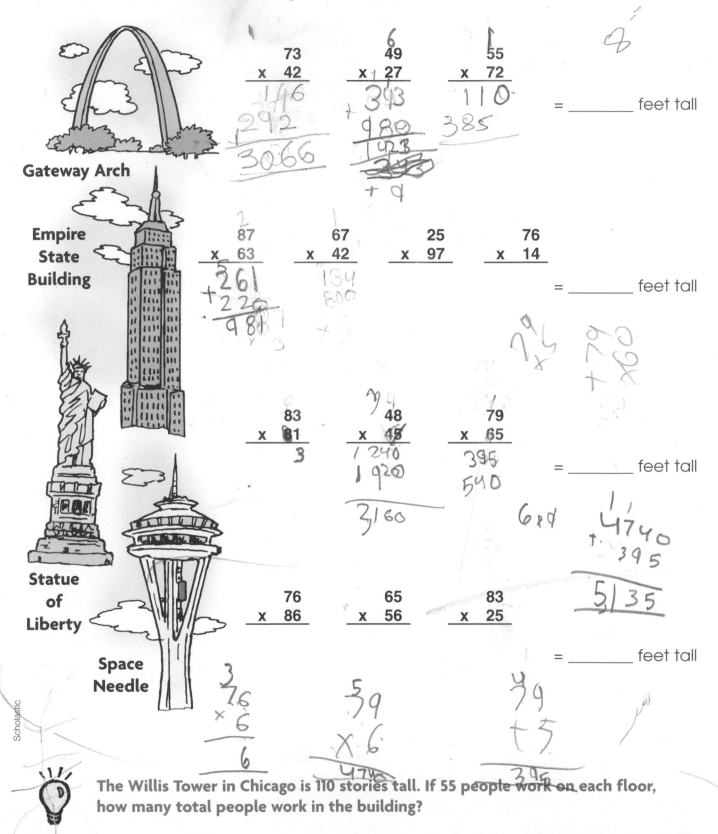

Gateway Arch

$$\begin{array}{r} 73 \\ \times\ 42 \\ \hline 146 \\ 292 \\ \hline 3066 \end{array}$$

$$\begin{array}{r} 49 \\ \times\ 27 \\ \hline 343 \\ 980 \\ \hline 1428 \end{array}$$

$$\begin{array}{r} 55 \\ \times\ 72 \\ \hline 110 \\ 385 \end{array}$$

= _____ feet tall

Empire State Building

$$\begin{array}{r} 87 \\ \times\ 63 \\ \hline 261 \\ +220 \\ \hline 481 \end{array}$$

$$\begin{array}{r} 67 \\ \times\ 42 \\ \hline 134 \\ 800 \end{array}$$

$$\begin{array}{r} 25 \\ \times\ 97 \end{array}$$

$$\begin{array}{r} 76 \\ \times\ 14 \end{array}$$

= _____ feet tall

$$\begin{array}{r} 83 \\ \times\ 81 \\ \hline 3 \end{array}$$

$$\begin{array}{r} 48 \\ \times\ 45 \\ \hline 1240 \\ 1920 \\ \hline 3,160 \end{array}$$

$$\begin{array}{r} 79 \\ \times\ 65 \\ \hline 395 \\ 540 \end{array}$$

= _____ feet tall

Statue of Liberty

$$\begin{array}{r} 4740 \\ +\ 395 \\ \hline 5135 \end{array}$$

Space Needle

$$\begin{array}{r} 76 \\ \times\ 86 \end{array}$$

$$\begin{array}{r} 65 \\ \times\ 56 \end{array}$$

$$\begin{array}{r} 83 \\ \times\ 25 \end{array}$$

= _____ feet tall

$$\begin{array}{r} 76 \\ \times\ 6 \\ \hline 6 \end{array}$$

$$\begin{array}{r} 79 \\ \times\ 6 \\ \hline 4740 \end{array}$$

$$\begin{array}{r} 79 \\ +\ 5 \\ \hline 395 \end{array}$$

The Willis Tower in Chicago is 110 stories tall. If 55 people work on each floor, how many total people work in the building?

To multiply with a 2-digit factor that requires regrouping, follow these steps.

1. Multiply by the ones digit.

2. Place a zero in the ones column.

3. Multiply by the tens digit.

4. Add to find the product.

$$
\begin{array}{r}
3 \\
46 \\
\times \ 26 \\
\hline
276
\end{array}
$$

$$
\begin{array}{r}
3 \\
46 \\
\times \ 26 \\
\hline
276 \\
0
\end{array}
$$

$$
\begin{array}{r}
3 \\
46 \\
\times \ 26 \\
\hline
276 \\
+ \ 920
\end{array}
$$

$$
\begin{array}{r}
3 \\
46 \\
\times \ 26 \\
\hline
276 \\
+ \ 920 \\
\hline
1,196
\end{array}
$$

Multiply. Then use the code to answer the riddle below.

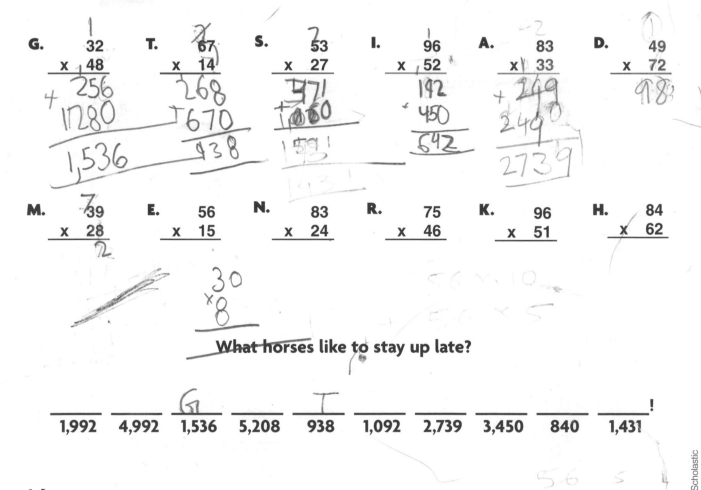

G.
$$
\begin{array}{r}
32 \\
\times \ 48 \\
\hline
256 \\
+ 1280 \\
\hline
1,536
\end{array}
$$

T.
$$
\begin{array}{r}
67 \\
\times \ 14 \\
\hline
268 \\
670 \\
\hline
938
\end{array}
$$

S.
$$
\begin{array}{r}
53 \\
\times \ 27 \\
\hline
371 \\
1060
\end{array}
$$

I.
$$
\begin{array}{r}
96 \\
\times \ 52 \\
\hline
192 \\
450 \\
\hline
642
\end{array}
$$

A.
$$
\begin{array}{r}
83 \\
\times \ 33 \\
\hline
249 \\
2490 \\
\hline
2739
\end{array}
$$

D.
$$
\begin{array}{r}
49 \\
\times \ 72 \\
\hline
983
\end{array}
$$

M.
$$
\begin{array}{r}
39 \\
\times \ 28 \\
\hline
2
\end{array}
$$

E.
$$
\begin{array}{r}
56 \\
\times \ 15 \\
\hline
\end{array}
$$

N.
$$
\begin{array}{r}
83 \\
\times \ 24 \\
\hline
\end{array}
$$

R.
$$
\begin{array}{r}
75 \\
\times \ 46 \\
\hline
\end{array}
$$

K.
$$
\begin{array}{r}
96 \\
\times \ 51 \\
\hline
\end{array}
$$

H.
$$
\begin{array}{r}
84 \\
\times \ 62 \\
\hline
\end{array}
$$

$$
\begin{array}{r}
30 \\
\times \ 8 \\
\hline
\end{array}
$$

What horses like to stay up late?

___ ___ G ___ T ___ ___ ___ ___ ___ !
1,992 4,992 1,536 5,208 938 1,092 2,739 3,450 840 1,431

Each of Farmer Gray's 24 horses eats 68 pounds of hay.
How many pounds of hay do the horses eat altogether?

Scholastic

Multiply.

A.

362	602	452	283	918	473
x 43	x 18	x 22	x 13	x 27	x 55

65

B.

540	417	308
x 38	x 56	x 61

C.

692	586	918
x 34	x 37	x 86

D.

467	598	861
x 42	x 29	x 73

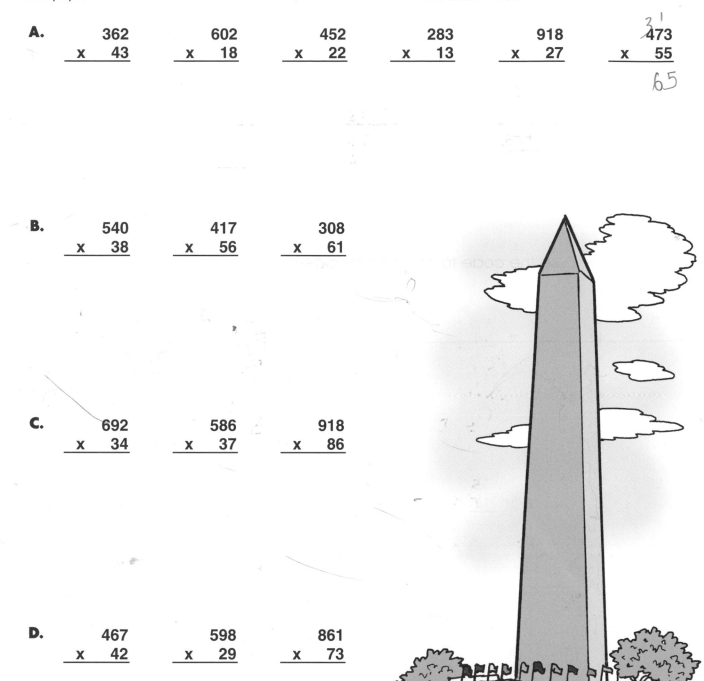

 The Washington Monument has 897 steps. If 42 people climb to the top, how many steps have they climbed altogether?

Scholastic

When a multiplication problem involves money, the product must have a dollar sign and a decimal point. The decimal point is placed between the ones digit and the tenths digit.

```
  6
  2
$3.71
x    94
 14.84
+ 333.90
$348.84
```

Remember to use a dollar sign and a decimal point.

Multiply. Then use the code to answer the riddle below.

N. $1.94
x   23

M. $0.79
x   25

I. $2.06
x   64

O. $0.68
x   45

A. $3.68
x   32

T. $9.54
x   19

F. $0.88
x   72

D. $0.93
x   94

E. $8.15
x   67

S. $7.43
x   92

R. $0.87
x   75

H. $6.92
x   83

Where do musicians buy instruments?

___ ___   ___ ___ ___
$117.76 $181.26 $181.26 $574.36 $546.05

___ ___ ___ ___   ___ ___ ___
$63.36 $131.84 $63.36 $546.05 $117.76 $44.62 $87.42

___ ___ ___ ___   ___ ___ ___ ___ ___!
$87.42 $131.84 $19.75 $546.05 $683.56 $181.26 $30.60 $65.25 $546.05

→ *Word problems that suggest equal groups often require multiplication.*

Write a number sentence for each problem. Solve.

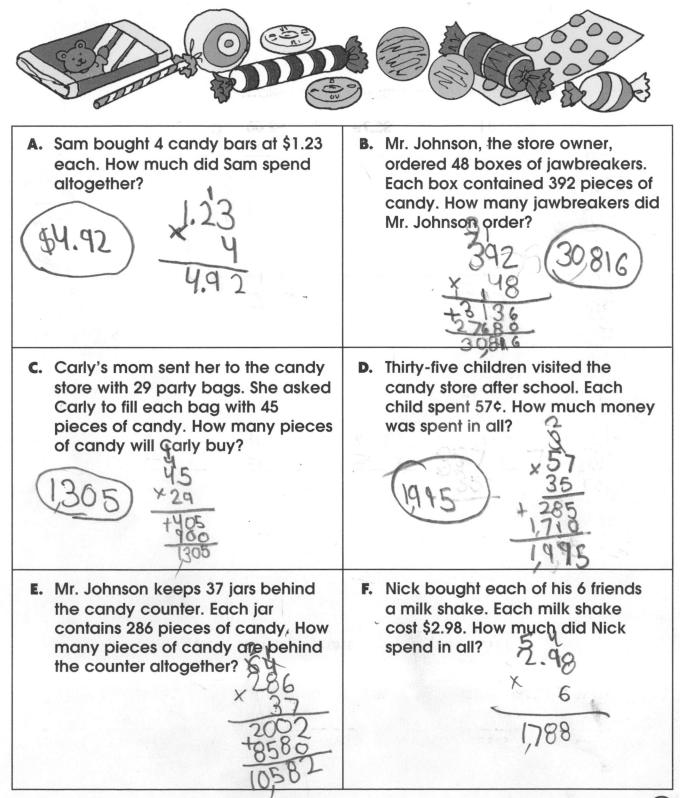

A. Sam bought 4 candy bars at $1.23 each. How much did Sam spend altogether?

$$\begin{array}{r} 1.23 \\ \times\quad 4 \\ \hline 4.92 \end{array}$$

$4.92

B. Mr. Johnson, the store owner, ordered 48 boxes of jawbreakers. Each box contained 392 pieces of candy. How many jawbreakers did Mr. Johnson order?

$$\begin{array}{r} 392 \\ \times\ 48 \\ \hline 3136 \\ +27680 \\ \hline 30816 \end{array}$$

30,816

C. Carly's mom sent her to the candy store with 29 party bags. She asked Carly to fill each bag with 45 pieces of candy. How many pieces of candy will Carly buy?

$$\begin{array}{r} 45 \\ \times\ 29 \\ \hline 405 \\ +900 \\ \hline 1305 \end{array}$$

1,305

D. Thirty-five children visited the candy store after school. Each child spent 57¢. How much money was spent in all?

$$\begin{array}{r} 57 \\ \times\ 35 \\ \hline 285 \\ +1710 \\ \hline 1995 \end{array}$$

1,995

E. Mr. Johnson keeps 37 jars behind the candy counter. Each jar contains 286 pieces of candy. How many pieces of candy are behind the counter altogether?

$$\begin{array}{r} 286 \\ \times\ 37 \\ \hline 2002 \\ +8580 \\ \hline 10582 \end{array}$$

F. Nick bought each of his 6 friends a milk shake. Each milk shake cost $2.98. How much did Nick spend in all?

$$\begin{array}{r} 2.98 \\ \times\quad 6 \\ \hline 1788 \end{array}$$

1,788

Scholastic

December 14.22

To divide means to make equal groups. Since multiplication also depends on equal groups, you can use the multiplication facts to help you learn the division facts.

$$\begin{array}{r} 8 \\ \times\ 6 \\ \hline 48 \end{array} \longrightarrow \quad 6\,\overline{)\,48\,}^{\,8}$$

Basic division facts are problems you will learn by memory. Divide.

A.

$$4\,\overline{)\,24\,}^{\,6} \quad -24 \quad \underline{0}$$

$$4\,\overline{)\,36\,}^{\,9} \quad -36 \quad 0$$

$$7\,\overline{)\,56\,}^{\,8} \quad -56 \quad 0$$

$$5\,\overline{)\,25\,}^{\,5} \quad -25 \quad 0$$

$$9\,\overline{)\,81\,}^{\,9} \quad -81 \quad 0$$

$$8\,\overline{)\,24\,}^{\,3} \quad -24 \quad 0$$

B.

$$5\,\overline{)\,45\,}^{\,9} \quad -45 \quad 0$$

$$8\,\overline{)\,72\,}^{\,9} \quad -72 \quad 0$$

$$4\,\overline{)\,28\,}^{\,7} \quad -28 \quad 0$$

$$6\,\overline{)\,42\,}^{\,7} \quad -42 \quad 0$$

$$6\,\overline{)\,36\,}^{\,6} \quad -36 \quad 0$$

$$1\,\overline{)\,9\,}^{\,9} \quad -9 \quad 0$$

C.

$$3\,\overline{)\,12\,}^{\,4} \quad -12 \quad 0$$

$$7\,\overline{)\,21\,}^{\,3} \quad -21 \quad 0$$

$$6\,\overline{)\,48\,}^{\,8} \quad -48 \quad 0$$

$$3\,\overline{)\,24\,}^{\,8} \quad -24 \quad 0$$

$$8\,\overline{)\,32\,}^{\,4} \quad -32 \quad 0$$

$$7\,\overline{)\,63\,}^{\,9} \quad -63 \quad 0$$

D.

$$8\,\overline{)\,64\,}^{\,8} \quad -64 \quad 0$$

$$7\,\overline{)\,49\,}^{\,7} \quad -49 \quad 0$$

$$5\,\overline{)\,30\,}^{\,6} \quad -30 \quad 0$$

$$9\,\overline{)\,27\,}^{\,3} \quad -27 \quad 0$$

$$6\,\overline{)\,6\,}^{\,1} \quad -6 \quad 0$$

$$3\,\overline{)\,15\,}^{\,5} \quad -15 \quad 0$$

Divide to learn an interesting fact.

In what year was television invented?

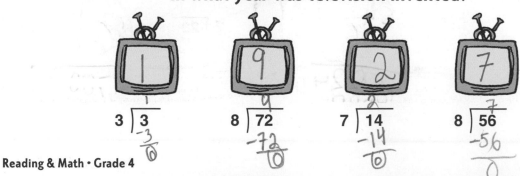

$$3\,\overline{)\,3\,}^{\,1} \quad -3 \quad 0$$

$$8\,\overline{)\,72\,}^{\,9} \quad -72 \quad 0$$

$$7\,\overline{)\,14\,}^{\,2} \quad -14 \quad 0$$

$$8\,\overline{)\,56\,}^{\,7} \quad -56 \quad 0$$

Scholastic

Each part of a division problem has a name.

$$5 \leftarrow \text{quotient}$$

$$\text{divisor} \rightarrow 9\overline{\smash{)}45} \leftarrow \text{dividend}$$

Divide.

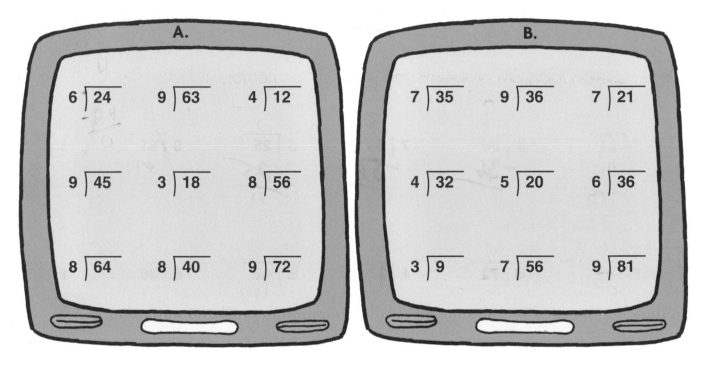

A.

$6\overline{\smash{)}24}$	$9\overline{\smash{)}63}$	$4\overline{\smash{)}12}$
$9\overline{\smash{)}45}$	$3\overline{\smash{)}18}$	$8\overline{\smash{)}56}$
$8\overline{\smash{)}64}$	$8\overline{\smash{)}40}$	$9\overline{\smash{)}72}$

B.

$7\overline{\smash{)}35}$	$9\overline{\smash{)}36}$	$7\overline{\smash{)}21}$
$4\overline{\smash{)}32}$	$5\overline{\smash{)}20}$	$6\overline{\smash{)}36}$
$3\overline{\smash{)}9}$	$7\overline{\smash{)}56}$	$9\overline{\smash{)}81}$

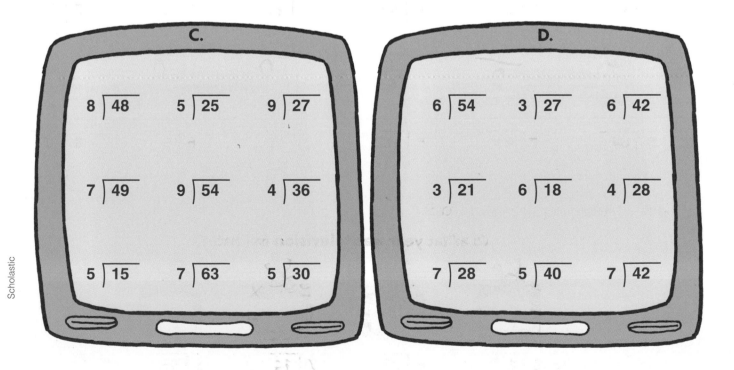

C.

$8\overline{\smash{)}48}$	$5\overline{\smash{)}25}$	$9\overline{\smash{)}27}$
$7\overline{\smash{)}49}$	$9\overline{\smash{)}54}$	$4\overline{\smash{)}36}$
$5\overline{\smash{)}15}$	$7\overline{\smash{)}63}$	$5\overline{\smash{)}30}$

D.

$6\overline{\smash{)}54}$	$3\overline{\smash{)}27}$	$6\overline{\smash{)}42}$
$3\overline{\smash{)}21}$	$6\overline{\smash{)}18}$	$4\overline{\smash{)}28}$
$7\overline{\smash{)}28}$	$5\overline{\smash{)}40}$	$7\overline{\smash{)}42}$

Scholastic

To divide with zeros, follow these samples.

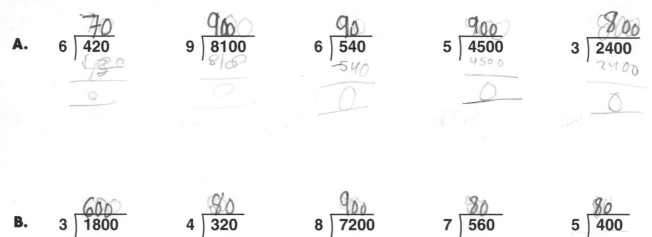

$$\begin{array}{r} 80 \\ 8 \overline{\smash{)}640} \end{array}$$

$64 \div 8 = 8$
$0 \div 8 = 0$
Add a zero to make 80.

$$\begin{array}{r} 800 \\ 8 \overline{\smash{)}6400} \end{array}$$

$64 \div 8 = 8$
$0 \div 8 = 0$
$0 \div 8 = 0$
Add 2 zeros to make 800.

Divide.

A. $6 \overline{\smash{)}420}$ $9 \overline{\smash{)}8100}$ $6 \overline{\smash{)}540}$ $5 \overline{\smash{)}4500}$ $3 \overline{\smash{)}2400}$

B. $3 \overline{\smash{)}1800}$ $4 \overline{\smash{)}320}$ $8 \overline{\smash{)}7200}$ $7 \overline{\smash{)}560}$ $5 \overline{\smash{)}400}$

C. $3 \overline{\smash{)}150}$ $4 \overline{\smash{)}360}$ $6 \overline{\smash{)}4800}$ $6 \overline{\smash{)}360}$ $8 \overline{\smash{)}640}$

Scholastic

$12 + 2x = 16$

$2x = 16 - 12$

$2x = 4$

To divide with a 3-digit dividend, follow these steps.

1.
$$7 \overline{)427}$$
6 ... 42

$7 \times \underline{} = 42$
$7 \times 6 = 42$

2.
$$7 \overline{)427}$$
6
$- 42 \downarrow$
07

Subtract.

Bring down the ones digit.

3.
$$7 \overline{)427}$$
61
$- 42 \downarrow$
07
$- 7$
0

$7 \times \underline{} = 7$
$7 \times 1 = 7$

Subtract.

Divide. Then use the code to answer the riddle below.

T. $4 \overline{)208}$ U. $6 \overline{)306}$ H. $9 \overline{)819}$ C. $3 \overline{)246}$ A. $4 \overline{)368}$

E. $8 \overline{)648}$ O. $7 \overline{)497}$ S. $4 \overline{)248}$ N. $2 \overline{)168}$ D. $4 \overline{)288}$

(E. work) 81, -64, -08, -8, 0

(O. work) 21, 4, 07, -7, 0

C. $4 \overline{)328}$ I. $3 \overline{)159}$ W. $5 \overline{)305}$ M. $9 \overline{)279}$! $4 \overline{)88}$

Why did the cat hang out near the computer?

___ ___   ___ ___ ___ ___ ___ ___   ___ ___
53   52   61   92   84   52   81   72   52   71

___ ___ ___ ___ ___   ___ ___ ___
82   92   52   82   91   52   91   81

___ ___ ___ ___ ___ ___
31   71   51   62   81   22

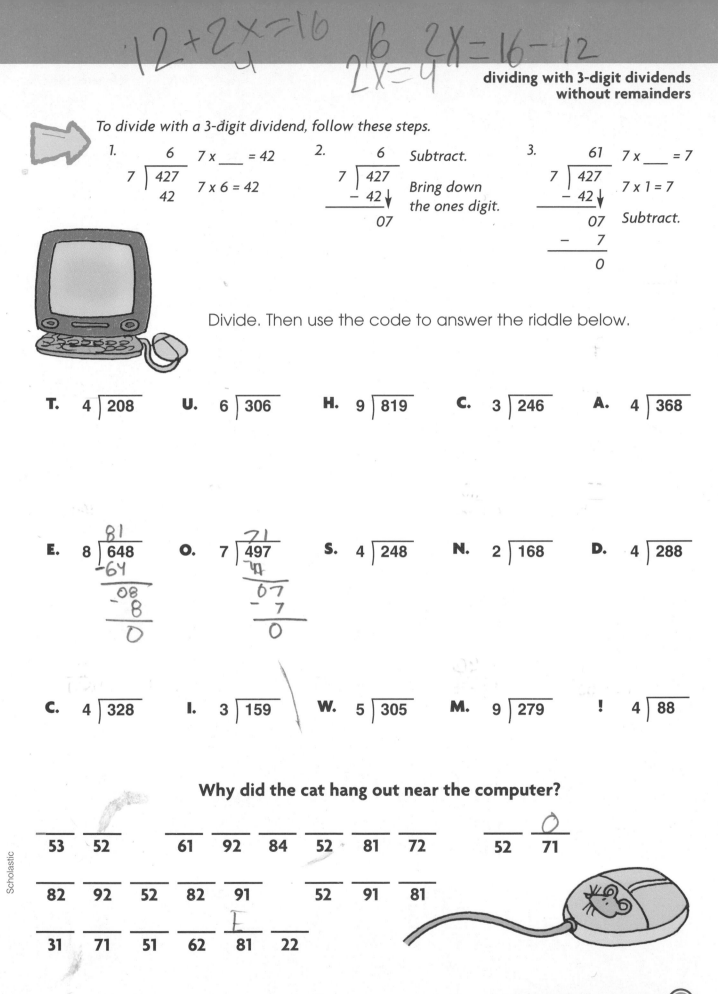

To divide with remainders, follow these steps.

1. Does 8 x ___ = 34? No! 2. Use the closest smaller dividend.
8 x 4 = 32

$8 \overline{)34}$

Anwser: _____

1. _____
2. _____

$\begin{array}{r} 4 \\ 8\overline{)34} \\ 32 \end{array}$

3. Subtract to find the remainder.

$\begin{array}{r} 4 \\ 8\overline{)34} \\ -32 \\ \hline 2 \end{array}$

4. The remainder is always less than the divisor.

$\begin{array}{r} 4\ R2 \\ 8\overline{)34} \\ -32 \\ \hline 2 \end{array}$

Divide. Then use the code to complete the riddle below.

E. 9)84 81 3→R=3	**L.** 3)29 -27 2→R=2 Questoun: is the left side line curved	**S.** 7)67 63 4→4=R	**O.** 5)24 20 4→R=4
T. 6)23 18 5→R=5	**N.** 6)479 42 -54 54	**P.** 6)39	**I.** 7)520 -49 3
O. 4)19	**A.** 8)70	**T.** 3)268 -24 28 27	**S.** 9)555 54 15 6
H. 4)231 20 37 36 1	**!** 7)459 42 35 4	**R.** 5)27	**N.** 8)795 -72 75 72 3

Emily: **Yesterday I saw a man at the mall with very long arms. Every time he went up the stairs he stepped on them.**

Jack: **Wow! He stepped on his arms?**

Emily:

___ ___ , ___ ___ ___ ___ ___
7 R5 4 R4   4 R3 9 R7   8 R2 5 R3 9 R3

___ ___ ___ ___ ___ ___ ___
9 R4 3 R5 8 R6 7 R3 5 R2 6 R1 6 R3

Dec 5 22

Scholastic

Word problems that give you a large group and ask you to make smaller, equal groups require division. Write a division problem. Solve.

A. The movie theater holds 988 people. It has 38 rows with an equal number of seats. How many seats are in each row?

26

B. A box of popcorn holds 972 kernels. If 18 friends share a box equally, how many kernels will each friend get?

$$\begin{array}{r} 54 \\ 18\overline{)972} \\ -90 \\ \hline 072 \\ -072 \\ \hline 000 \end{array}$$

(54)

C. The box office sold 4,020 tickets to 6 shows. The same number of people attended each show. How many tickets did they sell to each show?

$$\begin{array}{r} 670 \\ 6\overline{)4020} \\ -36 \\ \hline 420 \\ -420 \\ \hline 000 \end{array}$$

D. The theater sold 4,315 tickets over 5 days. The same number of tickets were sold each day. How many tickets did they sell each day?

$$\begin{array}{r} 863 \\ 5\overline{)4315} \\ -40 \\ \hline 315 \\ -30 \\ \hline 15 \\ 15 \end{array}$$

E. The soda fountain serves 7 types of drinks. On Saturday night, the theater served 952 drinks of the 7 drinks in equal amounts. How many drinks of each type were served?

$$\begin{array}{r} 136 \\ 7\overline{)952} \\ -9 \\ \hline 42 \\ -42 \\ \hline 0 \end{array}$$

F. The ticket office had 657 extra tickets. They were donated equally to 9 charities. How many tickets did each charity receive?

$$\begin{array}{r} 73 \\ 9\overline{)657} \\ -63 \\ \hline 27 \\ -27 \\ \hline 0 \end{array}$$

Dec 5-22

Multiplication & Division Practice Test

Fill in the bubble next to the correct answer.

1.

$$\begin{array}{r} 923 \\ \times\ 56 \end{array}$$

○ A   5,168

● B   51,688

○ C   54,718

○ D   45,188

2.   532 ÷ 7 =

● F   76

○ G   78

○ H   87

○ J   57

3.   Find the missing factor.

8 x ___9___ = 72

○ A   8

○ B   7

● C   9

○ D   3

4.

$$\begin{array}{r} 125 \\ \times\ 7 \\ \hline 875 \end{array}$$

● F   875

○ G   775

○ H   735

○ J   835

Multiplication & Division Practice Test

Choose a sticker to place here.

Fill in the bubble next to the correct answer.

5.

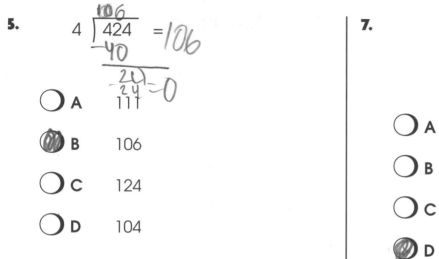

$$4 \overline{)424} = 106$$

- ○ A   111
- ● B   106
- ○ C   124
- ○ D   104

6. Find the missing factor.

___6___ × 9 = 54

- ○ F   5
- ○ G   9
- ○ H   7
- ● J   6

7.

$$\begin{array}{r} 2{,}564 \\ \times \quad 3 \\ \hline 7692 \end{array}$$

- ○ A   6387
- ○ B   8092
- ○ C   6789
- ● D   7692

8.

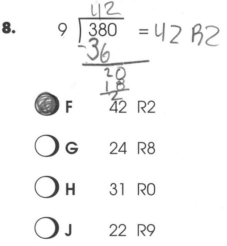

$$9 \overline{)380} = 42\ R2$$

- ● F   42 R2
- ○ G   24 R8
- ○ H   31 R0
- ○ J   22 R9

Scholastic

Fractions & Decimals

If your child likes to cook, he or she will find it very helpful to understand fractions. Most recipes have ingredients that are measured in fractions.

Decimals are important to understand because our money system is based on decimals.

What to Do

The activities in this section introduce your child to concepts related to fractions and decimals. Have your child complete the activities. Then together, review his or her work. Remember, answers, if you need them, have been provided at the back of the book. Reward your child with a sticker for work that is well done!

Keep On Going!

Look for opportunities to reinforce your child's understanding of fractions. For example, have your child cut a pan of brownies into 10 pieces. Ask questions such as: Justin ate 2 brownies. What fraction describes the amount of brownies he ate? What fraction describes the amount of brownies that are left?

A fraction consists of two parts.

$\frac{3}{4}$ The **numerator** tells how many parts are being identified.
The **denominator** tells the total number of equal parts in the whole.

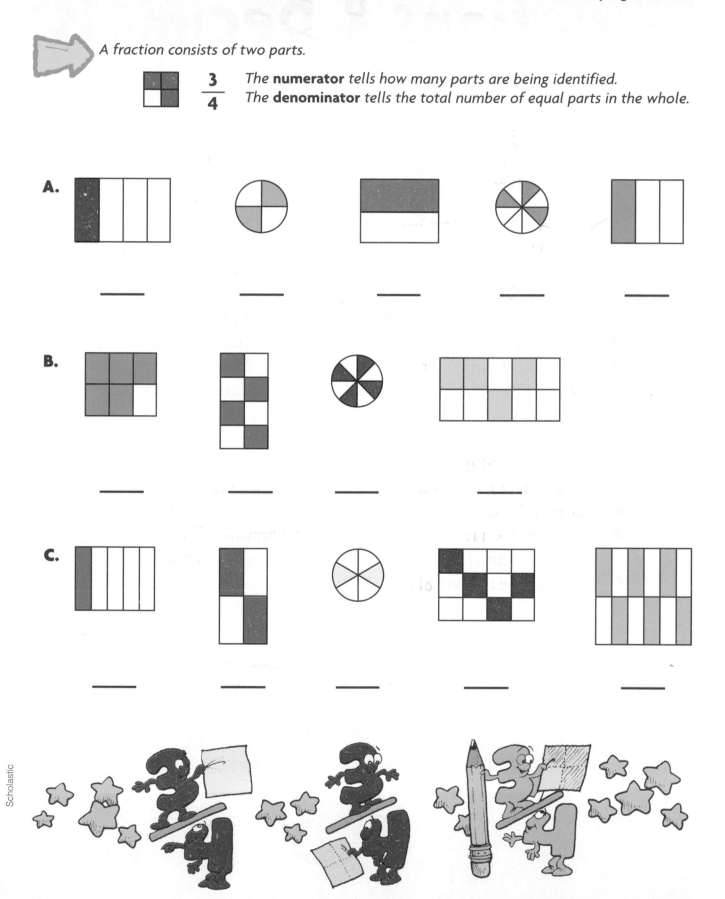

A.

_____   _____   _____   _____   _____

B.

_____   _____   _____   _____

C.

_____   _____   _____   _____   _____

12-14-22

Write the fraction that equals the part that is shaded.

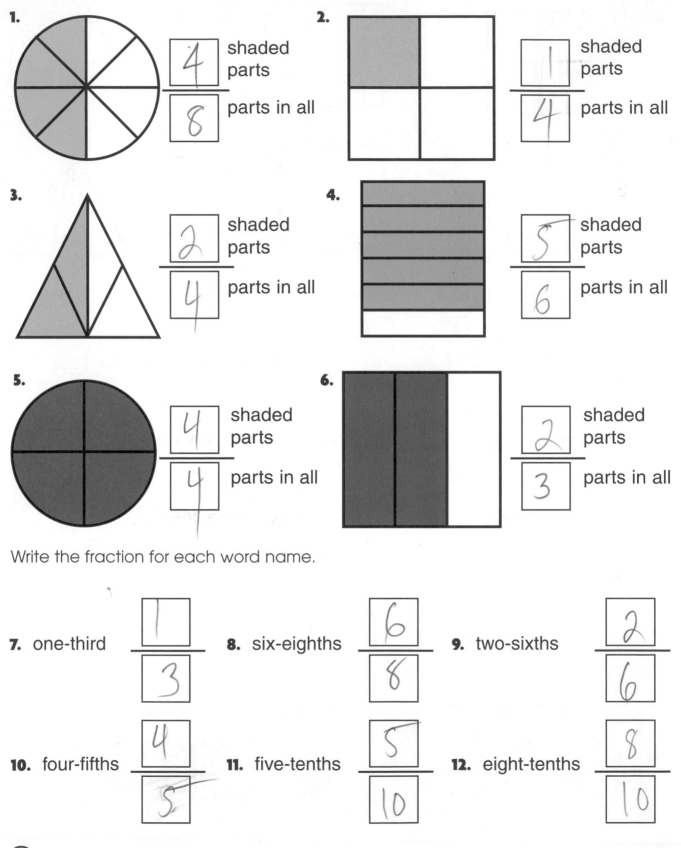

1. $\dfrac{4}{8}$ shaded parts / parts in all

2. $\dfrac{1}{4}$ shaded parts / parts in all

3. $\dfrac{2}{4}$ shaded parts / parts in all

4. $\dfrac{5}{6}$ shaded parts / parts in all

5. $\dfrac{4}{4}$ shaded parts / parts in all

6. $\dfrac{2}{3}$ shaded parts / parts in all

Write the fraction for each word name.

7. one-third $\dfrac{1}{3}$

8. six-eighths $\dfrac{6}{8}$

9. two-sixths $\dfrac{2}{6}$

10. four-fifths $\dfrac{4}{5}$

11. five-tenths $\dfrac{5}{10}$

12. eight-tenths $\dfrac{8}{10}$

Scholastic

12-14-22

Shade in the part of each shape that equals the fraction given.

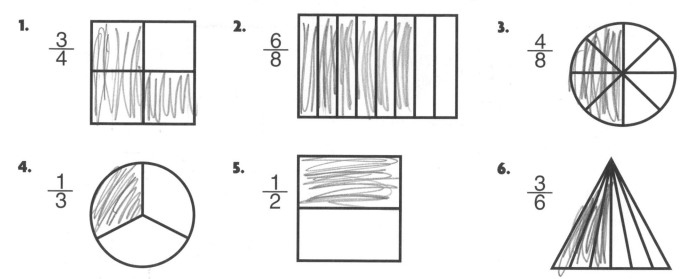

1. $\frac{3}{4}$ 2. $\frac{6}{8}$ 3. $\frac{4}{8}$

4. $\frac{1}{3}$ 5. $\frac{1}{2}$ 6. $\frac{3}{6}$

Write a fraction for each of the following.

7. Denominator 5, Numerator 2 $\frac{2}{5}$

8. Denominator 10, Numerator 6 $\frac{6}{10}$

9. Denominator 4, Numerator 1 $\frac{1}{4}$

10. Denominator 8, Numerator 7 $\frac{7}{8}$

11. Denominator 4, Numerator 6 $\frac{6}{4}$

12. Denominator 3, Numerator 2 $\frac{2}{3}$

Complete the pattern.

13. $\frac{1}{4}, \frac{2}{4}, \frac{3}{4}, 1, 1\frac{1}{4}, 1\frac{2}{4}$ $1\frac{3}{4}, 2, 2\frac{1}{4}, 2\frac{2}{4}$

Write the mixed number that names the shaded area.

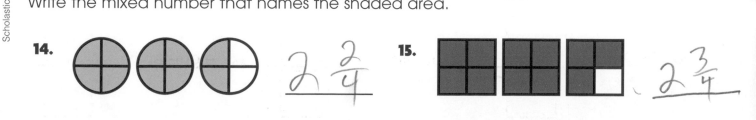

14. $2\frac{2}{4}$ **15.** $2\frac{3}{4}$

12-14-22

Equivalent fractions *have the same amount.*

$\frac{1}{2} = \frac{4}{8}$ $\frac{3}{6} = \frac{1}{2}$

Write each missing numerator to show equivalent fractions.

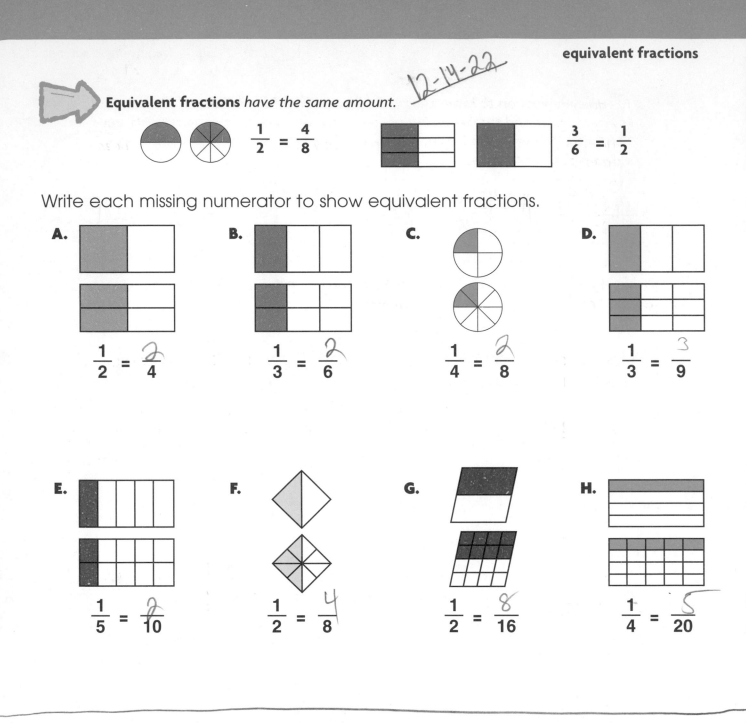

A. $\frac{1}{2} = \frac{2}{4}$

B. $\frac{1}{3} = \frac{2}{6}$

C. $\frac{1}{4} = \frac{2}{8}$

D. $\frac{1}{3} = \frac{3}{9}$

E. $\frac{1}{5} = \frac{2}{10}$

F. $\frac{1}{2} = \frac{4}{8}$

G. $\frac{1}{2} = \frac{8}{16}$

H. $\frac{1}{4} = \frac{5}{20}$

Write the number sentence that shows each set of equivalent fractions.

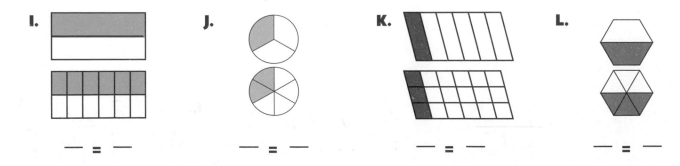

I.   ___ = ___

J.   ___ = ___

K.   ___ = ___

L.   ___ = ___

Scholastic

To reduce a fraction to lowest terms, find a common factor that will divide into both the numerator and the denominator. In the example below, the factor 2 will work. The factor 4, however, is better. When the only factor is 1, the fraction has been reduced to lowest terms.

12-14-22

$$\frac{4 \div 2}{8 \div 2} = \frac{2}{4}$$

Divide by 2. Can you divide again? Yes!

$$\frac{2 \div 2}{4 \div 2} = \frac{1}{2}$$

Divide by 2. Can you divide again? No!

$$\frac{4 \div 4}{8 \div 4} = \frac{1}{2}$$

Divide by 4. Can you divide again? No!

Choose the greatest common factor for each fraction from the box. Divide and reduce to lowest terms.

A. 3 2 4 $\dfrac{2 \div \boxed{2}}{4 \div \boxed{2}} = \dfrac{1}{2}$

B. 6 3 2 $\dfrac{6 \div \boxed{3}}{9 \div \boxed{3}} = \dfrac{2}{3}$

C. 4 5 2 $\dfrac{5 \div \boxed{5}}{10 \div \boxed{5}} = \dfrac{1}{2}$

D. 3 5 2 $\dfrac{10 \div \boxed{5}}{15 \div \boxed{5}} = \dfrac{2}{3}$

E. 2 4 6 $\dfrac{4 \div \boxed{2}}{8 \div \boxed{2}} = \dfrac{2}{4}$

F. 8 2 10 $\dfrac{10 \div \boxed{2}}{12 \div \boxed{2}} = \dfrac{5}{6}$

G. 2 8 3 $\dfrac{3 \div \boxed{3}}{6 \div \boxed{3}} = \dfrac{1}{2}$

H. 4 6 3 $\dfrac{3 \div \boxed{3}}{9 \div \boxed{3}} = \dfrac{1}{3}$

I. 2 7 4 $\dfrac{7 \div \boxed{7}}{14 \div \boxed{7}} = \dfrac{1}{2}$

J. 2 6 3 $\dfrac{6 \div \boxed{2}}{8 \div \boxed{2}} = \dfrac{3}{4}$

K. 5 10 3 $\dfrac{5 \div \boxed{5}}{15 \div \boxed{5}} = \dfrac{1}{3}$

L. 6 4 8 $\dfrac{4 \div \boxed{4}}{16 \div \boxed{4}} = \dfrac{1}{4}$

Scholastic

Date. Jan-26-2023 |4   22

Write the fraction for each shaded box. Reduce to lowest terms. Then draw the reduced fraction in the empty box.

A.

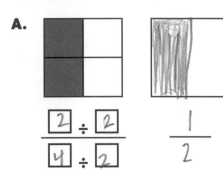

$$\frac{\boxed{2} \div \boxed{2}}{\boxed{4} \div \boxed{2}} \qquad \frac{1}{2}$$

B.

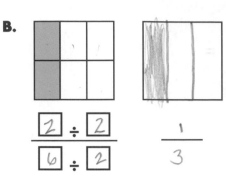

$$\frac{\boxed{2} \div \boxed{2}}{\boxed{6} \div \boxed{2}} \qquad \frac{1}{3}$$

C.

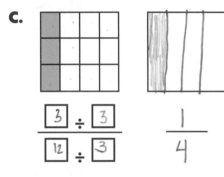

$$\frac{\boxed{3} \div \boxed{3}}{\boxed{12} \div \boxed{3}} \qquad \frac{1}{4}$$

D.

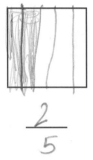

$$\frac{\boxed{6} \div \boxed{3}}{\boxed{15} \div \boxed{3}} \qquad \frac{2}{5}$$

E.

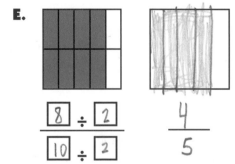

$$\frac{\boxed{8} \div \boxed{2}}{\boxed{10} \div \boxed{2}} \qquad \frac{4}{5}$$

F.

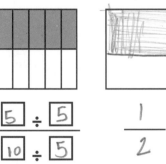

$$\frac{\boxed{5} \div \boxed{5}}{\boxed{10} \div \boxed{5}} \qquad \frac{1}{2}$$

G.

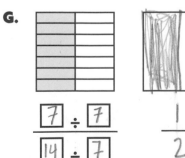

$$\frac{\boxed{7} \div \boxed{7}}{\boxed{14} \div \boxed{7}} \qquad \frac{1}{2}$$

H.

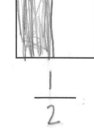

$$\frac{\boxed{6} \div \boxed{3}}{\boxed{9} \div \boxed{3}} \qquad \frac{2}{3}$$

Scholastic

Change each fraction to simplest form.

1. $\frac{10}{20} = \frac{5}{10}$

2. $\frac{6}{36} = \frac{1}{6}$

3. $\frac{3}{15} = \frac{1}{5}$

4. $\frac{9}{30} = \frac{3}{10}$

5. $\frac{25}{30} = \frac{5}{6}$

6. $\frac{5}{20} = \frac{1}{4}$

7. $\frac{2}{8} = \frac{1}{4}$

8. $\frac{6}{18} = \frac{1}{3}$

9. $\frac{16}{24} = \frac{8}{12}$

10. $\frac{20}{24} = \frac{10}{12}$

11. $\frac{14}{35} = \frac{2}{5}$

12. $\frac{12}{30} = \frac{6}{15}$

13. $\frac{10}{40} = \frac{1}{4}$

14. $\frac{15}{30} = \frac{5}{10}$

15. $\frac{4}{16} = \frac{2}{8}$

16. $\frac{4}{12} = \frac{2}{6}$

17. $\frac{15}{21} = \frac{5}{7}$

18. $\frac{14}{21} = \frac{2}{3}$

19. $\frac{12}{36} = \frac{6}{18}$

20. $\frac{21}{24} = \frac{7}{8}$

Scholastic

Reduce each fraction to lowest terms.
Then use the code to answer the riddle
below.

O. $\dfrac{2}{4} = \dfrac{1}{2}$

S. $\dfrac{4}{14} = \dfrac{2}{7}$

A. $\dfrac{10}{15} = \dfrac{2}{}$

B. $\dfrac{2}{32} = \dfrac{1}{}$

E. $\dfrac{2}{16} = \dfrac{1}{}$

! $\dfrac{2}{12} = \dfrac{1}{}$

T. $\dfrac{22}{24} = \dfrac{}{12}$

H. $\dfrac{4}{10} = \dfrac{2}{}$

D. $\dfrac{10}{100} = \dfrac{1}{}$

N. $\dfrac{2}{24} = \dfrac{1}{}$

M. $\dfrac{2}{26} = \dfrac{1}{}$

Y. $\dfrac{2}{28} = \dfrac{1}{}$

P. $\dfrac{4}{16} = \dfrac{}{4}$

R. $\dfrac{2}{8} = \dfrac{1}{}$

L. $\dfrac{2}{18} = \dfrac{1}{}$

Why was the math teacher crying?

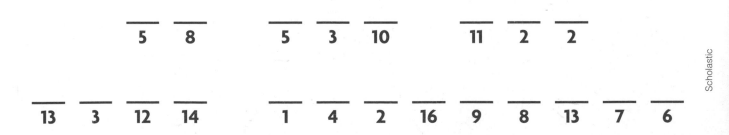

$\overline{}\ \overline{}\quad\overline{}\ \overline{}\ \overline{}\quad\overline{}\ \overline{}\ \overline{}$
  5   8   5   3   10   11   2   2

$\overline{}\ \overline{}\ \overline{}\ \overline{}\quad\overline{}\ \overline{}\ \overline{}\ \overline{}\ \overline{}\ \overline{}\ \overline{}\ \overline{}$
 13   3   12   14   1   4   2   16   9   8   13   7   6

Scholastic

In each fraction wheel, make the fractions equivalent to the fraction in the center.

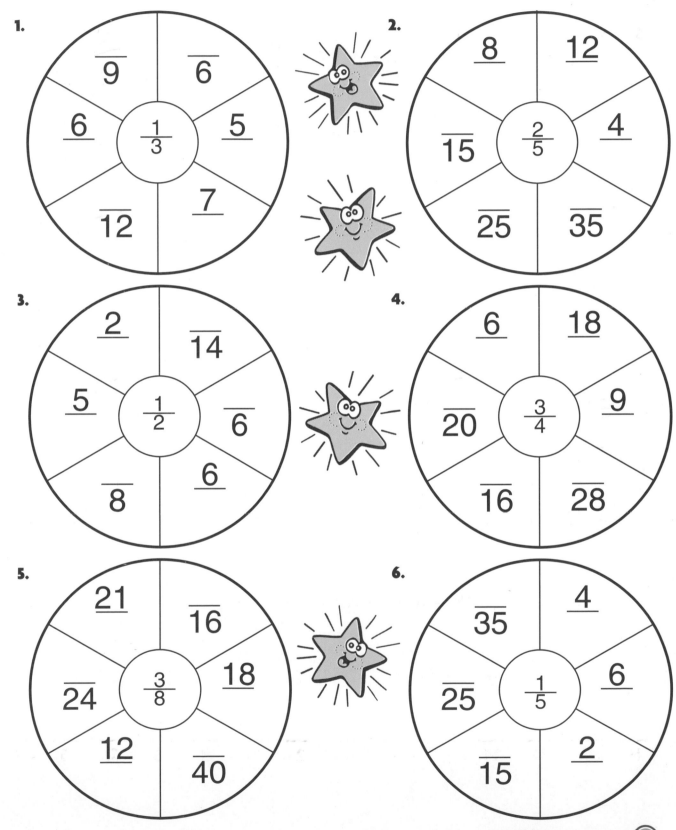

1.

Center: $\frac{1}{3}$

$\frac{}{9}$ $\frac{}{6}$ $\frac{6}{}$ $\frac{5}{}$ $\frac{}{12}$ $\frac{7}{}$

2.

Center: $\frac{2}{5}$

$\frac{8}{}$ $\frac{12}{}$ $\frac{}{15}$ $\frac{4}{}$ $\frac{}{25}$ $\frac{}{35}$

3.

Center: $\frac{1}{2}$

$\frac{2}{}$ $\frac{}{14}$ $\frac{5}{}$ $\frac{}{6}$ $\frac{}{8}$ $\frac{6}{}$

4.

Center: $\frac{3}{4}$

$\frac{6}{}$ $\frac{18}{}$ $\frac{}{20}$ $\frac{9}{}$ $\frac{}{16}$ $\frac{}{28}$

5.

Center: $\frac{3}{8}$

$\frac{21}{}$ $\frac{}{16}$ $\frac{}{24}$ $\frac{18}{}$ $\frac{12}{}$ $\frac{}{40}$

6.

Center: $\frac{1}{5}$

$\frac{}{35}$ $\frac{4}{}$ $\frac{}{25}$ $\frac{6}{}$ $\frac{}{15}$ $\frac{2}{}$

Change each improper fraction to a mixed number. Reduce to lowest terms.

Example: $\frac{15}{12} = 1\frac{3}{12} = 1\frac{1}{4}$

1. $\frac{9}{2} =$

2. $\frac{18}{5} =$

3. $\frac{10}{3} =$

4. $\frac{10}{6} =$

5. $\frac{8}{5} =$

6. $\frac{8}{6} =$

7. $\frac{9}{4} =$

8. $\frac{10}{9} =$

9. $\frac{7}{4} =$

10. $\frac{6}{4} =$

11. $\frac{11}{10} =$

12. $\frac{8}{3} =$

13. $\frac{26}{15} =$

14. $\frac{40}{24} =$

15. $\frac{25}{8} =$

16. $\frac{17}{4} =$

17. $\frac{9}{2} =$

18. $\frac{25}{3} =$

19. $\frac{8}{3} =$

20. $\frac{9}{8} =$

Scholastic

Change each improper fraction to a mixed number. Reduce to lowest terms.

1. $\dfrac{20}{8} =$

2. $\dfrac{24}{20} =$

3. $\dfrac{55}{12} =$

4. $\dfrac{19}{2} =$

5. $\dfrac{15}{4} =$

6. $\dfrac{7}{4} =$

7. $\dfrac{13}{11} =$

8. $\dfrac{11}{3} =$

9. $\dfrac{13}{4} =$

10. $\dfrac{13}{12} =$

11. $\dfrac{10}{8} =$

12. $\dfrac{12}{7} =$

13. $\dfrac{15}{9} =$

14. $\dfrac{35}{12} =$

15. $\dfrac{15}{8} =$

16. $\dfrac{16}{5} =$

17. $\dfrac{7}{4} =$

18. $\dfrac{4}{3} =$

19. $\dfrac{19}{6} =$

20. $\dfrac{10}{4} =$

Scholastic

Compare the fractions. Write >, <, or = in the blank.

> (more than)   < (less than)   = (equal)

1. $\dfrac{3}{4}$ ____ $\dfrac{2}{4}$

2. $\dfrac{4}{9}$ ____ $\dfrac{7}{9}$

3. $\dfrac{5}{6}$ ____ $\dfrac{1}{6}$

4. $\dfrac{7}{10}$ ____ $\dfrac{3}{10}$

5. $\dfrac{5}{8}$ ____ $\dfrac{3}{8}$

6. $\dfrac{7}{3}$ ____ $\dfrac{2}{3}$

7. $\dfrac{5}{6}$ ____ $\dfrac{11}{12}$

8. $\dfrac{4}{5}$ ____ $\dfrac{12}{15}$

9. $\dfrac{7}{12}$ ____ $\dfrac{5}{12}$

10. $\dfrac{5}{5}$ ____ $\dfrac{10}{10}$

11. $\dfrac{5}{9}$ ____ $\dfrac{11}{18}$

12. $\dfrac{2}{3}$ ____ $\dfrac{1}{2}$

13. $\dfrac{3}{5}$ ____ $\dfrac{4}{7}$

14. $\dfrac{3}{8}$ ____ $\dfrac{4}{5}$

15. $\dfrac{7}{8}$ ____ $\dfrac{5}{6}$

Scholastic

Write each mixed number as an improper fraction.
Example: $2\frac{3}{5} = (5 \times 2 = 10) + 3 = \frac{13}{5}$

1. $3\frac{1}{3} =$ **2.** $5\frac{1}{4} =$ **3.** $2\frac{3}{8} =$

4. $3\frac{2}{5} =$ **5.** $9\frac{4}{9} =$ **6.** $7\frac{2}{3} =$

7. $4\frac{1}{2} =$ **8.** $6\frac{2}{7} =$ **9.** $8\frac{4}{7} =$

10. $6\frac{1}{5} =$ **11.** $8\frac{1}{7} =$ **12.** $4\frac{3}{7} =$

13. $7\frac{2}{9} =$ **14.** $5\frac{3}{4} =$ **15.** $9\frac{3}{5} =$

16. $3\frac{4}{5} =$ **17.** $8\frac{3}{9} =$ **18.** $2\frac{1}{6} =$

19. $4\frac{5}{6} =$ **20.** $9\frac{1}{8} =$

Scholastic

Write each mixed number as an improper fraction.

1. $5\frac{5}{8}$ =

2. $3\frac{3}{7}$ =

3. $7\frac{3}{4}$ =

4. $9\frac{1}{6}$ =

5. $3\frac{3}{5}$ =

6. $4\frac{3}{8}$ =

7. $6\frac{1}{7}$ =

8. $4\frac{1}{5}$ =

9. $5\frac{1}{3}$ =

10. $8\frac{2}{9}$ =

11. $5\frac{4}{7}$ =

12. $6\frac{2}{3}$ =

13. $7\frac{2}{5}$ =

14. $4\frac{4}{5}$ =

15. $6\frac{1}{4}$ =

16. $8\frac{1}{8}$ =

17. $4\frac{3}{9}$ =

18. $3\frac{1}{2}$ =

19. $9\frac{4}{9}$ =

20. $7\frac{2}{7}$ =

Scholastic

To find the fractional part of a number, follow these steps.

1. Turn the whole number
   into a fraction.

2. Multiply the
   two fractions.

3. Divide the numerator
   by the denominator.

$$12 \rightarrow \frac{12}{1}$$

$$\frac{1}{3} \times \frac{12}{1} = \frac{12}{3}$$

$$3 \overline{\smash{)}12}^{\,4}$$

Find the fractional part of each number. Color each number in the picture.

A. $\frac{1}{3}$ of 9 =

B. $\frac{1}{5}$ of 10 =

C. $\frac{1}{4}$ of 20 =

D. $\frac{1}{2}$ of 10 =

E. $\frac{1}{6}$ of 12 =

F. $\frac{1}{7}$ of 14 =

G. $\frac{1}{3}$ of 12 =

H. $\frac{1}{5}$ of 25 =

I. $\frac{1}{3}$ of 6 =

J. $\frac{2}{3}$ of 6 =

K. $\frac{1}{4}$ of 28 =

L. $\frac{1}{5}$ of 30 =

M. $\frac{1}{9}$ of 18 =

N. $\frac{1}{3}$ of 15 =

O. $\frac{1}{4}$ of 16 =

P. $\frac{2}{5}$ of 10 =

Scholastic

To find the fractional part of a number, follow these steps.

1. Turn the whole number into a fraction.

$$9 \rightarrow \frac{9}{1}$$

2. Multiply the two fractions.

$$\frac{2}{3} \times \frac{9}{1} = \frac{18}{3}$$

3. Divide the numerator by the denominator.

$$3 \overline{)18} \quad 6$$

Find the fractional part of each number.

A. $\frac{3}{5}$ of 10 =

B. $\frac{1}{3}$ of 9 =

C. $\frac{3}{4}$ of 12 =

D. $\frac{2}{3}$ of 6 =

E. $\frac{4}{5}$ of 15 =

F. $\frac{2}{3}$ of 15 =

G. $\frac{3}{4}$ of 16 =

H. $\frac{5}{6}$ of 18 =

I. $\frac{4}{7}$ of 21 =

J. $\frac{3}{7}$ of 21 =

K. $\frac{5}{8}$ of 24 =

L. $\frac{3}{5}$ of 20 =

Scholastic

Find the missing term to make each pair of fractions equivalent.

Example: $\dfrac{2}{4} = \dfrac{8}{} = \dfrac{8}{16}$

1. $\dfrac{3}{4} = \dfrac{15}{}$ **2.** $\dfrac{4}{6} = \dfrac{12}{}$ **3.** $\dfrac{5}{8} = \dfrac{}{32}$ **4.** $\dfrac{4}{9} = \dfrac{16}{}$

5. $\dfrac{3}{5} = \dfrac{}{25}$ **6.** $\dfrac{3}{11} = \dfrac{9}{}$ **7.** $\dfrac{8}{9} = \dfrac{}{27}$ **8.** $\dfrac{3}{7} = \dfrac{}{21}$

9. $\dfrac{4}{5} = \dfrac{16}{}$ **10.** $\dfrac{2}{3} = \dfrac{}{9}$ **11.** $\dfrac{7}{10} = \dfrac{14}{}$ **12.** $\dfrac{5}{6} = \dfrac{}{36}$

Find the missing terms in each row of fractions.

13. $\dfrac{1}{3} = \dfrac{}{6} = \dfrac{}{9} = \dfrac{}{12} = \dfrac{}{15}$

14. $\dfrac{3}{4} = \dfrac{}{8} = \dfrac{}{12} = \dfrac{12}{} = \dfrac{15}{}$

15. $\dfrac{2}{3} = \dfrac{}{6} = \dfrac{6}{} = \dfrac{}{12} = \dfrac{10}{}$

16. $\dfrac{4}{5} = \dfrac{8}{} = \dfrac{}{15} = \dfrac{}{20} = \dfrac{20}{}$

Add the fractions and reduce to lowest terms.

Example: $\frac{1}{5} + \frac{4}{5} = \frac{5}{5} = 1$

1. $\frac{1}{2} + \frac{1}{2} =$

2. $\frac{2}{3} + \frac{1}{3} =$

3. $\frac{3}{10} + \frac{3}{10} =$

4. $\frac{3}{10} + \frac{7}{10} =$

5. $\frac{2}{9} + \frac{1}{9} =$

6. $\frac{2}{9} + \frac{5}{9} =$

7. $\frac{1}{8} + \frac{5}{8} =$

8. $\frac{2}{11} + \frac{5}{11} =$

9. $\frac{2}{7} + \frac{3}{7} =$

10. $\frac{3}{10} + \frac{9}{10} =$

11. $\frac{3}{5} + \frac{4}{5} =$

12. $\frac{3}{7} + \frac{4}{7} =$

13. $\frac{1}{5} + \frac{3}{5} =$

14. $\frac{3}{8} + \frac{1}{8} =$

15. $\frac{5}{12} + \frac{1}{12} =$

16. $\frac{4}{9} + \frac{2}{9} =$

17. $\frac{3}{11} + \frac{6}{11} =$

18. $\frac{1}{10} + \frac{3}{10} =$

Scholastic

Add the fractions and reduce to lowest terms.

1. $\dfrac{4}{5} + \dfrac{3}{4} =$

2. $\dfrac{1}{4} + \dfrac{1}{2} =$

3. $\dfrac{1}{2} + \dfrac{1}{7} =$

4. $\dfrac{2}{3} + \dfrac{3}{5} =$

5. $\dfrac{1}{5} + \dfrac{5}{6} =$

6. $\dfrac{5}{8} + \dfrac{1}{2} =$

7. $\dfrac{2}{3} + \dfrac{4}{9} =$

8. $\dfrac{2}{3} + \dfrac{1}{6} =$

9. $\dfrac{5}{16} + \dfrac{5}{8} =$

10. $\dfrac{3}{27} + \dfrac{5}{9} =$

11. $\dfrac{1}{10} + \dfrac{13}{20} =$

12. $\dfrac{2}{5} + \dfrac{1}{4} =$

13. $\dfrac{3}{18} + \dfrac{5}{9} =$

14. $\dfrac{1}{5} + \dfrac{7}{10} =$

15. $\dfrac{8}{11} + \dfrac{2}{3} =$

16. $\dfrac{4}{5} + \dfrac{1}{2} =$

17. $\dfrac{5}{6} + \dfrac{5}{12} =$

18. $\dfrac{2}{7} + \dfrac{10}{21} =$

Scholastic

In each box there are two fractions that add up to equal another number in the box. Draw a box around the two fractions that equal the third fraction. Draw a circle around the fraction that equals the sum of the other two fractions. The first one has been done for you.

1.

$$\frac{1}{6} \qquad \frac{2}{3}$$

$$\frac{5}{6} \qquad \frac{7}{8}$$

2.

$$\frac{3}{4} \qquad \frac{7}{8}$$

$$\frac{1}{8} \qquad \frac{5}{9}$$

3.

$$\frac{2}{3} \qquad \frac{3}{4}$$

$$\frac{1}{2} \qquad \frac{1}{6}$$

4.

$$\frac{3}{4} \qquad \frac{3}{8}$$

$$\frac{1}{4} \qquad \frac{5}{8}$$

5.

$$\frac{1}{7} \qquad \frac{2}{5}$$

$$\frac{23}{25} \qquad \frac{19}{35}$$

6.

$$\frac{1}{3} \qquad \frac{11}{15}$$

$$\frac{8}{15} \qquad \frac{2}{5}$$

7.

$$\frac{5}{8} \qquad \frac{2}{3}$$

$$\frac{1}{9} \qquad \frac{7}{9}$$

8.

$$\frac{3}{8} \qquad \frac{5}{8}$$

$$\frac{4}{7} \qquad \frac{1}{4}$$

9.

$$\frac{1}{5} \qquad \frac{3}{10}$$

$$\frac{1}{2} \qquad \frac{7}{10}$$

10.

$$\frac{17}{35} \qquad \frac{2}{7}$$

$$\frac{24}{35} \qquad \frac{2}{5}$$

11.

$$\frac{6}{14} \qquad \frac{1}{2}$$

$$\frac{2}{7} \qquad \frac{11}{14}$$

12.

$$\frac{17}{20} \qquad \frac{1}{4}$$

$$\frac{2}{5} \qquad \frac{3}{5}$$

Scholastic

Use the information below to rank the batting averages.

Baseball fans always argue about who's the best player. Everybody seems to have a favorite!

When it comes to finding the best hitter, though, no one can argue with batting averages. The batting average shows how often a baseball player gets a hit. It is a 3-digit decimal number, and looks like this: .328, .287, .311, .253. The larger the batting average is, the better the hitter is.

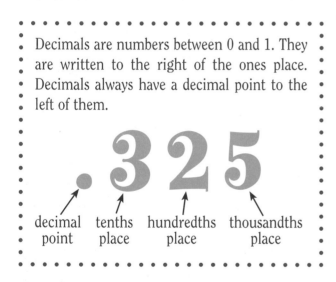

Decimals are numbers between 0 and 1. They are written to the right of the ones place. Decimals always have a decimal point to the left of them.

.325

decimal point | tenths place | hundredths place | thousandths place

Rank	Player (Team)	2015 Batting Average
☐	Yunel Escobar (Washington Nationals)	.314
☐	A. J. Pollock (Arizona Diamondbacks)	.315
☐	Buster Posey (San Francisco Giants)	.318
☐	Bryce Harper (Washington Nationals)	.330
☐	Paul Goldschmidt (Arizona Diamondbacks)	.321
☐	Miguel Cabrera (Detroit Tigers)	.338
☐	Joey Votto (Cincinnati Reds)	.314
☐	Dee Gordon (Miami Marlins)	.333
☐	Xander Bogaerts (Boston Red Sox)	.320
☐	José Altuve (Houston Astros)	.313

What to Do:

Read the chart of baseball players' batting averages from 2015. Rank the batting averages. This means number the batting averages in order from highest to lowest. (See Home Plate for help.) Write the numbers 1 to 10 in the boxes next to the names—1 for the highest average, 10 for the lowest. Ready? Play ball!

HOME PLATE

To rank decimal numbers:
- Start at the left.
- Compare the digits in the same place.
- Find the first place where the digits are different.
- The number with the smaller digit is the smaller number. Example: Rank .318 and .312

.318
↕↕↕
.312

So .312 is smaller than .318.

Circle the correct number for each number word given.

1. eight and ninety-two hundredths

a. 92.8   b. 8.92   c. 89.2   d. 892

2. four and six tenths

a. 4.06   b. 4.6   c. .46   d. 6.4

3. thirty-four and two hundredths

a. 342   b. 3.42   c. 34.02   d. 34.2

4. five tenths

a. .5   b. 5   c. .05   d. 50

5. twenty-three and sixteen hundredths

a. 23.16   b. 231.6   c. 2.316   d. 16.23

6. twenty-four hundredths

a. 240   b. .024   c. 2.4   d. .24

7. eight hundred two and fifty-three hundredths

a. 82.53   b. 802.53   c. 80,253   d. 825.3

8. seventy-four and two hundredths

a. 7,402   b. 7.42   c. 74.02   d. 74.2

9. thirty-three and nine tenths

a. 33.9   b. 33.09   c. 3.9   d. 3.39

10. four hundred twenty-two and fifty-four hundredths

a. 54.422   b. 42.254   c. 42.54   d. 422.54

If the number has a 5 in the ones place, color the shape green.
If the number has a 5 in the tenths place, color the shape pink.
If the number has a 5 in the hundredths place, color the shape yellow.
Finish the design by coloring the other shapes with colors of your choice.

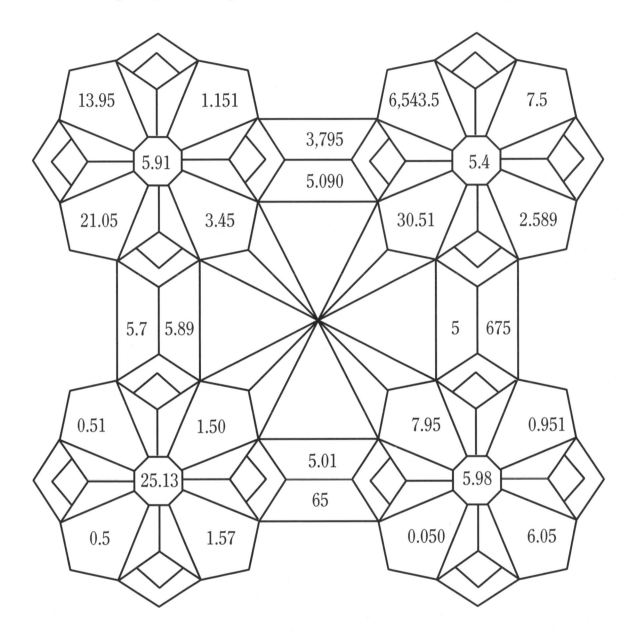

Taking It Further: Place the following decimals in the correct places on the lines below the dots: 4.9, 1.7, 2.5, and 0.2.

Match each decimal to the correct number word.

1.	.42		**a.**	thirteen and five tenths
2.	1.67		**b.**	thirty-eight and two hundredths
3.	7.5		**c.**	thirteen and five hundredths
4.	38.02		**d.**	forty-two hundredths
5.	597.1		**e.**	seventy-five hundredths
6.	.75		**f.**	six and seven tenths
7.	13.5		**g.**	five hundred ninety-seven and one tenth
8.	16.28		**h.**	seven and five tenths
9.	6.7		**i.**	one and sixty-seven hundredths
10.	13.05		**j.**	sixteen and twenty-eight hundredths

Write the number words for the following decimals.

11. 12.06

_____

12. 152.4

_____

13. .612

_____

14. 38.05

_____

15. 9.52

_____

Scholastic

Complete the crossnumber puzzle as if it were a crossword puzzle. Give each digit and decimal point its own square. Remember to align the decimal points and add any necessary zeros, then proceed as if you were adding whole numbers.

Across

- A. 1.3 + 2.4
- C. 2.2 + 2.18
- E. .3 + .25
- F. .3 + .3
- G. .56 + .34
- J. .4 + .17
- K. 6.93 + .23
- L. 1.18 + 3.12

Down

- A. 1.44 + 1.7
- B. 23.11 + 53.18
- C. 2.25 + 2.25
- D. 6.5 + 1.6
- F. .1604 + .11
- H. 20.8 + 3.5
- I. 1.367 + .333
- J. .2 + .16

Remember to include a decimal point and a dollar sign in the answer when adding money.

Add. Then use the code to answer the riddle below.

A. $63.54
 + 29.29

G. $65.35
 + 27.18

U. $24.12
 + 90.48

O. $15.79
 + 48.08

B. $27.60
 + 44.65

N. $77.88
 + 92.90

E. $86.91
 + 70.44

R. $39.75
 + 29.62

M. $103.90
 + 64.82

C. $291.26
 + 473.83

S. $485.13
 + 494.92

T. $630.57
 + 39.52

D. $184.64
 + 292.43

Y. $354.60
 + 261.74

F. $964.36
 + 252.04

W. $904.86
 + 95.82

Why are birds poor?

___ ___ ___ ___ ___ ___ ___
$72.25 $157.35 $765.09 $92.83 $114.60 $980.05 $157.35

___ ___ ___ ___ ___
$168.72 $63.87 $170.78 $157.35 $616.34
,

___ ___ ___ ___ ___ ___ ___ ___ ___ ___
$477.07 $63.87 $157.35 $980.05 $170.78 $670.09 $92.53 $69.37 $63.87 $1,000.68
!

___ ___ ___ ___ ___ ___ ___
$63.87 $170.78 $670.09 $69.37 $157.35 $157.35 $980.05

Scholastic

Round your answers to the nearest dollar. Circle the correct amount, then fill in the puzzle.

Across

A. $16.98 + $18.99 $36 $26

C. $24.85 + $29.99 $65 $55

E. $21.99 + $8.95 $31 $41

G. $218.04 + $67.90 $286 $386

I. $53.75 + $40.98 $105 $95

K. $7.99 + $19.70 $28 $22

L. $99.98 + 99.57 $300 $200

M. $65.75 + $20.90 $87 $97

O. $9.69 + $32.99 $40 $43

P. $588.95 + $14.90 $704 $604

Q. $3.75 + $9.99 $13 $14

R. $428.70 + $50.90 $480 $520

Down

B. $28.59 + $33.95 $69 $63

C. $39.25 + $18.70 $58 $42

D. $376.35 + $184.50 $521 $561

F. $7.28 + $11.69 $19 $16

H. $199.80 + $224.99 $525 $425

J. $399.95 + $126.99 $527 $566

M. $5.85 + $76.95 $83 $75

N. $39.80 + $13.99 $54 $62

O. $26.98 + $16.89 $44 $49

P. $48.95 + $18.99 $68 $66

Scholastic

When you make change, always start with the price. Count on from the price. Start with the coins that have the least value. Write the change from these purchases.

1. LAWN GAME

AMOUNT GIVEN $5.00

PRICE 3.45

CHANGE $ _____

2. YO-YO

AMOUNT GIVEN $3.00

PRICE 2.77

CHANGE $ _____

3. BIKE HELMET

AMOUNT GIVEN $10.00

PRICE 7.55

CHANGE $ _____

4. SOAP BUBBLES

AMOUNT GIVEN $2.00

PRICE 1.52

CHANGE $ _____

5. VIDEO GAME

AMOUNT GIVEN $20.00

PRICE 7.30

CHANGE $ _____

6. ACTION TOY

AMOUNT GIVEN $10.00

PRICE 6.49

CHANGE $ _____

7. SUNGLASSES

AMOUNT GIVEN $4.00

PRICE 3.68

CHANGE $ _____

8. BACKPACK

AMOUNT GIVEN $20.00

PRICE 9.35

CHANGE $ _____

9. JUMP ROPE

AMOUNT GIVEN $4.00

PRICE 3.17

CHANGE $ _____

10. MARKERS

AMOUNT GIVEN $5.00

PRICE 2.43

CHANGE $ _____

Scholastic

Figure it out!

1. Woovis the Dog found a $5 bill. Which item can he buy from the menu that will give the least change?

_____

DOGGIE DINER
BREAKFAST SHOP

MENU

Kibble $1.79
Mouse Crumbs $1.39
Table Scraps $2.49
Crumbs & Cheese $3.19
Deluxe Scraps $3.79

2. Molly Mouse gets Crumbs & Cheese for breakfast. She pays with the $5 bill. With the leftover money, what can Woovis buy to eat?

_____

3. Which item can Woovis buy with the $5 bill that will give the most change?

_____

4. Which two items can Woovis buy with the $5 bill so that he gets about $1 back in change?

_____

5. Woovis ordered two items from the menu and gave the cashier the $5 bill. But the two items cost more than $6.50. Which two items did Woovis order?

_____

SUPER CHALLENGE: Can Woovis use the $5 bill to buy three different items from the menu? Why or why not?

Scholastic

 *Always write a long subtraction problem vertically before solving it. When subtracting decimals, write each place-value column so the decimal points are aligned.*

$82.17 - 74.16 =$

$$\begin{array}{r} 82.71 \\ -74.16 \\ \hline \end{array}$$

Write each subtraction problem vertically. Subtract.

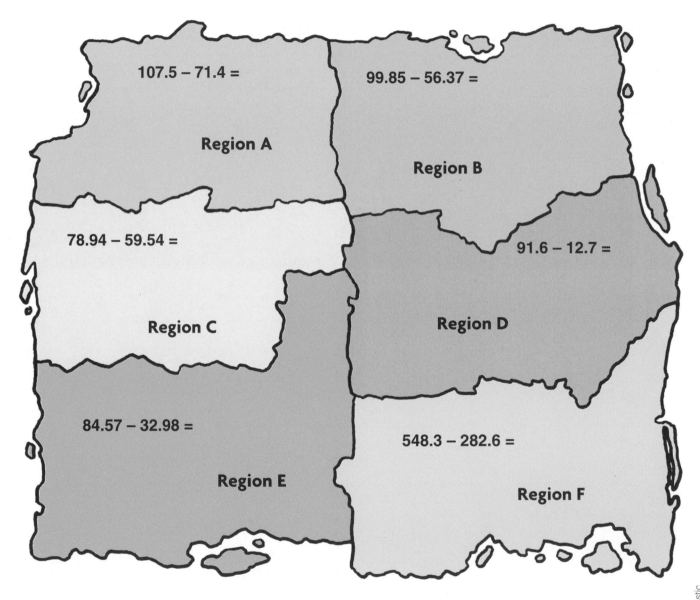

$107.5 - 71.4 =$

Region A

$99.85 - 56.37 =$

Region B

$78.94 - 59.54 =$

Region C

$91.6 - 12.7 =$

Region D

$84.57 - 32.98 =$

Region E

$548.3 - 282.6 =$

Region F

Mary traveled to two regions. Their difference is 24.08. What two regions did she visit?

Scholastic

Fractions & Decimals Practice Test

Fill in the bubble next to the correct answer.

1. $\dfrac{1}{4} + \dfrac{2}{12} =$

- ○ **A** $\dfrac{3}{12}$
- ○ **B** $\dfrac{5}{12}$
- ○ **C** $\dfrac{5}{4}$
- ○ **D** $\dfrac{4}{5}$

2. $56.4 + 3.37 =$

- ○ **F**   5.977
- ○ **G**   58.07
- ○ **H**   56.07
- ○ **J**   59.77

3. $\dfrac{1}{5} + \dfrac{1}{15} =$

- ○ **A** $\dfrac{3}{5}$
- ○ **B** $\dfrac{3}{15}$
- ○ **C** $\dfrac{1}{15}$
- ○ **D** $\dfrac{4}{15}$

4.
$$\begin{array}{r} 45.32 \\ -\ 7.18 \\ \hline \end{array}$$

- ○ **F**   38.14
- ○ **G**   32.64
- ○ **H**   37.74
- ○ **J**   32.14

Scholastic

Fractions & Decimals Practice Test

Fill in the bubble next to the correct answer.

5. Which fraction describes the shaded part of the square?

- ○ A $\frac{3}{8}$
- ○ B $\frac{5}{8}$
- ○ C $\frac{1}{2}$
- ○ D $\frac{2}{3}$

6. 51.05 + 1.15 =

- ○ F   52.2
- ○ G   53.5
- ○ H   54
- ○ J   51.75

7. Add. Change to a mixed number. Reduce to lowest terms.

$$\frac{3}{4} + \frac{3}{4} =$$

- ○ A $1\frac{1}{4}$
- ○ B $1\frac{2}{4}$
- ○ C $1\frac{1}{2}$
- ○ D $1\frac{3}{4}$

8.
$$\begin{array}{r} 9.03 \\ -\ 6.07 \\ \hline \end{array}$$

- ○ F   3.04
- ○ G   2.96
- ○ H   3.10
- ○ J   2.56

Scholastic

Word Problems

Word problems are fun to do. They can motivate your child to sharpen his or her addition, subtraction, multiplication, and division skills. They will also help your child develop strategies to solve more complex mathematical problems.

What to Do

Have your child work out the problems on each activity page. Review the answers together. For a quick check, look in the answer key at the back of the book.

Keep On Going!

Make up word problems for your child to solve based on things he or she likes to do. For example: You want to go to the movies. The ticket costs $6.50. You only have 50¢. How much more money will you need to buy a ticket? If you can earn $2.00 an hour pulling weeds, how many hours will you have to work to earn enough money to buy the ticket?

Choose the best answer to each question. Mark your answer. If the correct answer is not given, choose none of the above.

1. On Saturday, 73 people went to the two o'clock movie at the theater. Each person paid $4.00. How much money did the theater collect in all?
   Ⓐ $332.00
   Ⓑ $292.00
   Ⓒ $146.00
   Ⓓ $18.25
   Ⓔ none of the above

2. A total of 84 students are going on a field trip to the science museum. If 8 students can ride in each van, which number sentence should you use to find the number of vans needed for the field trip?
   Ⓕ $84 + 8 = \square$
   Ⓖ $84 - 8 = \square$
   Ⓗ $84 \times 8 = \square$
   Ⓙ $84 \div 8 = \square$
   Ⓚ none of the above

3. Mrs. Carver made 345 sandwiches for the school picnic. Students ate 286 of the sandwiches. How many sandwiches were left?
   Ⓐ 41
   Ⓑ 55
   Ⓒ 59
   Ⓓ 69
   Ⓔ none of the above

4. Jeremy uses 6 beads to make a dream catcher. How many dream catchers can he make with 92 beads?
   Ⓕ 12
   Ⓖ 14
   Ⓗ 15
   Ⓙ 16
   Ⓚ none of the above

5. Amanda jogged 4.9 miles on Monday and 7.3 miles on Wednesday. How many miles did she jog in all?
   Ⓐ 2.4 miles
   Ⓑ 3.6 miles
   Ⓒ 11.2 miles
   Ⓓ 12.4 miles
   Ⓔ none of the above

Choose the best answer to each question. Mark your answer. If the correct answer is not given, choose none of the above.

6. Robbie bought this jacket in a department store. He gave the clerk a $20.00 bill.

$16.95

How much change should Robbie get back?

Ⓕ $2.95
Ⓖ $3.05
Ⓗ $3.15
Ⓙ $4.05
Ⓚ none of the above

7. The school library had 10 books on Ancient Egypt. Arjun borrowed 2 books on Egypt. What fraction of the books did Arjun borrow?

Ⓐ $\frac{1}{4}$
Ⓑ $\frac{1}{6}$
Ⓒ $\frac{1}{5}$
Ⓓ $\frac{2}{3}$
Ⓔ none of the above

8. Bilbo has these marbles in his collection.

Bilbo's Marbles	
Cat's eye	105
Aggies	62
Glass	47

How many marbles does he have in all?

Ⓕ 104
Ⓖ 114
Ⓗ 204
Ⓙ 214
Ⓚ none of the above

9. Mr. Breen bought $1\frac{1}{2}$ pounds of cake flour and $2\frac{1}{2}$ pounds of bread flour. How much flour did he buy all together?

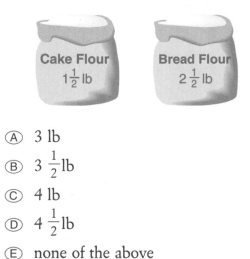

Cake Flour $1\frac{1}{2}$ lb   Bread Flour $2\frac{1}{2}$ lb

Ⓐ 3 lb
Ⓑ $3\frac{1}{2}$ lb
Ⓒ 4 lb
Ⓓ $4\frac{1}{2}$ lb
Ⓔ none of the above

Scholastic

Choose the best answer to each question. Mark your answer. If the correct answer is not given, choose none of the above.

10. Git works 28 hours each week. He worked 7 hours on Monday and 6 hours on Tuesday. How many more hours does he have to work this week?
- Ⓕ 41
- Ⓖ 22
- Ⓗ 21
- Ⓙ 15
- Ⓚ none of the above

11. Nina fell asleep on the sofa at 4:15 P.M. She woke up at 5:45 P.M. How long did she sleep?
- Ⓐ 1 hr 15 min
- Ⓑ 1 hr 30 min
- Ⓒ 1 hr 45 min
- Ⓓ 2 hr
- Ⓔ none of the above

12. Steve rode his bicycle across the United States. The trip took 64 days. How many weeks did the trip last?
- Ⓕ 6 weeks 4 days
- Ⓖ 8 weeks 6 days
- Ⓗ 9 weeks 1 day
- Ⓙ 10 weeks
- Ⓚ none of the above

13. A puppy named Max weighs 12 pounds. Max gains 2 pounds per week. At this rate, how much will Max weigh in 3 weeks?
- Ⓐ 14 lb
- Ⓑ 15 lb
- Ⓒ 17 lb
- Ⓓ 18 lb
- Ⓔ none of the above

14. Clem scored 34 points in a basketball game. Leo scored 26 points. Which number sentence should you use to find how many more points Clem scored?
- Ⓕ $26 + 34 = \square$
- Ⓖ $26 - 34 = \square$
- Ⓗ $34 \times 26 = \square$
- Ⓙ $34 \div 26 = \square$
- Ⓚ none of the above

15. Buzzy started watching a video at 9:30 A.M. The video lasted 80 minutes. At what time did the video end?
- Ⓐ 9:50 A.M.
- Ⓑ 10:30 A.M.
- Ⓒ 10:40 A.M.
- Ⓓ 10:50 A.M.
- Ⓔ none of the above

Scholastic

Choose the best answer to each question. Mark your answer. If the correct answer is not given, choose none of the above.

16. Jessica was baking. She added a 1/4 cup of milk and a 1/2 cup of water. Wat was the total amount of liquid added?

F. $\frac{3}{4}$

G. $\frac{1}{2}$

H. $\frac{3}{5}$

J. $\frac{1}{6}$

K. none of the above

17. At Joe's Adventure Golf, golf balls are kept in a large box. The chart shows how many balls of each color are in the box.

Color	Number
Red	24
Blue	12
Yellow	68
Green	20
Purple	35

If you reach into the box without looking and take one golf ball, which color are you most likely to get?

A. red

B. blue

C. yellow

D. green

E. none of the above

18. Keith uses 5 lemons to make 2 pitchers of lemonade.

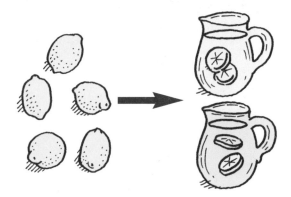

At this rate, how many lemons would Keith use to make 12 pitchers of lemonade?

F. 12

G. 15

H. 20

J. 30

K. none of the above

19. Dominic nailed two boards together in his dad's workshop. One board was 1/2 inch thick and the other was 3/8 inch thick. What was the combined thickness of the two pieces?

A. $\frac{7}{8}$ inch

B. $\frac{5}{6}$ inch

C. $\frac{3}{4}$ inch

D. $\frac{2}{3}$ inch

E. none of the above

Scholastic

Choose the best answer to each question. Mark your answer. If the correct answer is not given, choose none of the above.

20. Carla had $100. She spent $32.00 on groceries and $26.00 for gasoline. How much money did she have left?
- Ⓕ $42.00
- Ⓖ $58.00
- Ⓗ $68.00
- Ⓙ $74.00
- Ⓚ none of the above

21. Mr. Harrison drove 1150 miles in March, 2180 miles in April, and 1937 miles in May. How many miles in all did he drive in these 3 months?
- Ⓐ 4,937
- Ⓑ 5,567
- Ⓒ 5,267
- Ⓓ 6,000

22. Sam bought 50 stamps for $0.37 each. How much did he spend on stamps?
- Ⓕ $15.00
- Ⓖ $20.37
- Ⓗ $18.50
- Ⓙ $16.37

23. Members of the Kids' Club held a car wash one day to make money. They washed 74 cars in all. What else do you need to know to figure out how much money they made?
- Ⓐ how much they charged for each car
- Ⓑ what day the car wash was held
- Ⓒ how many members are in the club
- Ⓓ where the car wash was held
- Ⓔ none of the above

24. Sharon saved $620 last year. Her sister Kayla saved $75.00 less than that. How much did Kayla save?
- Ⓕ $535
- Ⓖ $545
- Ⓗ $555
- Ⓙ $695
- Ⓚ none of the above

25. Grace is reading a book that is 260 pages long. She read 24 pages on Monday, 30 pages on Tuesday, and 25 pages on Wednesday. How many pages does she have left to read?
- Ⓐ 79
- Ⓑ 181
- Ⓒ 206
- Ⓓ 230
- Ⓔ none of the above

Scholastic

Choose the best answer to each question. Mark your answer. If the correct answer is not given, choose none of the above.

1. The Jensons are driving from Buffalo to New York City. The distance is 419 miles. They have gone 250 miles so far. How many more miles do they have to go?
   - (A) 159
   - (B) 169
   - (C) 229
   - (D) 669
   - (E) none of the above

2. A total of 95 students will march in a parade for Memorial Day. They will march in rows of 6 students per row. Which number sentence should you use to find how many rows of students there will be?
   - (F) $95 \div 6 = \square$
   - (G) $95 - 6 = \square$
   - (H) $95 \times 6 = \square$
   - (J) $95 + 6 = \square$
   - (K) none of the above

3. In one hour, 74 cars went past a tollbooth. The driver of each car paid a $3.00 toll. How much money was collected in all?
   - (A) $77.00
   - (B) $212.00
   - (C) $222.00
   - (D) $252.00
   - (E) none of the above

4. Jamie made 76 jars of pickles. If he puts 8 jars in a box, how many boxes will he need for 76 jars?
   - (F) 7
   - (G) 8
   - (H) 9
   - (J) 10
   - (K) none of the above

5. Mrs. Grimes owned 11.6 acres of land. She sold 3.8 acres. How many acres of land does she have left?
   - (A) 6.8
   - (B) 7.3
   - (C) 7.7
   - (D) 8.8
   - (E) none of the above

Choose the best answer to each question. Mark your answer. If the correct answer is not given, choose none of the above.

6. Janelle bought this tool kit at a store. She gave the clerk a $20.00 bill.

$15.87

How much change should she receive?

Ⓕ $4.23
Ⓖ $4.13
Ⓗ $4.03
Ⓙ $3.13
Ⓚ none of the above

7. The table shows the number of children in each grade at the Clark School.

Grade	Number of Children
1	104
2	85
3	92

How many children are there in all?

Ⓐ 270
Ⓑ 271
Ⓒ 280
Ⓓ 291
Ⓔ none of the above

8. Karen hiked all three trails shown on the map.

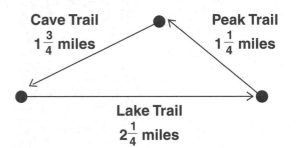

Cave Trail $1\frac{3}{4}$ miles

Peak Trail $1\frac{1}{4}$ miles

Lake Trail $2\frac{1}{4}$ miles

How far did she hike in all?

Ⓕ $5\frac{1}{4}$ miles
Ⓖ 5 miles
Ⓗ $4\frac{3}{4}$ miles
Ⓙ $4\frac{1}{4}$ miles
Ⓚ none of the above

9. Drew is 14 years older than his brother Clancy. Clancy is 3. How old is Drew?

Ⓐ 11
Ⓑ 13
Ⓒ 15
Ⓓ 17
Ⓔ none of the above

Scholastic

Choose the best answer to each question. Mark your answer. If the correct answer is not given, choose none of the above.

10. A soccer game started at 2:45 P.M. It ended at 4:30 P.M. How long did the game last?

- (F) 1 hr 15 min
- (G) 1 hr 30 min
- (H) 1 hr 45 min
- (J) 2 hr 15 min
- (K) none of the above

11. Rosa baby-sits for 24 hours each week. She baby-sat for 6 hours on Sunday and 4 hours on Wednesday. How many more hours does she have to baby-sit?

- (A) 14
- (B) 18
- (C) 20
- (D) 34
- (E) none of the above

12. Liam traveled for 4 weeks and 4 days. How many days is that all together?

- (F) 24
- (G) 28
- (H) 30
- (J) 36
- (K) none of the above

13. A pea plant is 16 inches tall. It grows 3 inches per week. At this rate, how tall will the plant be in 3 weeks?

- (A) 19 in.
- (B) 22 in.
- (C) 25 in.
- (D) 28 in.
- (E) none of the above

14. Mike ran 32 miles last week. Shem ran 26 miles. Which number sentence should you use to find how many more miles Mike ran?

- (F) $32 - 26 = \square$
- (G) $32 \div 26 = \square$
- (H) $26 - 32 = \square$
- (J) $26 + 32 = \square$
- (K) none of the above

15. Lynne started playing basketball at 4:30 P.M. She played for 40 minutes. At what time did she stop playing?

- (A) 5:00 P.M.
- (B) 5:10 P.M.
- (C) 5:20 P.M.
- (D) 5:40 P.M.
- (E) none of the above

Choose the best answer to each question. Mark your answer. If the correct answer is not given, choose none of the above.

16. Mr. Crowley was painting the windows on his house. It took 5 hours to paint 3 windows. At this rate, how long would it take to paint 18 windows?
   F 21 hours
   G 24 hours
   H 27 hours
   J 30 hours
   K none of the above

17. Hannah had $100.00. She spent $64.00 on food and $28.00 on music. How much did she have left?
   A $6.00
   B $8.00
   C $18.00
   D $32.00
   E none of the above

18. Steve earned $875 during the summer. Mandy earned $160 more than Steve. How much did Mandy earn?
   F $715
   G $935
   H $985
   J $1025
   K none of the above

19. A 4th-grade class went to the Nature Center on a field trip. They spent a total of $124 for tickets. What else do you need to know to figure out how much each ticket cost?
   A where the Nature Center was
   B what day the trip took place
   C the name of the Nature Center
   D how many students went on the trip

20. Saul makes $19 an hour at his job. About how much will he earn in 28 hours?
   F $30–$40
   G $50–$60
   H $300–$400
   J $500–$600

21. A factory made 1130 brooms on Monday, 2940 brooms on Tuesday, and 1800 brooms on Wednesday. About how many brooms were made in all?
   A 8000
   B 7000
   C 6000
   D 5000

Scholastic

Solve the following problems and find your answer in the code boxes below. To solve the riddle, write the word from each problem in the code box with the matching answer.

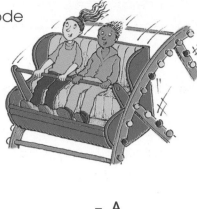

How do mice celebrate when they have moved from one house to another?

1. A small aircraft cruises at an average speed of 160 miles an hour.

   • What distance would be covered after 6 hours of flying? _____ = A

2. As a member of the reading club, Kristy set a goal for herself. In 20 days she wanted to read three books with a total page count of 1,000 pages.

   • How many pages would she need to read every day? _____ = THEY

3. The Boy Scouts were involved in planting seedlings. There were 28 scouts and each scout planted 237 seedlings.

   • How many total seedlings were planted? _____ = MOUSE

4. One thousand two hundred twenty-five was the total number of rides that 35 friends took on a Ferris wheel.

   • What number of rides would each friend have taken? _____ = PARTY

5. Danielle just turned 10 years old. Her friends want to calculate how many months have passed since she was born.

   • How many months ago was Danielle born? _____ = HAVE

6. The distance between two large cities is 538 miles. A salesman travels that distance 14 times each month.

   • How far does the salesman travel per month? _____ = WARMING

Scholastic

50	120	960	6,636	7,532	35

Solve each of the problems below. Write your answer in the space provided next to the problem. Write the word from the problem above the correct answer in the code box below. Find all the answers to decode the riddle.

What do you do if you have a sick canary?

1. Ms. Goodman drives 120 miles to and from work each day.
 • How far does she travel in 25 days?   _____ = TO

2. Tire World had a special sale on summer tires for $75 a tire. The owner of a fleet of taxis spent $900 on tires.
 • How many tires did he purchase for his taxis?   _____ = FOR

3. Monica is the scorekeeper for her school's basketball team. In the last 12 games the team averaged 68 points per game.
 • What is the total number of points the team has scored?   _____ = THE

4. Juan achieved some great scores on his last five math tests. His total score for the five tests was 460.
 • What was Juan's average score for each math test?   _____ = HURRY

5. Billy delivers 68 newspapers each day to the houses on his street. Altogether he has delivered 4,624 papers so far.
 • How many days has Billy delivered papers?   _____ = TWEETMENT

6. A large transport truck travels 397 miles every day making grocery deliveries to a supermarket chain.
 • How far would the truck travel in 3 weeks?   _____ = VET

92	3,000	816

8,337	12	68

.

Scholastic

Solve the following problems and find your answer in the code boxes below. To solve the riddle, write the word from each problem in the code box with the matching answer.

How do we know the little witch was feeling much better?

1. At the end of August, Mrs. Kim purchased school outfits for her daughters. She spent $319.71 on her three daughters.
   • What is the average amount that she spent on each daughter?   _____ = **FOR**

2. While shopping at the mall Mr. Gibson paid $5.40 for three dozen (or 36) cookies.
   • What is the cost of a single cookie?   _____ = **OUTSIDE**

3. Julian has a part-time job mowing lawns in his neighborhood. He mows one lawn each afternoon, except Sunday, and earns $4.50 per lawn.
   • How much does Julian earn each week?   _____ = **A**

4. Mrs. Wilson's class baked, iced, and sold 480 cupcakes to the students at their school.
   • How much did the class make from their sale if the cupcakes sold for $0.50 each?   _____ = **SHE**

5. Keon has been delivering papers for a full year. Each month for a year, Keon deposited $7.50 into his bank account. He has exactly enough money to buy a scooter.
   • What is the price of the scooter?   _____ = **SPELL**

6. The Millers were having a corn roast to celebrate their son's Little League victory. The farmer's market was selling corn for $4.00 per dozen.
   • How much did they pay for 9 dozen ears of corn?   _____ = **WENT**

$240.00	$36.00	$0.15	$106.57	$27.00	$90.00

Solve the following problems and find your answer in the code boxes below. To solve the riddle, write the word from each problem in the code box with the matching answer.

1. Jamal bought 65 stamps for 37 cents each. He also bought 10 stamps for 83 cents each.

- How much did Jamal spend on stamps?

_____ = BE

2. Four friends went out to dinner. They shared the bill of $99.24 equally among them all.

- What amount did each person pay?   _____ = HAS
- If they each contributed $25.00, what would their change be?   _____ = TO

3. John was saving money for his college tuition. He had $1,090.85 in the bank. He deposited $210.00, but a week later he took out $75.00 to buy a surfboard.

- How much does John now have in the bank?   _____ = CHOCOLATE

4. A furniture store had a special on sofas and coffee tables. It sold 15 sofas at $599.00 each and earned a total of $3,015.00 from the sale of 28 coffee tables.

- How much did the store make during its sale?   _____ = IT

5. A farmer's fruit stand sold 84 baskets of cherries for $3.49 per basket. The sale of peaches raised $65.

- How much money did the fruit stand bring in from the cherries and peaches?   _____ = MOUSSE

What's a French cat's favorite dessert?

$12,000	$24.81	$0.76	$32.35	$1,225.85	$358.16

Word Problems Practice Test

Fill in the bubble next to the correct answer.

1. Kim just turned 10 years old. Her mother is four times older than Kim. How old is Kim's mother?

   ○ **A**   34

   ○ **B**   43

   ⊗ **C**   40

   ○ **D**   14

2. Umair bought a notebook for $1.39 and two pens for $1.49 each. How much money did he spend?

   ⊗ **F** $4.37

   ○ **G** $4.97

   ○ **H** $3.97

   ○ **J** $4.55

3. The fastest flamenco dancer does 16 heel taps per second. How many heel taps would the dancer do in one minute?

   ○ **A**   940

   ○ **B**   960

   ○ **C**   160

   ⊗ **D**   660

   60×16

4. Maria watched a movie that started at 1:45 PM and ended at 4:15 PM. How long was the movie?

   ○ **F**   2 hours

   ⊗ **G**   2 and $\frac{1}{2}$ hours

   ○ **H**   2 hours and 45 minutes

   ○ **J**   3 hours and 15 minutes

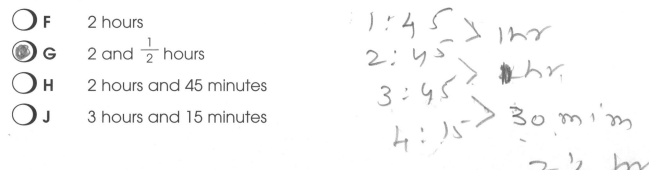

1:45 ⟶ 1 hr
2:45
3:45 ⟶ 1 hr
4:15 ⟶ 30 min

$2\frac{1}{2}$ hr

Scholastic

Word Problems Practice Test

Fill in the bubble next to the correct answer.

5. Jessie paid for a friend's birthday present with a $20.00 bill. She received $4.82 change. How much did the birthday present cost?

○ **A** $15.18

○ **B** $14.75

○ **C** $15.25

○ **D** $12.50

6. A busload of 48 tourists paid a total of $240 for a five-hour tour of the city. How much did each tourist pay for the tour?

○ **F** $7.50

○ **G** $5.55

○ **H** $5.00

○ **J** $6.00

7. There were 294 cars in the parking lot. Forty-eight of the cars were green, 36 were brown, 62 were white, and the rest of the cars were black. How many black cars were there?

○ **A**   248

○ **B**   168

○ **C**   236

○ **D**   148

8. The Johnson twins walk to and from school each day, and they walk home for lunch and back again. The distance from their home to school is $\frac{3}{8}$ mile. What is the total distance they walk each day going to and coming from school?

○ **F** $1\frac{3}{8}$ miles

○ **G** $1\frac{1}{8}$ miles

○ **H** $1\frac{1}{2}$ miles

○ **J** $1\frac{5}{8}$ miles

Scholastic

Get Ready for Grade 5

What Your Child Should Know to Prepare for Grade 5

Reading/Language Arts

- identify and use compound words

- identify run-on sentences and fix them

- identify parts of speech such as pronouns and prepositions

- use key reading skills such as sequence, classifying, cause/effect, inference, and compare/contrast

- understand and use key grammar and writing skills to build strong, interesting sentences and to write paragraphs in a variety of modes: expository, persuasive, descriptive

Mathematics

- identify geometric shapes

- understand concepts related to time and money

- understand concepts related to decimals

- develop strategies to solve word problems using addition, subtraction, multiplication, division, fractions, decimals, and time

A Word Sandwich

The words in boldface below can be sandwiched between two other words to create new compound words. Choose the correct boldface word for each example and write the compound words it makes on the blanks. Your choice must work as both the ending of the first word and the beginning of the second. The first one has been done for you.

HINT: Each word in the list is used only once.

crow   ever   water   fire   flower

hand   light   out   over   post   top

1. cook _____ *book* _____ mark
cookbook, bookmark

2. sun _____ pot
_____

3. scare _____ bar
_____

4. sleep _____ flow
_____

5. tree _____ soil
_____

6. flash _____ house
_____

7. what _____ green
_____

8. work _____ side
_____

9. wild _____ proof
_____

10. back _____ cuff
_____

11. goal _____ card
_____

12. under _____ front
_____

Each group of letters is missing either the prefix *dis-* or *trans-,* or the suffix *-or* or *-ic* to make it a real word. Your job is to figure out which prefix or suffix works best. Write the word formed and its meaning in the space provided. There is only one correct answer for each. You may use a dictionary to check your answers.

Examples:

obey ➜ adding *dis-* in the front makes it "disobey"

mythic ➜ adding *-ic* at the end makes it "mythic"

LETTERS	DIS-, TRANS-, -OR, OR -IC?	WORD FORMED	MEANING?
1. direct			
2. poet			
3. plant			
4. inspect			
5. like			
6. port			
7. counsel			
8. honest			

YOUR TURN

Look at the words formed and their definitions above, then take a guess at the meanings of the suffixes or prefixes used with them. Use a dictionary to check your guess.

dis- _____

trans- _____

-or _____

-ic _____

Scholastic

A **pronoun** is a word that takes the place of a noun or nouns. Pronouns show number. They indicate one or more than one.

Read the sentences. Write a pronoun on the line that could take the place of the underlined words.

1. Talent shows can make people nervous. _____

2. A talent show gives people a chance to show off. _____

3. My younger brother was in the talent show at my school. _____

4. Lots of people clapped loudly for my brother. _____

5. My older sister did not want to be in the show. _____

6. I did not blame my older sister. _____

7. I was nervous about being in the talent show, too. _____

8. Pam, Alicia, and I decided to sing a round. _____

9. People clapped politely for Pam, Alicia, and me. _____

10. We thanked the audience members for applauding. _____

11. You can ask Mrs. Renko about how well we did! _____

12. Now my sister is thinking about being in a show. _____

13. I asked my parents if my brother, sister, and I could practice at home. _____

14. Next year, the talent show will be even better! _____

Scholastic

*An **irregular verb** does not form the past tense or past participle by adding -ed. The **past participle** is the form of the verb used with* have, has, *or* had.

A. On the line, write the past tense or the past participle form of the verb in parentheses ( ).

1. I _____ I lost my math book. (think)

2. My friend had _____ a fancy seashell. (find)

3. Ed _____ his new puppy to my house. (bring)

4. Have you _____ the new coach? (meet)

5. She _____ she would get the team in shape. (say)

6. My neighbors _____ me for baby-sitting. (pay)

7. John _____ the football. (catch)

8. The little boy _____ his balloon tightly. (hold)

9. I have _____ about learning a new sport. (think)

10. The first night, I _____ the new puppy in my room. (keep)

11. Denise _____ a gold locket in the park the other day. (find)

12. We have already _____ for our tickets. (pay)

13. My sister has _____ a cold. (catch)

14. Maya has _____ a journal for many years. (keep)

15. Steve and I _____ in first grade. (meet)

B. Use each of the following verbs in a sentence.

      write   **wrote**   **have written**

1. _____

2. _____

3. _____

Scholastic

Moonwalkers on City Streets

Do you need some exercise? Do you want to see some city sights? Perhaps you want to assert your rights as a pedestrian in a city designed for cars. Then you might want to join a group called Moonwalkers in Bethlehem, Pennsylvania. The Moonwalkers meet once a week at night. Then they stride through their city, up hills, down streets, over bridges, and along canals. What are some other reasons that people enjoy moonwalking? They get to meet other members of their community, and they enjoy being out at night.

Find five causes and one effect in the passage. Write them on the map.

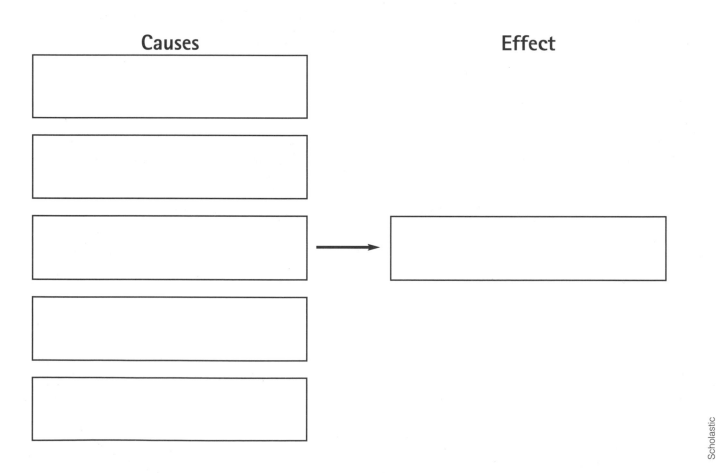

Causes

Effect

Scholastic

Double Dakota

Both North and South Dakota are midwestern states on the Great Plains. If you visit Bismarck, you'll be in the capital of North Dakota. South Dakota's capital is Pierre. While in South Dakota, you might travel through the Black Hills. The faces of four presidents—George Washington, Thomas Jefferson, Abraham Lincoln, and Theodore Roosevelt—are carved into Mount Rushmore there. Other interesting South Dakota sights are the dry landscape of Badlands National Park and bison roaming in Custer State Park. In North Dakota, you might visit the International Peace Garden on the Canadian border.

Find facts in the passage about North and South Dakota. Write the facts under the correct headings on the Venn diagram. Under "Both," write facts that are true of both states.

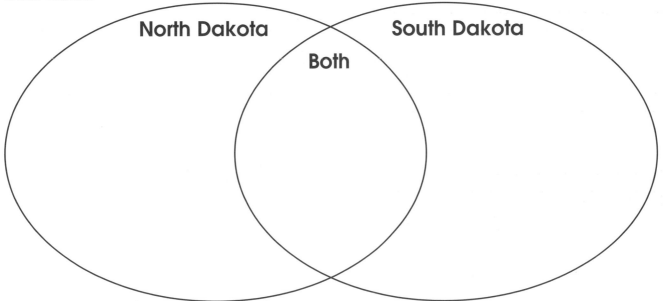

Presidential Passages

George Washington, the first President of the United States, took office in 1789. The first president to live in the White House, however, was John Adams. He and his wife, Abigail, moved there in 1800. Since then, technology has changed the lives of presidents. In 1833, Andrew Jackson was the first president to ride on a train. James Polk was the first president to be photographed in 1849. Benjamin Harrison was the first president to have electricity in the White House in 1891.

Presidential firsts also relate to advances in communications. In 1993, William Clinton was the first president to have email in the White House. In 1955, Dwight Eisenhower was the first president to appear on color TV. The first president to make a radio broadcast from the White House was Calvin Coolidge in 1925.

Write eight events on the time line in the correct order.

1750   1800   1850   1900   1950   2000

MORE! Discover which president was the first to ride on a steamboat, in a car, and on an airplane.

Scholastic

Colorful Events

History is full of colorful events. Television first appeared in living color in 1953. People began taking color photographs in 1935. Colorful music history was made in 1970 when a frog puppet named Kermit croaked out the song "Bein' Green." The year 1968 marked a milestone in another hue with the release of the movie *The Yellow Submarine* starring the Beatles. Traffic signals appeared in 1920. Another colorful event occurred in 1927 when bathtubs and sinks—once only available in white—were sold in tones such as Spring Green, Autumn Brown, and Horizon Blue for the first time.

Add five events in the correct place on the time line.

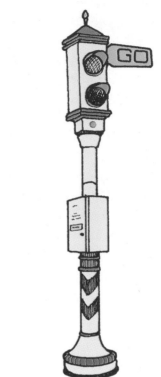

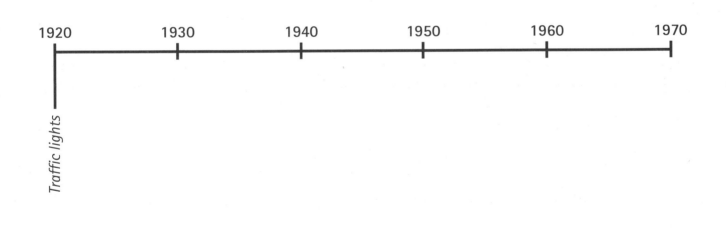

1920   1930   1940   1950   1960   1970

Traffic lights

On the Radar Screen

You may have heard of radar, but do you know what the word means? *Radar* stands for "radio detection and ranging." Radar waves have many important uses in everyday life. Radar signals aid air-traffic control in keeping track of planes. Burglar alarms use radar to detect the movements of intruders. Radar helps predict the weather. In baseball, radar measures the speed of pitches. Police use radar to detect drivers who are speeding. Radar even plays a role in the workings of microwave ovens.

Decide what the main idea of the paragraph is. Write it in the center circle. Find details from the paragraph that tell about the topic. Write them in the web.

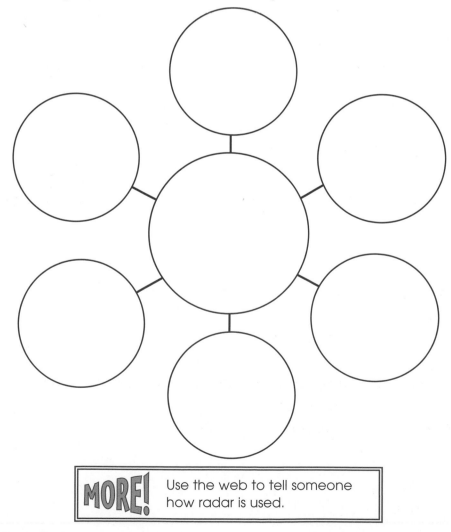

MORE! Use the web to tell someone how radar is used.

Scholastic

Choose the word that means the same, or nearly the same, as the underlined word in each sentence.

1. The teacher asked the students to <u>extend</u> the line.
    A. shorten   C. lengthen
    B. erase   D. cat

2. We were afraid he would make a <u>grave</u> mistake as he worked very quickly.
    F. foolish   H. honest
    G. sudden   J. serious

3. Although we tried very hard, we were told that it was a <u>futile</u> attempt.
    A. hopeless   C. dangerous
    B. brave   D. final

4. Before we started to play, the coach said we had to <u>discuss</u> the rules.
    F. learn   H. dislike
    G. write down   J. talk over

5. It was hard to believe her <u>incredible</u> story.
    A. imaginary   C. dislike
    B. unbelievable   D. true

6. Even though it was getting dark, we were told to continue to watch <u>intently</u>.
    F. angrily   H. attentively
    G. silently   J. secretly

7. We tried to <u>convince</u> a friend to help us at the carnival.
    A. promise   C. visit
    B. ask   D. persuade

8. Not only was the shipment of high quality, it also boasted <u>infinite</u> variety.
    F. imitation   H. unlimited
    G. colorful   J. detailed

Choose the word whose meanings fit both sentences.

1. The children always _____ from
the car when we stop for snacks.
The _____ of lightning came so
close to us.
- A. race
- B. bolt
- C. flash
- D. hurry

2. My mother uses a special fingernail
_____ when she does her nails.
Our teacher always has us stand in
single _____ before going to the bus.
- F. file
- G. rows
- H. gloss
- J. cream

3. How many records did the singer
_____ last year?
I love to go to the _____ aisle to
see what is fresh.
- A. design
- B. fish
- C. perform
- D. produce

4. Susan got a new fishing _____ for
her birthday.
The sudden turn made me _____
and fall off the seat of the bus.
- F. rod
- G. jump
- H. reel
- J. shout

5. We waited for the bell to _____
before going home.
She found her _____ right where
you said.
- A. pen
- B. sound
- C. sweater
- D. ring

6. What will you _____ on our
vacation?
The old trunk showed signs of
_____ .
- F. want
- G. take
- H. wear
- J. abuse

7. She turned the _____ on.
It was easy to carry because it was
_____ .
- A. TV
- B. light
- C. small
- D. lamp

8. This floor appears to be _____ .
Did anyone else hear that loud
_____ ?
- F. noise
- G. flat
- H. sound
- J. level

The subject and verb in a sentence must agree. A singular subject takes a singular verb. A plural subject takes a plural verb.

When the subject is singular, add an -s to a regular verb in the present tense.

<u>Nina</u> celebrates many holidays.   (singular subject-singular verb)
The <u>neighbors</u> celebrate many holidays.   (plural subject-plural verb)

Find a match for each puzzle piece. Then write the complete sentence.

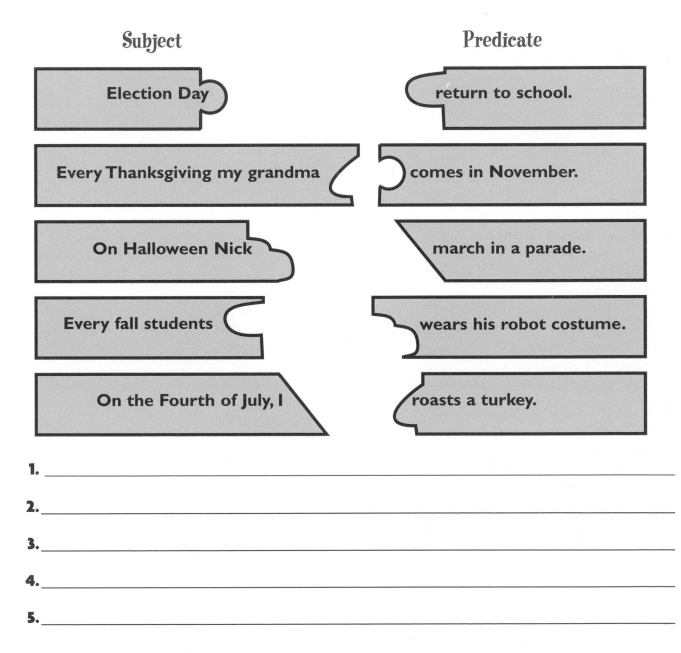

Subject

- Election Day
- Every Thanksgiving my grandma
- On Halloween Nick
- Every fall students
- On the Fourth of July, I

Predicate

- return to school.
- comes in November.
- march in a parade.
- wears his robot costume.
- roasts a turkey.

1. _____

2. _____

3. _____

4. _____

5. _____

Scholastic

Complete each sentence step. First add a verb to the subject. Then add an adverb to build each sentence. Look at the example at the right.

Example:

| Swans |
| Swans glide. |
| Swans glide gracefully. |

1.

| Turkeys |
| |
| |

2.

| Penguins |
| |
| |

3.

| Robins |
| |
| |

4.

| Ducks |
| |
| |

5.

| Geese |
| |
| |

6.

| Hens |
| |
| |

7.

| Parrots |
| |
| |

8.

| Vultures |
| |
| |

Think of an adjective to describe each of the subjects in your completed sentences.

Scholastic

Do you sometimes run together several ideas into one long, run-on sentence?

According to my grandma, it is a good idea to eat chicken soup when you have a cold and believe it or not, scientists agree with her the protein in the soup fights the stuffiness by thinning out the lining of your sinuses I think chicken soup tastes better than medicine, so the next time I have a cold I'm going to follow my grandmother's advice.

You can easily fix a run-on sentence by rewriting each complete idea as a separate sentence. Begin each sentence with a capital letter and end it with the correct punctuation mark.

According to my grandma, it is a good idea to eat chicken soup when you have a cold. Believe it or not, scientists agree with her! The protein in the soup fights the stuffiness by thinning out the lining of your sinuses. I think chicken soup tastes better than medicine, so the next time I have a cold I'm going to follow my grandmother's advice.

Rewrite each run-on sentence correctly.

1. Did you know that carrots really are good for your eyes there is a vitamin in this crunchy orange root called beta-carotene that helps lower the risk of eye disease and so the next time you find carrot sticks in your lunch don't trade them or toss them away munch away in good health instead?

_____

_____

_____

2. Do you like potato chips, cookies, cake, and ice cream if you're like me, you probably do and I'm sure you also know that these wonderful taste treats are considered to be junk food and it is a good idea to eat small amounts of food with a lot of fat, oil, sugar, and salt?

_____

_____

_____

3. Think about all the foods you eat and are they nutritious and do they have all the vitamins and minerals your body needs to be healthy, or are they full of fats, sugar, and salt make healthful choices because you are what you eat.

_____

_____

_____

Scholastic

Future-tense verbs tell about action that will happen in the future. Use *will* with a verb to show the future tense.

Complete this school fair poster. Add verbs in the future tense to show what everyone will do. Use a different verb for each performer.

Come to Our School Fair!

Buster _____ a bone on his nose.

Jack _____ his unicycle.   Lily _____ magic tricks.

Marcus _____ prizes.   Heather _____ popcorn and drinks.

Scholastic

Think of two or more things to add to the poster.

A **preposition** often helps tell where something is.

How many stars can you find? They are hidden around the park. Add a preposition from the box to each clue to tell where the stars are.

between	on	under	against
behind	in	over	around

Clues:

1. _____ a bench

2. _____ a sand pail

3. _____ the baby's stroller

4. _____ two litter baskets

5. _____ the corner

6. _____ the fence

7. _____ Keith's foot

8. _____ the tree

The clues are prepositional phrases. Use each prepositional phrase in a sentence.

PHONE CALL featuring Molly and Squirmy

GRAMMAR WORKSHOP

How do subjects and verbs agree?

Singular subjects take singular verbs.
Wrong: One parent **are** at home.   Right: One parent **is** at home.

Plural subjects take plural verbs.
Wrong: Both parents **is** at home.   Right: Both parents **are** at home.
Wrong: Molly and Squirmy **plays** games. Right: Molly and Squirmy **play** games.

Circle the correct form of the verb.

1. Molly and Squirmy (is/are) good friends.

2. For a mouse, Molly (talk/talks) on the phone quite a bit.

3. Squirmy (don't/doesn't) talk very much on the phone.

4. Molly and her family (has/have) two telephone lines.

5. Sometimes, Squirmy (get/gets) a busy signal on both lines.

6. Woovis and Moovis (call/calls) Squirmy on the phone.

7. No one (is/are) home.

8. The answering machine (pick/picks) up the call.

Scholastic

HOW MANY MINUTES OF EXERCISE DO YOU NEED TO WORK OFF THE CALORIES FOUND IN VARIOUS FOODS? FIND OUT BY COMPLETING THESE MATH SENTENCES.

	FOOD AND CALORIES		SWIMMING MIN.		WALKING MIN.		RUNNING MIN.		BIKING MIN.
1	POUND CAKE 1 slice	142	17	+10 =		−19 =		+14 =	
2	FRIED EGG	108	13	+8 =		−15 =		+11 =	
3	BANANA	127	15	+9 =		−17 =		+13 =	
4	HAMBURGER	350	44	+23 =		−48 =		+35 =	
5	2 PORK CHOPS	260	31	+19 =		−36 =		+26 =	
6	ORANGE	73	9	+5 =		−10 =		+7 =	
7	HOT DOG	290	34	+22 =		−40 =		+29 =	
8	½ CUP POTATO SALAD	99	12	+7 =		−13 =		+9 =	
9	GRILLED CHEESE SANDWICH	286	34	+21 =		−39 =		+28 =	
10	6-8 ROASTED PEANUTS	86	10	+7 =		−12 =		+8 =	
11	22 GRAPES	70	8	+5 =		−9 =		+7 =	

Fill in the missing numbers.

A.
$$\begin{array}{r} 3\ \square\ 7 \\ -\ \square\ 2\ \square \\ \hline 2\ 2\ 2 \end{array}$$

B.
$$\begin{array}{r} 7\ \square\ 9 \\ -\ 1\ 2\ 9 \\ \hline \square\ 2\ \square \end{array}$$

C.
$$\begin{array}{r} 4\ \square\ 6 \\ -\ \square\ 3\ \square \\ \hline 2\ 1\ 8 \end{array}$$

D.
$$\begin{array}{r} 5\ \square\ \square \\ -\ 4\ 6\ 6 \\ \hline \square\ 0\ 6 \end{array}$$

E.
$$\begin{array}{r} 3\ 2\ 4 \\ -\ \square\ 8\ \square \\ \hline 1\ \square\ 5 \end{array}$$

F.
$$\begin{array}{r} 5\ 3\ \square \\ -\ 1\ \square\ 6 \\ \hline \square\ 1\ 3 \end{array}$$

Hey, you'll do fine!

G.
$$\begin{array}{r} \square\ 1\ \square \\ -\ 3\ \square\ 0 \\ \hline 2\ 7\ 3 \end{array}$$

H.
$$\begin{array}{r} 5\ \square\ \square \\ -\ 3\ 7\ 6 \\ \hline \square\ 4\ 5 \end{array}$$

I.
$$\begin{array}{r} 8\ 9\ 5 \\ -\ \square\ 7\ \square \\ \hline 2\ \square\ 8 \end{array}$$

J.
$$\begin{array}{r} 5\ 1\ 8 \\ -\ \square\ \square\ \square \\ \hline 3\ 8\ 0 \end{array}$$

CIRCLE THE FRACTION WHICH BEST REPRESENTS THE SECTION OF THE FLAG NEXT TO THE ARROW.

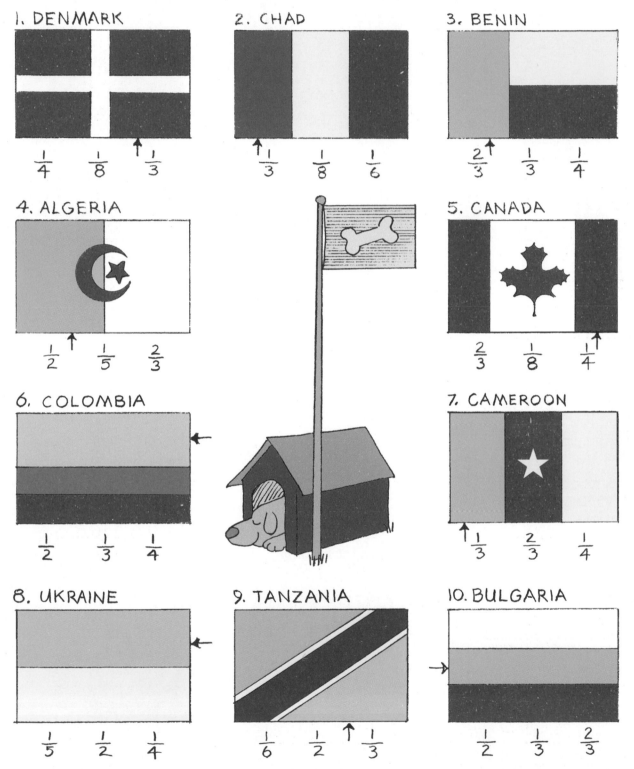

1. DENMARK

$\frac{1}{4}$ $\frac{1}{8}$ $\frac{1}{3}$

2. CHAD

$\frac{1}{3}$ $\frac{1}{8}$ $\frac{1}{6}$

3. BENIN

$\frac{2}{3}$ $\frac{1}{3}$ $\frac{1}{4}$

4. ALGERIA

$\frac{1}{2}$ $\frac{1}{5}$ $\frac{2}{3}$

5. CANADA

$\frac{2}{3}$ $\frac{1}{8}$ $\frac{1}{4}$

6. COLOMBIA

$\frac{1}{2}$ $\frac{1}{3}$ $\frac{1}{4}$

7. CAMEROON

$\frac{1}{3}$ $\frac{2}{3}$ $\frac{1}{4}$

8. UKRAINE

$\frac{1}{5}$ $\frac{1}{2}$ $\frac{1}{4}$

9. TANZANIA

$\frac{1}{6}$ $\frac{1}{2}$ $\frac{1}{3}$

10. BULGARIA

$\frac{1}{2}$ $\frac{1}{3}$ $\frac{2}{3}$

Fractions for lunch! Well, even if you don't have an appetite for pickle pizza, we hope you'll have an appetite for math! Answer the questions below.

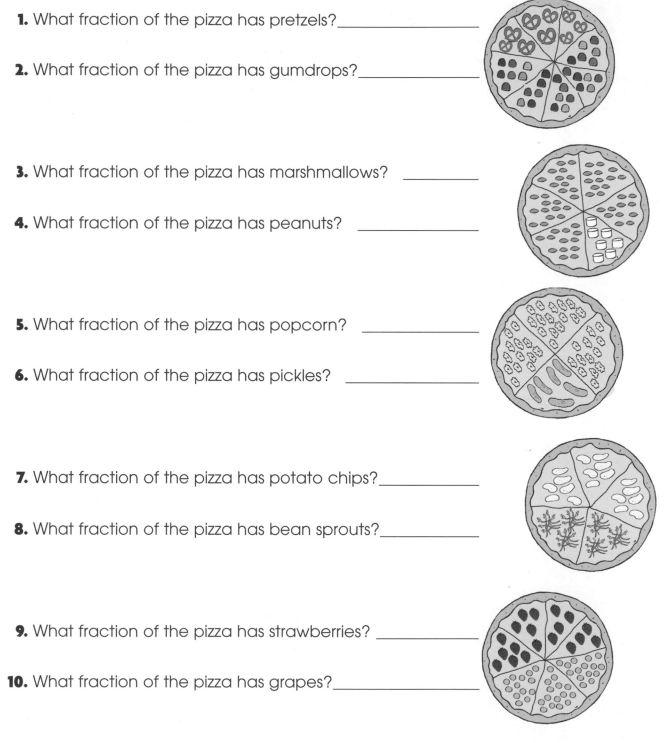

1. What fraction of the pizza has pretzels?_____

2. What fraction of the pizza has gumdrops?_____

3. What fraction of the pizza has marshmallows? _____

4. What fraction of the pizza has peanuts? _____

5. What fraction of the pizza has popcorn? _____

6. What fraction of the pizza has pickles? _____

7. What fraction of the pizza has potato chips?_____

8. What fraction of the pizza has bean sprouts?_____

9. What fraction of the pizza has strawberries? _____

10. What fraction of the pizza has grapes?_____

Scholastic

These construction workers have a big job ahead of them. They're building decimals. You can help. Read the clues on each house. Then write the correct decimal on the roof of each house.

1. 1 in the ones place
7 in the tenths place
7 in the hundredths place

5. 9 in the ones place
4 in the tenths place
4 in the hundredths place

8. 6 in the ones place
7 in the tenths place
6 in the hundredths place

2. 8 in the ones place
7 in the tenths place
0 in the hundredths place

6. 6 in the ones place
0 in the tenths place
5 in the hundredths place

9. 1 in the tens place
2 in the ones place
5 in the tenths place
6 in the hundredths place

3. 3 in the ones place
0 in the tenths place
9 in the hundredths place

7. 0 in the ones place
1 in the tenths place
5 in the hundredths place

10. 2 in the tens place
4 in the ones place
9 in the tenths place
9 in the hundredths place

4. 3 in the ones place
9 in the tenths place
0 in the hundredths place

Scholastic

ELAPSED TIME IS TIME THAT HAS PASSED.
DETERMINE THE ELAPSED TIME
FOR EACH EVENT BELOW.

THE EVENT	WRITE THE ELAPSED TIME
1. MOVIE STARTS AT 5:40 PM AND ENDS AT 8:00 PM	
2. STORE OPENS AT 8:15 AM AND CLOSES AT 6:00 PM	
3. TRAIN LEAVES AT 9:20 AM AND ARRIVES AT 3:40 PM	
4. CEREMONY BEGINS AT 11:05 AM AND ENDS AT 11:55 AM	
5. TOUR STARTS AT 3:45 PM AND ENDS AT 5:10 PM	
6. PARADE BEGINS AT 10:10 AM AND ENDS AT 11:15 AM	
7. PLANE TAKES OFF AT 1:40 PM AND LANDS AT 9:32 PM	
8. DINNER WILL BEGIN AT 5:00 PM AND LAST UNTIL 6:10 PM	
9. MEETING STARTS AT 7:15 AM AND LASTS UNTIL 8:05 AM	

Scholastic

FRANK'S GARDEN CENTER AND BARRY'S NURSERY ARE HAVING A SALE OF FLOWERING BUSHES. WRITE THE PRICE PER BUSH TO FIND WHICH MAN HAS THE BETTER BUY. WRITE HIS NAME, TOO.

	FRANK'S GARDEN CENTER		BARRY'S NURSERY
1.	4 for $12.80	OR	7 for $27.86
2.	8 for $58.16	OR	7 for $51.10
3.	2 for $29.08	OR	3 for $46.11
4.	5 for $34.00	OR	9 for $62.00
5.	6 for $46.20	OR	8 for $49.60
6.	9 for $51.30	OR	5 for $23.50
7.	8 for $72.40	OR	5 for $47.30
8.	8 for $37.60	OR	7 for $37.80

1. _____

2. _____

3. _____

4. _____

5. _____

6. _____

7. _____

8. _____

Want to buy a flowering bush cheap?

Help! Sam Sorter needs to sort these items according to shape. You can help.
Write the name of the shape of each item on the lines provided.

cone   **cube**   **sphere**   **cylinder**   **rectangular prism**

1. dice _____

2. balloon _____

3. can of paint _____

4. cereal box _____

5. planet Mars _____

6. hockey puck _____

7. globe _____

8. bowling ball _____

9. funnel _____

10. suitcase _____

11. pen _____

12. AA battery _____

13. megaphone _____

14. paper towel roll _____

Scholastic

HOW MANY TRIANGLES OR SQUARES ARE THERE IN THESE
GEOMETRIC FIGURES? CLUE: THEY OVERLAP.

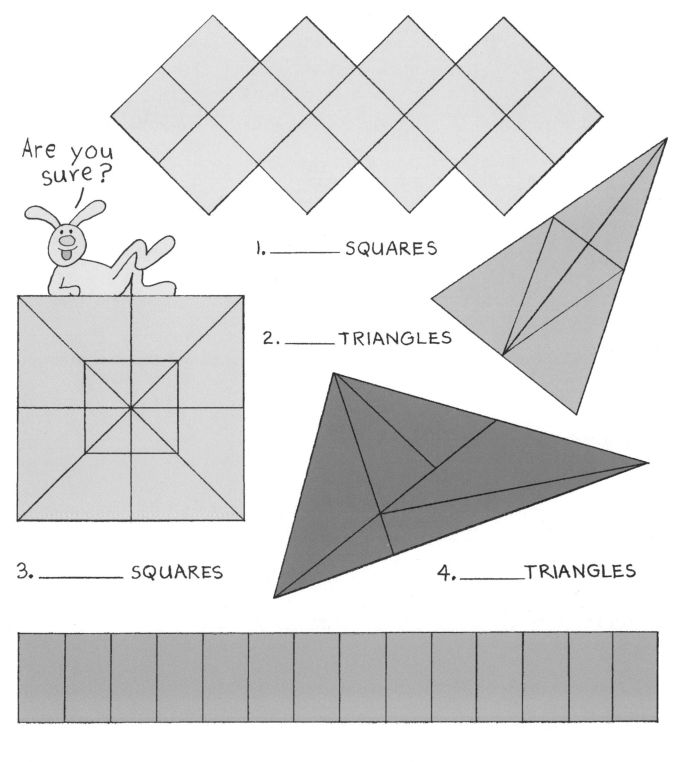

1. _____ SQUARES

2. _____ TRIANGLES

3. _____ SQUARES

4. _____ TRIANGLES

5. _____ SQUARES

Terrell and his brother and sister play in a band called 3-Tee.
Answer questions 1 and 2 about the band.

1. At a recent music festival, 3-Tee played for an hour. Each of its songs is between 3 and 4 minutes long. About how many songs did the band play in an hour?
   Ⓐ fewer than 10
   Ⓑ between 10 and 15
   Ⓒ between 15 and 20
   Ⓓ more than 20

2. At a concert, 3-Tee sold 89 CDs for $10.99 each. About how much money did the group make?
   Ⓕ $89.00
   Ⓖ $99.00
   Ⓗ $990.00
   Ⓙ $1100.00

Connie plays basketball for her middle school team. Answer questions 3–5 about the team.

3. Connie has scored a total of 32 points in 8 games this season. Which number sentence should you use to find out how many points Connie has averaged per game?
   Ⓐ $32 + 8 = \square$
   Ⓑ $32 \times \square = 8$
   Ⓒ $32 \div 8 = \square$
   Ⓓ $32 - \square = 8$

4. At a recent game, Connie and her friend Tanya together scored half the points for their team. The team scored 54 points. What else do you need to know to figure out how many points Connie scored?
   Ⓕ how many points the other team scored
   Ⓖ whether Connie scored more points than Tanya
   Ⓗ whether Connie and Tanya's team won
   Ⓙ how many points Tanya scored

5. Last year, Connie's team scored a total of 1045 points. The season was 20 games long. How many points did the team average per game?
   Ⓐ fewer than 50
   Ⓑ between 50 and 55
   Ⓒ between 55 and 60
   Ⓓ more than 60

Scholastic

6. Kami's dad buys night crawlers to use as bait for fishing. If night crawlers cost $2.39 per carton, about how much does Kami's dad pay for 3 cartons of night crawlers?

- F $3.00
- G $5.50
- H $7.50
- J $9.00

7. At several supermarkets, bananas cost between 20 and 25 cents a pound. Which is the best estimate of the cost of 4 pounds of bananas?

- A $0.90
- B $1.20
- C $1.50
- D $1.80

8. Ty and his friends went to the video arcade. They used a total of 30 game tokens. Each person used the same number of tokens. What else do you need to know to find how many tokens each person used?

- F how many people got tokens
- G how much the tokens cost
- H how much each game cost
- J how many tokens were left

9. There are 42 people going on a trip to the aquarium. Each van can hold 8 people. To get everyone there, they will have to send at least how many vans?

- A 5
- B 6
- C 8
- D 9

10. Doug works at the pet store. He makes $7.50 per hour. Last week he earned a total of $210. Which is closest to the number of hours he worked?

- F 300 hours
- G 30 hours
- H 10 hours
- J 3 hours

11. Jun has to make 60 gallons of punch for the school fair. Each can of powdered-drink mix makes 7.5 gallons. Write a number sentence he could use to find out how many cans of powdered-drink mix he needs.

_____

12. Four friends are waiting in line at the movie theater. Jenny is standing directly in front of Ted. Ann is not first or last in line. Gary is standing behind Ann. Draw a picture or diagram showing the order in which the friends are standing.

Scholastic

Solve each problem. If your answer is not given, mark "None of these."

A new sporting goods store just opened at the mall. Answer questions 1–3 about the store.

Kevin and his friends went on a bike trail ride. Answer questions 4–6 about the trail ride.

1. At the grand opening, Sportsmart had a special on tennis balls.

TENNIS BALLS
2 cans $5.00   1 can $3.00

Jack bought 5 cans of tennis balls. How much did he spend?
Ⓐ $25
Ⓑ $15
Ⓒ $13
Ⓓ $8
Ⓔ None of these

2. On Saturday, 1032 people visited the new store. On Sunday, 988 people visited. How many people visited the store over the weekend?
Ⓕ 1910
Ⓖ 1940
Ⓗ 2010
Ⓙ 2020
Ⓚ None of these

3. The new store has 12,400 square feet of display space. The Camping and Hiking section takes up 2,230 square feet. How many square feet of display space are there in the rest of the store?
Ⓐ 9270
Ⓑ 10,170
Ⓒ 10,220
Ⓓ 10,230
Ⓔ None of these

4. In the first hour of the trail ride, Kevin rode 8.95 miles. In the second hour, he rode 9.1 miles. How many miles did he ride in the first 2 hours?
Ⓕ 9.86
Ⓖ 17.15
Ⓗ 17.96
Ⓙ 18.5
Ⓚ None of these

5. It took the group 5 hours to ride 45.5 miles. How many miles per hour did they ride on average?
Ⓐ 9.1
Ⓑ 10.4
Ⓒ 10.9
Ⓓ 11.0
Ⓔ None of these

6. Eight people completed the entire 90-mile trail ride. Four people completed 50 miles of the ride. In all, how many miles did these 12 bikers ride?
Ⓕ 770
Ⓖ 790
Ⓗ 850
Ⓙ 920
Ⓚ None of these

Scholastic

Marty's dad has been collecting music for many years. Answer questions 7–9 about his collection.

7. Marty's dad has three times as many jazz CDs as he has classical CDs. If he has 42 jazz CDs, how many classical CDs does he have?

Ⓐ 14
Ⓑ 21
Ⓒ 39
Ⓓ 126

8. Marty wants to tape three of his dad's old record albums. The first album is 39 minutes long. The second is 34.4 minutes long. The third is 29.6 minutes long. What is the shortest tape Marty can use to tape all three albums?

Ⓕ 60 minutes
Ⓖ 90 minutes
Ⓗ 110 minutes
Ⓙ 120 minutes

9. Marty's dad has 200 cassette tapes: $\frac{1}{4}$ of them are rock music, and $\frac{3}{8}$ are jazz music. What fraction of the tapes are either rock or jazz music?

Ⓐ $\frac{3}{4}$
Ⓑ $\frac{7}{8}$
Ⓒ $\frac{5}{8}$
Ⓓ $\frac{2}{3}$

Abra's class is painting a mural on one of the school walls. Answer questions 10–12 about the mural.

10. So far the class has painted $\frac{1}{3}$ of the mural. How much of the mural is left to paint?

Ⓕ $\frac{1}{2}$
Ⓖ $\frac{1}{3}$
Ⓗ $\frac{2}{3}$
Ⓙ $\frac{3}{4}$

11. Each member of the class has been given a 1.5-foot long section to paint. There are 26 students in the class. How long is the mural?

Ⓐ 32 feet
Ⓑ 36 feet
Ⓒ 39 feet
Ⓓ 42 feet

12. The class keeps all of the paintbrushes they are using in 2 racks. Each rack holds the same number of brushes. There are 48 brushes in all, and each rack has 4 full rows of brushes. How many brushes are in each row?

Ⓕ 6
Ⓖ 8
Ⓗ 10
Ⓙ 12

Answer Key

READING/LANGUAGE ARTS
Spelling

Page 14
A. a: basic, radio, glacier; ai: daily, brain, explain;
a_e: erase, escape; ay: crayon, stray;
ey: obey, they; eigh: eighth, neighbor, freight
B. precipitation*; hail*

Page 15
A. 1. eighth 2. explain 3. obey 4. crayon
5. freight 6. stray;

Dear Jane,
  I saw a glashier on the basik dailey boat tour.
I cannot erajs the magnificent image from my
brane. I asked the captain and crew if I could raydio
my neighber. However, thay were too busy trying to
excap the bad weather. Talk to you soon.
                                    Sincerely,
                                    Daisy

C. 7. hail 8. temperature 9. precipitation
10. thermometer 11. humidity 12. hurricane

Page 16
about/family: beach, ecology, eager, agreed,
either; famous/nibble: jockey, neither, field,
monkey, feast; niche/young: species, secret,
queen, yield, seaweed

Page 17
1. monkey 2. ecology 3. eager 4. feast
5. queen 6. seaweed 7. either ALGAE
8. species, beach 9. field, neither
10. yield, agreed 11. jockey, secret
12. crocodile 13. biologist 14. rhinoceros
15. orangutan 16. leopard

Page 18
one syllable: flight, type, mile, rhyme, prize;
two syllables: delight, surprise, apply, myself,
mighty; three syllables: icicle, decided, finally,
diagram, idea
B. library*; biography*

Page 19
A.

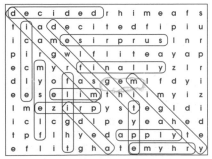

B. forward: decided, finally, apply;
backward: surprise, mile, rhyme, prize;
down: icicle, flight, type, myself;
diagonally: diagram, delight, mighty, idea
C. 1. biography 2. library 3. glossary
4. fiction 5. dictionary 6. finish

Page 20
o: poem, echo, introduce, cocoa;
o_e: spoke, wrote, awoke, grove;
oa: coast, throat, goal, cocoa;
ow: shown, narrow, tomorrow, shadow;
two long-o sounds: cocoa
B. ocean*

Page 21
1. cocoa 2. poem 3. coast 4. tomorrow
5. grove 6. introduce 7. wrote 8. shadow
9. echo 10. throat 11. shown 12. awoke
13. narrow 14. goal 15. spoke 16. ocean
17. discovery 18. geography 19. valley
20. continent 21. challenger deep

Page 22
u: huge, view, rescue, few, refuse, value, accuse;
oo: clue, school, prove, juice, fruit, crew, issue,
bruise

Page 23
A. 1. juice 2. huge 3. crew 4. clue 5. rescue
6. fruit 7. bruise 8. view

Luke just read the latest issew of the
skool newspaper. An author of one of the
articles was trying to acuse Luke's class of
making the mess in the lunchroom last
tuesday. Luke knew this was not true. He
decided he must pruve it to more than a fuw
students. Luke interviewed the custodian. The
custodian agreed that Luke's class did not
refuze to clean up. In fact, the custodian
added that they knew the valew of a clean
lunchroom. Luke now had his proof.

C. rhythm, harmony, musical, performance,
orchestra; MOZART

Page 24
nouns: moisture, council, boundary,
downtown, mountain, allowance, oyster;
verbs: destroy, allow, avoid, employ, boiled,
disappoint, found; both: voyage

Page 25
A. 1. found 2. mountain 3. oyster 4. avoid
5. allowance 6. employ 7. voyage 8. council
9. boiled 10. allow 11. moisture 12. boundary
13. disappoint 14. downtown 15. destroy
B. About seven quarts of oxygen are required
to run a one hundred yard dash.

Page 26
atomic/freckle: cracker, clerk, attic, frantic,
attack; handicap/picture: nickel, picnic,
heroic, hockey, hawk; pink/trademark: tractor,
rocket, shriek, plastic, stack

Page 27
A. 1. attack 2. hockey 3. hawk 4. attic
5. plastic 6. rocket 7. shriek 8. clerk, cracker
9. rocket, heroic 10. picnic, frantic
11. tractor, stack; B. Olympic, competition,
skiing, snowboarding, athletes, skeleton

Page 28
one syllable: ledge, pledge, bridge, judge,
edge, budge, urge; two syllables: package,
message, garbage, damage, luggage, manage;
three syllables: average, discourage

Page 29
A. 1. manage, damage 2. judge, edge;
3. pledge, ledge 4. package, message
5. urge, badge, luggage 6. average, bridge
7. discourage, garbage
B. 1. nutrition 2. vegetable 3. mineral
4. vitamin 5. protein 6. trillion

Page 30
distance, instance, princess, recess, saucer,
science, sentence, silence, since, slice, source,
spice, spruce, succeed, surface

Page 31
1. princess 2. science 3. saucer 4. recess
5. spice 6. sentence 7. spruce 8. slice
9. source 10. distance 11. since 12. silence
13. succeed 14. instance 15. surface
16. cricket 17. ladybug 18. grasshopper
19. insects 20. antenna 21. stink bug

Page 32
a: woman, balance, animal, instant, hospital;
e: garden, problem, students, frighten, different;
o: person, custom, bottom, season, opinion

Page 33
A. 1. balance 2. problem 3. hospital
4. woman 5. animal 6. instant 7. bottom
8. custom 9. opinion

All the studints from Mr. melby's class
met in front of the school early saturday
morning. It was spring, the seson to plant their
class gardon. Each persin was to plant a
diferent kind of seed. Mr. Melby was in
charge of creating a scarecrow to frightin the
crows away. They calculated that if every
student planted 50 seeds, the class would
plant 1,250 seeds altogether. How many
students are in Mr. Melby's class?

B. 25; C. 1. graph 2. fraction 3. geometry
4. multiplication 5. division 6. google

Page 34
A. one vowel: forty, truly; two vowels: once,
meant, young, island, toward, answer, often;
three vowels: another, against, beauty,
calendar, machine, cousin

Page 35
A. 1. island 2. cousin 3. forty 4. machine
5. beauty 6. calendar

Wunce upon a time there was a yung boy who would not study. He ment to study, but he always forgot. Thus, he would ofen need to guess an anser because he truely did not know it. While walking tward his house after school, he decided to lean aginst a tree. He watched a squirrel nibble on a nut. Anuther squirrel scampered up the tree. the squirrels were so fascinating the boy decided to learn about them. That night he discovered how interesting it is to study.

C. 7. sculpture 8. landscape 9. masterpiece 10. artistic 11. portrait 12. Mona Lisa

Page 36
caboose/knee: geese, calves, children, halves, cacti; knew/scene: loaves, oxen, scarves, mice, knives; shallow/wonderful: wolves, teeth, thieves, women, shelves

Page 37
1. calves 2. geese 3. halves 4. teeth 5. shelves 6. cacti 7. oxen 8. knives 9. thieves 10. scarves 11. women 12. mice 13. loaves 14. children 15. wolves 16. geckos
B. reptiles, vertebrates, alligators, tortoises, predators

Reptils are cold-blooded vertebractes. this means that their body temperatures stay about the same temperature as their surroundings. Alligaters, lizards, snakes, and tortuises are examples of these scaly-skinned animals. Many reptiles are preddators, which means they hunt other animals for food.

Pages 39–40
1. C 2. G 3. B 4. F 5. B 6. H 7. B 8. C

Vocabulary
Page 42
A. 1. phon 2. tact 3. clam 4. son 5. aud 6. spec 7. vis 8. vid 9. claim 10. scop 11. dic; B. Review definitions; refer to a dictionary.

Page 43
Review definitions; refer to a dictionary.

Page 44
1. discontinued 2. disconnect 3. dishonest 4. disappear 5. discover 6. disagree, disapprove 7. dislike 8. disobey

Page 45
1. eastward 2. heartily 3. resident 4. treacherous 5. American 6. government 7. zoology 8. necessity 9. noiseless 10. weaken 11. Washington

Page 46
A. 1. extraordinary, uncommon 2. desiring, jealous 3. relation, family 4. feebleness, fragility 5. money-making, prosperous 6. glad, cheerful 7. kingliness, monarchy 8. friendship, fellowship B. 1. ship 2. hood

Page 47
A. 1. joyous 2. leadership 3. remarkable 4. kinship 5. profitable 6. neighborhood 7. royalty 8. envious 9. frailty 10. brotherhood
B. 1. neighborhood 2. princess 3. leadership 4. taker

Page 48
A. 1. act, behave 2. carry, tote 3. bowl, tank 4. pipe, channel 5. retelling, account 6. wet, watery 7. diver, explorer; B. 1. aqua 2. port 3. port

Page 49
A. 1. porter 2. report 3. aqueduct 4. portable 5. aquarium 6. transport 7. aquanaut 8. aquamarine 9. aquatic 10. comport; B. 1. aquamarine 2. tent 3. transport 4. report

Page 50
A. 1. favored, liked 2. painter, sculptor 3. crowded, populated 4. creative, skilled 5. company, organization 6. people, inhabitants 7. object, tool; B. 1. art 2. corp 3. corp

Page 51
A. 1. populous 2. artisan 3. corporal 4. artist 5. artifact 6. corporation 7. popular 8. corps 9. population 10. artistic; B. 1. popular 2. artisan 3. corporal 4. corps

Page 52
A. 1. g 2. d 3. f 4. b 5. a 6. c 7. e
B. 1. geo 2. photo 3. auto

Page 53
A. 1. geography 2. photogenic 3. automatic 4. geometry 5. telephoto 6. autograph 7. photocopier 8. geology 9. photograph 10. autobiography; B. 1. geology 2. autobiography 3. photograph 4. photocopier

Page 54
1. conductor 2. professor 3. hairdresser 4. architect 5. custodian 6. paratrooper 7. astronaut 8. physician 9. geologist 10. cashier 11. archaeologist 12. astronomer

Page 55
1. inform; topple 2. stamen; macaw 3. pond; inform 4. temple; stamen 5. macaw; temple 6. topple; pond

Page 56
1. fly up in the air 2. used to tell time 3. can be read 4. instruments 5. bodies of water 6. roadways 7. types of beds 8. types of hats

Page 57
1. dogs 2. weather 3. types of drinks 4. parts of the face 5. meats 6. liquid measurements 7. landforms 8. geometric shapes

Page 58
1. A 2. C 3. B 4. B 5. B 6. B 7. A 8. A

Page 59
1. failed 2. flatter 3. scolded 4. accomplishment 5. jealous 6. immediately 7. undecided 8. exaggerate 9. relax 10. wasted 11. clumsy 12. nonexistent

Page 60
A. 1. slurp 2. rumble 3. sizzle 4. crunched 5. thud 6. burp 7. crackled 8. clomped 9. screech 10. rumble
B. Review sentences and onomatopoeic words.

Page 61
1. shrimp 2. unfinished 3. half 4. bitter 5. serious 6. ugly 7. misunderstood 8. sorrow 9. whisper 10. minor 11. inside 12. original 13. estimate 14. random 15. awfully

Page 62
1. German 2. Hindi 3. Chinese 4. Dutch 5. French 6. Italian 7. Yiddish 8. Japanese 9. Spanish 10. Turkish 11. Yiddish 12. Spanish 13. German 14. Italian 15. Spanish 16. French

Page 63
1. Malay 2. Italian 3. Japanese 4. Italian 5. French 6. Italian 7. Japanese 5. Italian
B. 1. paddy 2. corduroy

Page 64
A. 1. futon 2. umbrella 3. gong 4. trampoline 5. judo 6. opera 7. paddy 8. corduroy 9. depot 10. ravioli; B. 1. bong 2. puddle 3. depot 4. tumbling

Page 65
A. 1. f 2. e 3. a 4. g 5. c 6. b 7. d
B. 1. mayo 2. dorm 3. flu

Page 66
1. dorm 2. mayo 3. drape 4. deli 5. gym 6. flu 7. gas 8. condo 9. vet 10. disco
B. 1. condo 2. flu 3. vet 4. shop

Page 67
A. 1. skyscraper 2. laptop 3. monorail 4. hatchback 5. astronaut 6. nylons
B. 1. suburb 2. jazz 3. takeout 4. infomercial

Page 68
A. 1. hatchback 2. nylon 3. astronaut 4. jazz 5. skyscraper 6. laptop 7. infomercial 8. takeout 9. suburbs 10. monorail
B. 1. skyscraper 2. hatchback 3. thread 4. takeout

Page 69
A. 1. mock up, model 2. run, extend 3. first, precede 4. error, mistake 5. cut, trim 6. assignment, specialty 7. writer, journalist
B. 1. masthead 2. widow

Page 70
1. beat 2. crop 3. typo 4. stringer 5. masthead 6. dummy 7. bleed 8. scoop 9. headline 10. widow; B. 1. typo 2. scoop 3. widow 4. reporter

Page 71
1. when a picture goes to the edge of a page
2. when a newspaper publishes a big story before anyone else, this is what it's called
3. when you cut off a part of a picture
4. a reporter who is not on a newspaper staff but sends in stories
5. a model of how a page will look
6. the area or subject that a reporter covers
7. the names of a newspaper's publishers and editors are listed on this
8. a word on a line by itself at the end of a paragraph

Page 72
A. 1. bamboo 2. rush 3. popcorn 4. calm
5. ballroom 6. scarecrow 7. hobble 8. clear
B. 1. slugabed 2. polliwog

Page 73
1. bonkers 2. dillydally 3. bamboozle
4. polliwog 5. hobnob 6. gobbledygook
7. scalawag 8. ballyhoo 9. slugabed
10. poppycock; B. 1. sleepyhead 2. you're late 3. scalawag 4. excited

Page 74
month: Jan., Feb., Mar., Apr., Aug., Sept., Oct., Nov., Dec.; address: St., Rd., Ave.;
person: Gov., Pres.; address and person: Dr.

Page 75
A. 2. Sept. 3. Apr. 4. Nov. 5. Aug. 6. Oct.
7. Mar. 8. Jan. 9. Dec. 10. Pres., Ave.
11. Gov., St. 12. Dr., Rd.; B. 1. gov-er-nor
2. cap-i-tal 3. sen-a-tor 4. gov-ern-ment
5. pres-i-dent

Page 76
OK, NE, AR, OR, CT, DE, NJ, SC, ME, FL, WY, GA, ID, WI, IL, IA, KY, CO, MD, MN, MS, UT, VA, WV, TN, MA, KS, MO, MT, NV, NH, NM, NY, NC, ND, OH, AL, MI, PA, RI, CA, IN, HI, SD, AK, TX, VT, WA, AZ, LA

Page 77
1. ordinary, graceless 2. big-hearted, gleaming
3. weird, baffled 4. trustworthy, big-hearted
5. graceless, trustworthy 6. red, ordinary
7. gleaming, unsteady 8. baffled, weird
9. unsteady, swift 10. alert, solid 11. swift, red 12. solid, alert

Page 78
1. dry, moist 2. innocent, guilty 3. narrow, narrow 4. darken, lighten 5. hustle, dawdle
6. lower, hoist 7. minor, minor 8. failure, success 9. scarce, plentiful 10. sloppy, sloppy
11. brand-new, second-hand

Page 79
A. 1. boulder 2. sweet 3. boar 4. metal
B. 1. vein 2. vain

Page 80
A. 1. suite 2. boulder 3. mettle 4. vain
5. sweet 6. bolder 7. metal 8. bore 9. veins
10. boar; B. 1. gumdrop 2. spoon 3. bore
4. rock

Page 81
1. The Vain Bore 2. Bolder Ways to Cook Sweet Food 3. Working with Metal 4. Your Veins and You 5. Decorating a Suite with Bolder Colors
6. The Boar Adventure: A Story of Real Mettle

Page 82
1. still, moving, stationery 2. tight, loose, taught 3. up-to-date, outdated, currant
4. change, maintain, altar 5. prohibited, permitted, band 6. braver, meeker, boulder
7. rough, smooth, course 8. hurtful, kind, crewel 9. total, difference, some 10. thin, thick, shear 11. origin, death, berth
12. presence, absence, attendants

Page 83
A. 1. a 2. a 3. a 4. b 5. b 6. b
B. 1. prune 2. grouse 3. grouse 4. prune

Page 84
1. desert 2. prune 3. grouse 4. desert
5. sewer 6. bass 7. bass 8. grouse
9. sewer 10. prune; B. 1. no 2. no 3. no

Page 85
1. illegible 2. immigrate 3. anecdote 4. cease
5. disprove 6. conscious 7. formerly 8. adopt
9. bizarre 10. cooperation 11. access
12. message

Page 86
1. litter 2. thorough 3. farther 4. latter
5. envelope 6. comma 7. dessert 8. breathe
9. descent 10. alley 11. breath 12. alley
13. coma 14. descent 15. thorough 16. envelop
17. farther 18. desert 19. latter 20. liter

Pages 93–94
1. B 2. G 3. C 4. G 5. D 6. J 7. A 8. H

Reading Comprehension Skills
Page 97
1. Southwest: many-storied homes, steep-walled canyons, Apache and Navajo, buttes, Arizona, New Mexico, and southern Colorado; Eastern Woodlands: wigwam and longhouses, fishing, cold winters, warm summers, Iroquois and Cherokee, bordered what now is Canada; Both: made pottery, hunting, excellent craftspeople, corn, beans, and squash
2. large, multiple-family dwellings 3. The northern area was colder than the southern area.

Page 99
5, 1, 6, 2, 4, 3; Review sentences.
2. article, amusingly, credited, version, PECOS BILL, PECOS BILL

Page 100
A. 1. before 2. then 3. when 4. after
5. soon 6. next 7. while 8. after 9. finally
10. now; B. at last, after, then, first, next

Page 101
Making a Pie Crust: 2, 1, 4, 3; Changing a Tire: 3, 2, 1, 4; Baking a Cake: 4, 2, 1, 3; Feeding the Cat: 3, 1, 2, 4

Pages 102–103
Answers will vary. Sample main ideas: Letter one—Except for the bugs, Tyler and his new friends are having fun at camp.; Letter two—Tyler's mom is worried about his bug bites, and she wants him to start being nice to the other campers.; Letter three—Tyler is having a great time at camp, has some new friends, and is having fun playing tricks on other campers.; Letter four—Steven is sad he could not go to camp and remembers the fun he had at camp last year.

Page 105
1. between Virginia and Maryland on the Potomac River 2. It is the capital of the U.S.; it's the headquarters of the federal government; it is the symbol of our history; it is home to many important historical landmarks. 3. George Washington, Abraham Lincoln, Thomas Jefferson, Franklin D. Roosevelt 4. Americans who fought the Korean and Vietnam Wars 5. National World War II Memorial 6. It honors Americans who fought and supported the U.S. during World War II. 7. 1941–1945 8. Rainbow pool, two giant arches, a ring of stone columns, a wall covered with gold stars 9. Each star represents 100 Americans who died fighting in World War II. 10. Bob Dole 11. "Freedom is not free…it must be earned." 12. Many businesses, private groups, and schools donated money to this cause.

Page 107
1. formal 2. residence 3. reception
4. entertained 5. adorned 6. guide 7. wing
8. mansion 9. tour 10. incredible 11. huge
12. visitors 13. vary 14. five hundred seventy

Page 109
1. hard worker, quick-acting, brave, fast-thinking 2. scared, alarmed, helpless
3. Review opinion 4. B, E, L, L, E, E 5. Henry Heimlich 6. Hawaii; Mount Waialeale 7. just under 2" 8. Answers will vary.

Page 110–111
1. Tuesday and Wednesday 2. Monday
3. Review child's ideas 4. Thursday and Friday
5. Review answer. 6. sunny and warm so they can do all of the outdoor activities they were hoping to do 7. lingering 8. athletic
9. cooler with drinks, goggles, sunglasses, sunscreen 10. Review paragraph.

Page 113
A. colonists; America; The colonists wanted to control themselves and have more say in decision making but Britain wouldn't allow it; They outlined their freedom in the Declaration of Independence.
B. 1. imposed 2. permanent 3. delegates
4. soldiers 5. brave 6. friction 7. immigrate
8. independence 9. prosper

Scholastic

Pages 114–115
1. B, C, A 2. a. E, C b. C, E c. E, C d. E, C
3. Since it was a beautiful day, Janie and Jake's mom was taking them to the beach. 4. Janie—Hayley had just had Janie over to play last week; Jake—Charlie and Jake went everywhere together. 5. Review answer.

Page 116
1. Jupiter 2. Uranus 3. Neptune
4. Earth 5. Saturn 6. Mercury 7. Mars
8. Venus

Page 117
Washington: Grant; Arizona: Spencer; Pennsylvania: Kara; Massachusetts: Jack; Maine

Page 119
Dairy: milk, yogurt, ice cream, vanilla milk shake, cheese; Vegetables: carrots, peas, corn, broccoli, cauliflower; Grains: oatmeal, wheat bread, rice, crackers, pasta; Fruits: banana, apple, grapes, strawberries, pear; Meat & Fish: chicken nuggets, ham, hamburger, fish sticks, pork chops; Fats/Sweets: chocolate chip cookies, candy bar, doughnuts, chocolate cake, cheesecake 1. eat right and exercise
2. hamburger, chicken, ribs 3. Review choices.
4. E, C 5. T, J, K, A, T A, T, J, J, K

Page 120
1. Spring 2. Mother's Day 3. because they are having a sale 4. Flower Power is having a buy one, get one free sale. 5. The sale ends on Tuesday.

Page 121
1. They love Florida 2. They are sad.
3. They think it sounds like a fun, interesting part of the country.
4.

Pages 122–123
1. Most whales are enormous creatures.
2. Whales might look a lot like fish, but the two are very different. 3. Whales can be divided into two groups—baleen and toothed.
4. Blubber is very important to whales and has many purposes. 5. Review that main ideas are written. 6. Whale: can hold breath for a long time, tail fin sideways, lungs; Fish: gills, live in ponds, tail fin up and down; Both: live in oceans, people love to watch

Page 125
1. O, O, F, O, F, F, F, O 2. Review facts.
3. Review opinion. 4. brave, cautious, strong, daring, athletic 5. long climbing poles, ice ax, oxygen mask 6. Review opinion. 7. Review opinion.

Page 126
1. O 2. F 3. F 4. O 5. O 6. F 7. F 8. O
9. O 10. F 11. O 12. O 13. O 14. O

Pages 127–128
1. C 2. G 3. A 4. J 5. C 6. H 7. A 8. A
9. G 10. C 11. G

Reading Passages
Page 131
1. A 2. H

Page 133
1. B 2. H 3. Words that come from people's names 4. He loved to play cards and did not want to stop a game to eat so he invented the sandwich, which he could eat while he played.
5. Bloomers are pants that are worn under a dress. The name came from the inventor, Amelia Bloomer.

Page 135
1. A 2. H 3. Fertilizers used on crops pollute the water. 4. Author is not happy about the ways people have changed the Everglades. Review answer.

Page 137
1. B 2. H 3. Review answer. 4. He helps people less fortunate than himself; he donates money to worthy causes.

Page 139
1. A 2. G 3. The two types of whales are those with teeth and those without. Toothed whales have sharp teeth used to catch, bite, and kill their prey. Whales without teeth have baleens, which are used to filter bits of food from the water. 4. A dolphin is one type of whale but there are many other whales (that are not dolphins).

Page 141
1. C 2. G 3. They forced him and his people to move far away from their home.
4. Review. 5. Review opinion.

Pages 142–144
A. 1. D 2. F 3. D;   B. 1. C 2. F 3. C;
C. 1. C 2. J 3. A 4. G; D. 1. A 2. G 3. D;
E. 1. A 2. J 3. D 4. G

Pages 145–146
1. C 2. F 3. D 4. A 5. H 6. B

Grammar/Writing
Page 148
1. C 2. B 3. D 4. B 5. B 6. D 7. B 8. A
9. B 10. C 11. B 12. B 13. D 14. D

Page 149
1–12 Review proper nouns chosen.
14. character 15. sports team 16. continent
17. singer 18. car 19. book/movie 20. state
21. Great Lake 22. month 23. day of the week 24. president

Page 150
1. an 2. a 3. a 4. An 5. an 6. an 7. a 8. a
9. a 10. a 11. a 12. a 13. An 14. a 15. an

Page 151
1. it 2. me 3. you 4. I 5. him 6. us 7. them
8. her, she 9. we, them 10. it 11. you 12. us

Page 152
Possible answers: 1. our 2. his 3. Her 4. their
5. your 6. Our 7. Our 8. his 9. their 10. its
11. my 12. your 13. his 14. their 15. Our

Page 153
A. 1. We, S 2. us, O 3. You, S 4. I, S 5. it, O
6. her, O 7. them, O 8. She, S B.1. They sent a postcard to us. 2. It was addressed to him.
C. Review sentences.

Page 154
1. C 2. F 3. B 4. H 5. B 6. H 7. A 8. J

Page 155
A. 1. of mountains, rivers, and lakes 2. on the walls; of his room 3. to the scenes; in the pictures 4. on a camping trip 5. in a backpack and knapsack 6. from his father's mug 7. in the mountains; for hours 8. at the Lost Lake 9. on their journey 10. at a quiet place; for the night 11. in a tent 12. from the wind and rain 13. to his father 14. on their camping trip; B. Review sentences for prepositional phrases.

Page 156
1. D 2. B 3. A 4. B 5. A 6. C 7. B 8. B
9. A 10. C 11. C 12. A

Page 157
1. C 2. B 3. D 4. A 5. C 6. A 7. B 8. B

Page 158
1. C 2. D 3. B 4. B 5. A 6. B 7. A 8. A
9. B 10. B 11. A 12. A 13. D

Page 159
A. 1. older 2. loudest 3. biggest 4. quieter
5. higher 6. softer 7. brightest 8. saddest
B. 1. hottest, more than two 2. warmer, two
3. colder, two 4. tallest, more than two
5. longer, two 6. friendliest, more than two
7. younger, two 8. liveliest, more than two

Page 160
Sample sentences: 1. It rains very rarely in the desert. 2. Animals move very slowly in the heat. 3. A cactus grows slowly. 4. Thirsty creatures drink very eagerly. 5. You should always drink water when you are in the desert.

Page 161
1. b 2. c 3. a 4. c 5. a 6. a 7. d 8. d

Page 162
1. S 2. E 3. S 4. Q 5. C 6. E 7. C 8. E
9. Q 10. C 11. S 12. Q

Page 163
A. S, S, P, S, S, P, P, S   P, P, P, P, S, S, P, S
B. 1. Half a loaf is better than none.
2. One good turn deserves another.
3. One rotten apple spoils the whole barrel.
4. The show must go on.
5. Every cloud has a silver lining.
6. The early bird catches the worm.
7. A rolling stone gathers no moss.
8. Haste makes waste.

Page 164
1. The Caspian Sea, the world's largest lake, covers an area about the same size as Montana. 2. The Komodo dragon, a member of the monitor family, can grow to a length of 10 feet. 3. Our closest star, the sun, is estimated to be more than 27,000,000° F. 4. Ronald W. Reagan, our nation's 40th president, worked as a Hollywood actor for almost 30 years. 5. Georgia, the state that grows the most peanuts, harvests over 2 billion pounds each year. 6. Jackie Robinson, who played for the Brooklyn Dodgers, was the first African American to play in the major leagues.

Page 165
Possible sentences: 1. My brothers built a tree house in the old oak tree in our backyard. 2. Jim made a sturdy rope ladder for the tree house. 3. Kyle bought a gallon of brown paint. 4. Kyle and Jim finished painting the walls in an hour. 5. Jim painted a "no trespassing" sign on the tree house door. 6. A curious squirrel leaped from a branch into their tree house. 7. The unexpected visitor startled my unsuspecting brothers. 8. The frightened squirrel leaped out of the house in a big hurry.

Page 166
1. but 2. and 3. or 4. and 5. or 6. but 7. and 8. but 9. or 10. but 11. and 12. or 13. but 14. but

Page 167
Possible sentences: 1. I watched a movie while I waited for my parents to get home. 2. My brother was in his room because he had homework to do. 3. The power went out before the movie was over. 4. I wasn't concerned since this happens all the time. 5. I didn't mind the dark at first until I heard a scratching sound. 6. I started to look around when I found my flashlight 7. I was checking the living room when I caught Alex trying to hide.

Page 168
1. My sister Annie has always participated in sports, and many say she's a natural. 2. Soccer, basketball, and softball are fun, but she wanted a new challenge. 3. My sister talked to my brother and me, and we were honest with her. 4. I told Annie to go for it, but my brother told her to stick with soccer or basketball. 5. Will Dad convince her to try skiing, or will he suggest ice skating?

Page 169
1. While Gina answered the phone, Marta watched for the bus. 2. Just as Gina said "Hello," the caller hung up. 3. Unless they hurried, the girls were going to miss the one o'clock show. 4. By the time they got to the corner, the bus had already come and gone.

5. After the girls had waited for a half hour, the next bus to town finally showed up. 6. Since they missed the earlier show, the girls decided to catch the four o'clock show. 7. Since Gina bought the tickets first, they wouldn't have to stand on line later. 8. Even though it was early, Gina and Marta were at the theater by three o'clock. 9. Once they were inside, they bought a tub of popcorn and drinks.

Page 170
1. I'd like a bike, a pair of in-line skates, and a snowboard for my birthday. 2. Well, my friend, you can't always have what you want when you want it. 3. No, but I can always hope! 4. My friends and I skate all year long, and we snowboard during the winter. 5. I used to like skateboarding, but now I prefer snowboarding and in-line skating. 6. What sports games or hobbies do you enjoy most, Jody? 7. I learned to ski last year, and now I'm taking ice-skating lessons. 8. Skiing, ice skating, and skateboarding are all fun things to do. 9–12. Review that directions have been followed.

Pages 171–173
Review that directions have been followed.

Page 174
Answers will vary. 1. any indoor sport such as indoor hockey 2. any dessert such as ice cream, pudding, etc. 3. a type of shark such as the great white shark 4. string instruments 5. a jungle in South America such as the Amazon 6. Huron, Ontario, Michigan, Erie, or Superior 7. specific careers such as a doctor, nurse, etc. 8. one person vehicles such as a motorcycle 9. Mars 10. example of a dinosaur such as T-rex

Pages 175–176
Review that directions have been followed.

Page 177
1. b 2. c 3. a 4. b 5. c 6. c

Page 178
The trumpet and the violin are both musical instruments that are played in orchestras. However, there are some differences. The trumpet is a brass instrument. It has a mouthpiece and has three valves. On the other hand, the violin is a wood instrument. It has four strings and is played with a bow. Both instruments take practice to play.

Pages 179–184
Review that directions have been followed.

Page 185
1. C 2. J 3. C 4. G 5. A 6. G 7. D 8. F

Page 186
think about the fastest car you've ever seen in the Indianapolis 500 race⊙ that's about how fast a peregrine falcon dives⊙ it actually reaches speeds over 200 miles an hour⊙ how incredibly fast they are⊙ peregrine falcons are also very powerful birds⊙ did you know that they can catch and kill their prey in the air using their sharp claws⊙ what's really amazing is that peregrine falcons live in both the country and in the city⊙ keep on the lookout if you're ever in New York City⊙ believe it or not, it is home to several falcons⊙

Page 187
Missing words: you, country, friend, students, days, half, learn, year, month, summer, vacation, begins, Japan, education, age, schools, students, high, hard, take, college

Page 189
1. C 2. H 3. D 4. F or H 5. B 6. J 7. C 8. J

Page 190
1. C 2. F 3. A 4. F 5. B 6. H 7. B 8. F or G

Pages 191–193
1. C 2. J 3. A 4. H 5. C 6. J 7. C 8. F 9. C 10. H 11. C 12. G

MATH
Addition & Subtraction
Page 195
1. 55 2. 72 3. 24 4. 53 5. 31 6. 21 7. 80 8. 41 9. 21 10. 71 11. 103 12. 68 13. 35 14. 43 15. 61 16. 84 17. 91 18. 107 19. 69 20. 29

Page 196
1. 111 2. 121 3. 86 4. 90 5. 99 6. 99 7. 85 8. 71 9. 99 10. 133 11. 76 12. 94 13. 158 14. 136 15. 76 16. 98 17. 115 18. 77 19. 115 20. 90

Page 197
1. 4,730 2. 2,405 3. 2,822 4. 7,920 5. 4,744 6. 6,132 7. 2,310 8. 6,845 9. 2,067 10. 9,128 11. 4,655 12. 3,173 13. 9,175 14. 4,236 15. 2,104 16. 5,870 17. 2,360 18. 4,578 19. 7,670 20. 1,857

Page 198
A. 15,981 19,341 10,397 8,990
B. 12,218 12,188 11,929 10,984
C. 18,990 16,767 20,310 16,971
D. 17,759 15,984 14,487 18,510
EXTRA 39,651

Page 199
Z. 1,371 B. 632 R. 1,211 Q. 1,522 S. 1,201 X. 761 I. 9,107 C. 4,053 Y. 10,155 A. 14,024 Y. 9,122 L. 103,468 P. 76,076 E. 82,373 F. 92,228 D. 539,396 O. 651,951 R. 1,059,472 BIRDS OF PREY

Page 200
H. 9,122 L. 12,548 I. 18,975 A. 17,531 E. 10,322 O. 17,200 C. 18,506 T. 14,123 M. 13,590 N. 130,752 U. 111,110 Y. 182,920 R. 136,131 ONLY ON THE NORTH AMERICAN CONTINENT

Scholastic

Page 201
1. 7,901 2. 12,300 3. 7,148 4. 12,885
5. 11,695 6. 15,019 7. 15,944 8. 10,404
9. 9,207 10. 9,816 11. 8,915 12. 11,303
ONE WEARS TROUSERS. THE OTHER PANTS!

Page 202
1. 18 2. 18 3. 17 4. 19 5. 15 6. 16
7. 18 8. 15 9. 15 10. 17 11. 17 12. 18
13. 18 14. 16 15. 16 16. 17 17. 22 18. 18
19. 15 20. 19 21. 17 22. 15 23. 18 24. 18
25. 18

Page 203
A. 13 B. 18 C. 16 D. 15 E. 15 F. 15
G. 17 H. 19 I. 17 J. 15 K. 20 L. 14
M. 14 N. 12 O. 14 P. 15 Q. 13 R. 17
S. 15 T. 14 U. 20 V. 22

Page 204
A. $12.89 + $28.53 + $28.53 = $69.95
B. $23.95 + $17.23 + $76.82 = $118.00
C. $7.96 + $9.96 + $5.96 = $23.88
D. $9.29 + $7.90 + $1.39 = $18.58
E. $79.00 + $ 99.75 = $178.75
F. $1.75 + $1.75 + $1. 75 = $5.25

Page 205
1. 5,104 2. 9,221 3. 4,732 4. 6,528 5. 803
6. 1,161 7. 3,106 8. 3,114 9. 9,159 10. 112
11. 2,106 12. 236 13. 1,515 14. 337 15. 8,613
16. 241

Page 206
1. 464 2. 63 3. 416 4. 73 5. 179 6. 699
7. 240 8. 164 9. 119 10. 506 11. 376 12. 479

Page 207
1. 3,338 2. 4,729 3. 2,579 4. 4,819 5. 8,858
6. 3,689 7. 7,046 8. 857 9. 2,491 10. 3,875
11. 5,252 12. 5,583 13. 874 14. 1,988
IN THE BLEACHERS

Page 208
1. a. 5,708 b. 4,834 c. 1,052 d. 491 e. 3
2. a. 7,187 b. 5,708 c. 2,812 d. 1,034 e. 7
3. a. 8,245 b. 6,879 c. 2,980 d. 1,383 e. 4
4. a. 4,609 b. 2,656 c. 818 d. 126 e. 9
Colts: 37 Panthers: 49 PANTHERS WON

Page 209
1. 3 2. 9 3. 14 4. 0 5. 8 6. 5
7. 11 8. 16 9. 4 10. 10 11. 15 12. 7
13. 1 14. 6 15. 12 16. 13 17. 2
TWO HUNDRED BILLION

Page 210
A. 5 B. 2 C. 9 D. 8 E. 1 F. 5 G. 3 H. 9
I. 6 J. 3 K. 5 L. 9 M. 9 N. 2 O. 6 P. 8
Q. 2 R. 8 S. 7 T. 9 2527 m.p.h.

Page 211
A. 1,246 − 879 = 367
B. 4,128 − 1,839 = 2,289
C. 6,283 − 2,496 = 3,787
D. 947.6 − 289.9 = 657.7
E. 8,612 − 4,985 = 3,627
F. 3,290 − 2,391 = 899

Pages 212–213
1. A 2. F 3. D 4. G 5. A 6. G 7. C 8. F

Multiplication & Division
Page 215
A. 144, 168, 292   B. 399, 567, 168
C. 196, 512, 456, 315, 184, 492
D. 855, 462, 747, 768, 112, 480
EXTRA 604 meters

Page 216
A. 560, 3,000, 27,000, 440, 240, 12,000
B. 490, 36,000, 5,400, 42,000, 3,500, 360
C. 48,000, 480, 240, 4,500, 24,000, 400

Page 217
Gateway Arch: 3,066, 1,323, 3,960, 630 feet;
Empire State Building: 5,481, 2,814, 2,425,
1,064, 1,454 feet; Statue of Liberty: 6,723,
2,160, 5,135, 305 feet; Space Needle: 6,536,
3,640, 2,075, 605 feet; Empire State Building
should be circled.
EXTRA 6050 people

Page 218
G. 1,536 T. 938 S. 1,431 I. 4,992 A. 2,739
D. 3,528 M. 1,092 E. 840 N. 1,992 R. 3,450
K. 4,896 H. 5,208; NIGHTMARES
EXTRA 1632 pounds

Page 219
A. 15,566 10,836 9,944 3,679 24,786 26,015
B. 20,520 23,352 18,788
C. 23,528 21,682 78,948
D. 19,614 17,342 62,853 EXTRA 37,674 steps

Page 220
N. $44.42 M. $19.75 I. $131.84 O. $30.60
A. $117.76 T. $181.26 F. $63.36 D. $87.42
E. $546.05 S. $683.56 R. $65.25 H. $574.36
AT THE FIFE AND DIME STORE

Page 221
A. $1.23 x 5 = $4.92   B. 48 x 392 = 18,816
C. 29 x 44 = 1,305   D. 35 x $0.57 = $19.95
E. 286 x 37 = 10,582   F. $2.98 x 6 = $17.88

Page 222
A. 6, 9, 8, 5, 9, 3 B. 9, 9, 7, 7, 6, 9 C. 4, 3, 8, 8, 4, 9
D. 8, 7, 6, 3, 1, 5 EXTRA 1927

Page 223
A. 4, 7, 3, 5, 6, 7, 8, 5, 8 B. 5, 4, 3, 8, 4, 6, 3, 8, 9
C. 6, 5, 3, 7, 6, 9, 3, 9, 6 D. 9, 9, 7, 7, 3, 7, 4, 8, 6

Page 224
A. 70, 900, 90, 900, 800
B. 600, 80, 900, 80, 80 C. 50, 90, 800, 60, 80

Page 225
T. 52 U. 51 H. 91 C. 82 A. 92 E. 81
O. 71 S. 62 N 84 D. 72 C. 82 I. 53
W. 61 M. 31 !. 22
IT WANTED TO CATCH THE MOUSE!

Page 226
E. 9R3 L. 9R2 S. 9R4 O. 4R4 T. 3R5
N. 7R5 P. 6R3 I. 7R3 O. 4R3 A. 8R6
T. 8R2 S. 6R1 H. 5R3 !. 6R3 R. 5R2
N. 9R7 NO, ON THE STAIRS!

Page 227
Z. 742 N. 583R3 T. 262R3 S. 748 B. 618R6
P. 356 D. 394 C. 542R6 U. 857 O. 921
A. 921R4 Y. 672   SUNDAY

Page 228
S. 604   U. 908 W. 50R10   X. 130
G. 20R16 B. 308 R. 20R6   J. 902
A. 601   E. 20R22 Y. 320   T. 705
STAR WARTS

Page 229
A. 26 seats B. 54 kernels C. 670 tickets
D. 863 tickets E. 136 drinks F. 73 tickets

Pages 230–231
1. B 2. F 3. C 4. F 5. B 6. J 7. D 8. F

Fractions & Decimals
Page 233
A. 1/4, 2/4, 1/2 3/8, 1/3
B. 5/6, 4/8, 4/8, 4/10
C. 1/5, 2/4, 2/6, 4/12, 6/12

Page 234
1. 4/8 2. 1/4 3. 2/4 4. 5/6 5. 4/4
6. 2/3 7. 1/3 8. 6/8 9. 2/6 10. 4/5
11. 5/10 12. 8/10

Page 235

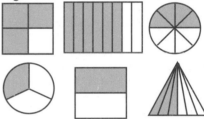

7. 2/5 8. 6/10 9. 1/4 10. 7/8 11. 6/4
12. 2/3 13. 1 3/4, 2, 2 1/4, 2 2/4 14. 10/4
15. 11/4

Page 236
A. 2 B. 2 C. 2 D. 3 E. 2 F. 4 G. 8 H. 5
I. 1/2 = 6/12 J. 1/3 = 2/6 K. 1/6 = 3/18
L. 1/2 = 3/6

Page 237
A. 2, 1/2 B. 3, 2/3 C. 5, 1/2 D. 5, 2/3
E. 4, 1/2 F. 2, 5/6 G. 3, 1/2 H. 3, 1/3
I. 7, 1/2 J. 2, 3/4 K. 5, 1/3 L. 4, 1/4

Page 238
A. 2/4 ÷ 2/2 = 1/2   B. 2/6 ÷ 2/2 = 1/3
C. 3/12 ÷ 3/3 = 1/4   D. 6/15 ÷ 3/3 = 2/5
E. 8/10 ÷ 2/2 = 4/5   F. 5/10 ÷ 5/5 = 1/2
G. 7/14 ÷ 7/7 = 1/2   H. 6/9 ÷ 3/3 = 2/3

Page 239
1. 1/2 2. 1/6 3. 1/5 4. 3/10 5. 5/6
6. 1/4 7. 1/4 8. 1/3 9. 2/3 10. 5/6
11. 2/5 12. 2/5 13. 1/4 14. 1/2 15. 1/4
6. 1/3 17. 5/7 18. 2/3 19. 1/3 20. 7/8

Page 240
O. 2 S. 7 A. 3 B. 16 E. 8 !. 6 T. 11 H. 5
D. 10 N. 12 M. 13 Y. 14 P. 1 R. 4 L. 9
HE HAD TOO MANY PROBLEMS!

Page 241
1. 3/9, 2/6, 5/15, 7/21, 4/12, 6/18
2. 8/20, 12/30, 4/10, 14/35, 10/25, 6/15
3. 2/4, 7/14, 3/6, 6/12, 4/8, 5/10
4. 6/8, 18/24, 9/12, 21/28, 12/16, 15/20
5. 21/56, 6/16, 18/48, 15/40, 12/32, 9/24
6. 7/35, 4/20, 6/30, 2/10, 3/15, 5/25

Page 242
1. 4 1/2 2. 3 3/5 3. 3 1/3 4. 1 2/3
5. 1 3/5 6. 1 1/3 7. 2 1/4 8. 1 1/9 9. 1 3/4
10. 1 1/2 11. 1 1/10 12. 2 2/3 13. 1 11/15
14. 1 2/3 15. 3 1/8 16. 4 1/4 17. 4 1/2
18. 8 1/3 19. 2 2/3 20. 1 1/8

Page 243
1. 2 1/2 2. 1 1/5 3. 4 7/12 4. 9 1/2 5. 3 3/4
6. 1 3/4 7. 1 2/11 8. 3 2/3 9. 3 1/4 10. 1 1/12
11. 1 1/4 12. 1 5/7 13. 1 2/3 14. 2 11/12
15. 1 7/8 16. 3 1/5 17. 1 3/4 18. 1 1/3
19. 3 1/6 20. 2 1/2

Page 244
1. > 2. < 3. > 4. > 5. > 6. > 7. < 8. =
9. > 10. = 11. < 12. > 13. > 14. < 15. >

Page 245
1. 10/3 2. 21/4 3. 19/8 4. 17/5 5. 85/9
6. 23/3 7. 9/2 8. 44/7 9. 60/7 10. 31/5
11. 57/7 12. 31/7 13. 65/9 14. 23/4 15. 48/5
16. 19/5 17. 75/9 18. 13/6 19. 29/6 20. 73/8

Page 246
1. 45/8 2. 24/7 3. 31/4 4. 55/6 5. 18/5
6. 35/8 7. 43/7 8. 21/5 9. 16/3 10. 74/9
11. 39/7 12. 20/3 13. 37/5 14. 24/5 15. 25/4
16. 65/8 17. 39/9 18. 7/2 19. 85/9 20. 51/7

Page 247
A. 3 B. 2 C. 5 D. 5 E. 2 F. 2 G. 4 H. 5
I. 2 J. 4 K. 7 L. 6 M. 2 N. 5 O. 4 P. 4

Page 248
A. 6 B. 3 C. 9 D. 4 E. 12 F. 10 G. 12
H. 15 I. 12 J. 9 K. 15 L. 12

Page 249
1. 20 2. 18 3. 20 4. 36 5. 15 6. 33
7. 24 8. 9 9. 20 10. 6 11. 20 12. 30
13. 2, 3, 4, 5 14. 6, 9, 16, 20 15. 4, 9, 8, 15
16. 10, 12, 16, 25

Page 250
1. 1 2. 1 3. 3/5 4. 1 5. 1/3 6. 7/9 7. 3/4
8. 7/11 9. 5/7 10. 1 1/5 11. 1 2/5 12. 1
13. 4/5 14. 1/2 15. 1/2 16. 2/3 17. 9/11 18. 2/5

Page 251
1. 1 11/20 2. 3/4 3. 9/14 4. 1 4/15
5. 1 1/30 6. 1 1/8 7. 1 1/9 8. 5/6
9. 15/16 10. 2/3 11. 3/4 12. 13/20
13. 13/18 14. 9/10 15. 1 13/33
16. 1 3/10 17. 1 1/4 18. 16/21

Page 252
Review that directions have been followed.

Page 253
Ranking from highest to lowest:
1. Miguel Cabrera (.338) 2. Dee Gordon (.333)
3. Bryce Harper (.330) 4. Paul Goldschmidt
(.321) 5. Xander Bogaerts (.320) 6. Buster
Posey (.318) 7. A. J. Pollock (.315) 8. Yunel
Escobar (.314) 9. Joey Votto (.314) 10. José
Altuve (.313)

Page 254
1. b 2. b 3. c 4. a 5. a 6. d 7. b 8. c 9. a 10. d

Page 255
0 — 1 — 2 — 3 — 4 — 5

  (0.2)   (1.7) (2.5)   (4.9)

Page 256
1. d 2. i 3. h 4. b 5. g 6. e 7. a 8. j 9. f
10. c 11. twelve and six hundredths
12. one hundred fifty-two and four tenths
13. six hundred twelve thousandths
14. thirty-eight and five hundredths
15. nine and fifty-two hundredths

Page 257
ACROSS: A. 3.7 C. 4.38 E. .55 F. .6 G. .9
J. .57 K. 7.16 L. 4.3; DOWN: A. 3.14 B. 78.29
C. 4.5 D. 8.1 F. .2704 H. 24.3 I. 1.7 J. .36

Page 258
$92.83 G. $92.53 U. $114.60 O. $63.87
B. $72.25 N. $170.78 E. $157.35 R. $69.37
M. $168.72 C. $765.09 S. $980.05 T. $670.09
D. $477.07 Y. $616.34 F. $1216.40 W. $1000.68
BECAUSE MONEY DOESN'T GROW ON TREES!

Page 259

Page 260
1. $1.55 2. 23¢ 3. $2.45 4. 48¢ 5. $12.70
6. $3.51 7. 32¢ 8. $10.65 9. 83¢ 10. $2.57

Page 261
1. Deluxe Scraps 2. Kibble or Mouse Crumbs
3. Mouse Crumbs 4. Table Scraps and Mouse
Crumbs 5. Crumbs & Cheese and Deluxe Scraps
Super Challenge: No. The cost of the three
cheapest items is more than $5.

Page 262
A. 36.1 B. 43.48 C. 19.4 D. 78.9 E. 51.59
F. 265.7 EXTRA: Region C & B

Pages 263–264
1. B 2. J 3. D 4. F 5. B 6. F 7. C 8. G

Word Problems
Page 266–270
1. B 2. J 3. C 4. H 5. E 6. G 7. C 8. J
9. C 10. J 11. B 12. H 13. D 14. K 15. D
16. F 17. C 18. J 19. A 20. F 21. C 22. H
23. A 24. G 25. B

Pages 271–274
1. B 2. F 3. C 4. J 5. E 6. G 7. E 8. F
9. D 10. H 11. A 12. K 13. C 14. F 15. B
16. J 17. B 18. K 19. D 20. J 21. C

Page 275
1. 960 2. 50 3. 6636 4. 35 5. 120 6. 7532
THEY HAVE A MOUSE WARMING PARTY

Page 276
1. 3000 2. 12 3. 816 4. 92 5. 68 6. 8337
HURRY TO THE VET FOR TWEETMENT

Page 277
1. $106.57 2. $.15 3. $27 4. $240 5. $90 6. $36
SHE WENT OUTSIDE FOR A SPELL

Page 278
1. $32.35 2. $24.81, $.76 3. $1,225.85
4. $12,000 5. $358.16
IT HAS TO BE CHOCOLATE MOUSSE

Pages 279–280
1. C 2. F 3. B 4. G 5. A 6. H 7. D 8. H

GET READY FOR GRADE 5
Page 282
2. flower, sunflower, flowerpot 3. crow,
scarecrow, crowbar 4. over, sleepover,
overflow 5. top, treetop, topsoil 6. light,
flashlight, lighthouse 7. ever, whatever,
evergreen 8. out, workout, outside 9. fire,
wildfire, fireproof 10. hand, backhand,
handcuff 11. post, goalpost, postcard
12. water, underwater, waterfront

Page 283
1. -or, director, someone who directs 2. -ic,
poetic, relating to poetry 3. trans-, transplant,
to move something to another place 4. -or,
inspector, person who inspects 5. dis-,
dislike, not liking 6. trans-, transport, to
move from one place to another using a
vehicle or ship 7. -or, counselor, someone
who counsels 8. dis-, dishonest, not honest
dis-: not; trans-: across; -or: a person who; -ic:
relating to

Page 284
1. They 2. It 3. He 4. him 5. She 6. her
7. it 8. We 9. us 10. them 11. her 12. she
13. them 14. it

Page 285
A. 1. thought 2. found 3. brought 4. met
5. said 6. paid 7. caught 8. held 9. thought
10. kept 11. found 12. paid 13. caught
14. kept 15. met; B. Answers will vary.

Scholastic

Page 286

Causes: need some exercise, want to see some city sights, assert rights as pedestrian in a city designed for cars, meet other members of the community, enjoy being out at night; Effect: enjoy moonwalking

Page 287

North Dakota: Bismarck is capital, International Peace Garden, located on Canadian border; South Dakota: Pierre is capital, Black Hills, Mount Rushmore, Badlands National Park, bison roaming in Custer State Park; Both: midwestern states on the Great Plains

Page 288

1789: George Washington is the first president of the U.S.

1800: John Adams is the first president to live in the White House.

1833: Andrew Jackson is the first president to ride on a train.

1849: James Polk is the first president to be photographed.

1891: Benjamin Harrison is the first president to have electricity in the White House.

1925: Calvin Coolidge is the first president to make a radio broadcast from the White House.

1955: Dwight Eisenhower is the first president to appear on color TV.

1993: William Clinton is the first president to have e-mail in the White House.

Page 289

1927: Bathtubs and sinks are available for sale in many colors.

1935: Color photography becomes available.

1953: TV first appears in living color.

1968: The Beatles' *The Yellow Submarine* is released.

1970: frog puppet Kermit croaks song "Bein' Green."

Page 290

Main Idea: Radar waves have many important uses in everyday life.

Details: 1. Radar aids air-traffic control in keeping track of planes. 2. Burglar alarms use radar to detect movement of intruders. 3. Radar helps predict weather. 4. Radar measures the speed of pitches in baseball. 5. Police use radar to detect drivers who are speeding. 6. Radar has a role in the workings of microwave ovens.

Page 291

1. C 2. J 3. A 4. J 5. B 6. H 7. D 8. H

Page 292

1. B 2. F 3. D 4. H 5. D 6. H 7. B 8. H

Page 293

1. Election Day comes in November. 2. Every Thanksgiving my grandma roasts a turkey. 3. On Halloween Nick wears his robot costume. 4. Every fall students return to school. 5. On the Fourth of July, I march in a parade.

Page 294

Review that directions have been followed.

Page 295

Review that directions have been followed.

Page 296

Answers will vary. (Buster) will balance, (Jack) will ride, (Lily) will do, (Marcus) will win, (Heather) will sell

Page 297

1. on 2. in 3. over 4. between 5. around 6. against 7. under 8. behind

Page 298

1. are 2. talks 3. doesn't 4. have 5. gets 6. call 7. is 8. picks

Page 299

1. 27, 8, 22	2. 21, 6, 17	3. 24, 7 20
4. 67, 19, 54	5. 50, 14, 40	6. 14, 4, 11
7. 56, 16, 45	8. 19, 6, 15	9. 55, 16, 44
10. 17, 5, 13	11. 13, 4, 11	

Page 300

A. 4, 1, 5   B. 4, 6, 0   C. 5, 2, 8   D. 7, 2, 1
E. 1, 9, 3   F. 9, 2, 4   G. 6, 3, 4   H. 2, 1, 1
I. 6, 7, 1   J. 1, 3, 8

Page 301

1. 1/4 2. 1/3 3. 1/3 4. 1/2 5. 1/4
6. 1/2 7. 1/3 8. 1/2 9. 1/3 10. 1/3

Page 302

1. 3/8 2. 5/8 3. 1/6 4. 5/6 5. 3/4
6. 1/4 7. 3/5 8. 2/5 9. 4/7 10. 3/7

Page 303

1. 1.77 2. 8.70 3. 3.09 4. 3.90 5. 9.44
6. 6.05 7. .15 8. 6.76 9. 12.56 10. 24.99

Page 304

1. 2 h 20 m	2. 9 h 45 m	3. 6 h 20 m
4. 50 m	5. 1 h 25 m	6. 1 h 5 m
7. 7 h 52 m	8. 1 h 10 m	9. 50 m

Page 305

1. $3.20, $3.98, Frank's; 2. $7.27, $7.30, Frank's; 3. $14.54, $15. 37, Frank's; 4. $6.80, $6.89, Frank's; 5. $7.70, $6.20, Barry's; 6. $5.70, $4.70; Barry's; 7. $9.05, $9.46, Frank's; 8. $4.70, $5.40, Frank's

Page 306

1. cube 2. sphere 3. cylinder 4. rectangular prism 5. sphere 6. cylinder 7. sphere 8. sphere 9. cone 10. rectangular prism 11. cylinder 12. cylinder 13. csone 14. cylinder

Page 307

1. 17 2. 13 3. 10 4. 15 5. 13

Pages 308–309

1. C 2. H 3. C 4. J 5. B 6. H 7. A 8. F 9. B
10. G 11. 60 ÷ 7.5 12. Review picture; Jenny, Ted, Ann, Gary

Pages 310–311

1. C 2. J 3. B 4. K 5. A 6. J 7. A
8. H 9. C 10. H 11. C 12. F

Scholastic